# Structural Engineering
## -two centuries of British achievement

This first edition, for sale exclusively to
members of the Institution of Structural Engineers,
commemorates the 75th Anniversary of its
Foundation and the 50th Anniversary of
the Granting of a Royal Charter, and is
limited to 1 000 copies of which
this is number 448

*President 1983-1984*

*Secretary*

# Structural
## -two centuries

Editor: Dr A. R. Collins MBE

# Engineering
# of British achievement

Tarot Print Limited

Published by TAROT PRINT LIMITED
Suite 4a, 71-75 High Street, Chislehurst, Kent BR7 5AG
for the Institution of Structural Engineers
11 Upper Belgrave Street, London SW1X 8BH

First published, October 1983

Edited by A.R. Collins MBE, DSc, FEng, FIStructE, FICE

Design, artwork and production by
TAROT DESIGN ASSOCIATES LIMITED

Designer: Bill Stotesbury MSIAD, MISTC

Production Director: Richard W. Fairbrass

Production Coordinator: Chris Miller NNEB

Studio: Sallyanne Rowe BA(Hons), Jim McIntosh

Picture Research: John Bancroft DipArch (Nottm), RIBA

Authors:
S.C.C. Bate CBE, BSc(Eng), PhD, CEng, FIStructE, FICE
P. Campbell JP, DIC, CEng, FIStructE, MSocIS(France), MASCE, ACIArb, MConsE
P.T. Dunican CBE, FEng, FIStructE, FICE, FIEI
Professor E. Happold BSc, FEng, FIStructE, FICE, FCIoB, Hon FRIBA
T. Harley-Haddow OBE, CEng, FIStructE, FICE, FRIBA, FRIAS, FRSA, MConsE
R.J. Mainstone DEng, CEng, FIStructE, MICE, FRSA, FSA, Hon FRIBA
C.D. Morgan OBE, FCIS
F. Newby MA(Cantab), CEng, FIStructE, MConsE, Hon FRIBA
R.J.M. Sutherland BA, FIStructE, FICE, FIHE, MConsE

The publishers also wish to acknowledge the special help
given by Derek J. Clark FCIS, R.J.W. Milne BSc,
Barry Scanes BA(Hons), Gerald Young and the members of the
75th Anniversary Editorial Panel of the Literature
Committee of the Institution of Structural Engineers



ISBN 0 946756 00 7



Phototypeset in Great Britain by Text Filmsetters Limited, Orpington, Kent.

Additonal setting by Delco Photoset, Bexley, Kent.

Printed and bound in Yugoslavia by Delo Printing Works, Ljubljana.

# Contents

# Foreword

Richard Collins

A.R. Collins MBE, DSc, FEng, FIStructE, FICE.

Dr A.R. Collins, a Past-President of the Institution of Structural Engineers, has, throughout his career, been engaged in research on civil and structural engineering first as an assistant to the late Sir William Glanville at the Building Research Station (now Establishment) and the Road Research Laboratory (now the Transport and Road Research Laboratory), then as Director of Research of the Cement and Concrete Association and, finally, as Director of the Construction Industry Research and Information Association.

His own research was concerned primarily with the properties and use of concrete and especially with the proportioning of concrete mixtures and his method of dealing with this problem was widely used throughout the industry. During the War he became involved in studying the effects of explosions on structures including the work that defined the requirements for the attack on the German dams and accurately forecast the results.

At the C & CA and CIRIA, he was concerned primarily with planning, managing and funding research in construction technology and with the application of the results by industry and, in this role, he served on the councils and committees of a number of British and international bodies including the Councils of the Institutions of Civil and Structural Engineers and the British Standards Institution. He has also served as Vice-Chairman of the Parliamentary and Scientific Committee and was elected to the Fellowship of Engineering in 1978.

Man first began building about 10000 years ago when he became a farmer and needed shelter for himself and his harvests. For most of the time since then, building remained a craft-based activity. Even today, the basic skills of brickwork, masonry, and carpentry, are much the same as they were in ancient times.

The design and construction of building structures in the modern sense originated in the second half of the 18th century as a result of the Industrial Revolution which created a demand for new and larger types of structure and produced new materials that could be used in their construction. As a result, the old rules-of-thumb and craft skills became inadequate and designers had to try to calculate the forces imposed on their structures and make experiments to determine the strength of the materials they proposed to use. This in turn led to the evolution of a new profession of designers in Britain who called themselves 'civil engineers' as the civilian equivalent of their military colleagues to whom the title 'engineer' had been applied previously.

In 1818 a group of these civil engineers formed a society which they called 'The Institution of Civil Engineers' to act as a centre for the exchange of knowledge and as a means of establishing standards training, professional integrity, and behaviour, to ensure that members of the new profession gained the trust and confidence of their clients and employers.

The rapid expansion in the scope of engineering technology, however, soon made it necessary for engineers to specialise in various ways and, from the middle of the 19th century onwards, a number of more specialised institutions were founded, of which The Institution of Structural Engineers is one.

The design of structures as a separate speciality grew out of the development of reinforced concrete at the beginning of the 20th century which, in 1908, led to the formation of the Concrete Institute to act as a focus for the new techniques and a centre through which those in practice could have an influence on the regulations then being prepared by various public authorities. In 1922 the Institute decided to widen the scope of its interests to include all forms of structural engineering and it was reformed as 'The Institution of Structural Engineers' which, in 1934 was granted a Royal Charter. The Institution is now recognised as the leading professional body for structural engineering in Britain and has a total membership of some 15000 of whom 4000 live and work in other countries all over the world.

The purpose of this book is primarily to celebrate the 75th Anniversary of the foundation of the Institution as the Concrete Institute in 1908, in the form of an illustrated history of structural engineering since the Industrial Revolution as seen through the eyes of eight eminent members of the Institution. Each author has dealt with a defined period, and has prepared a short introductory essay and a running commentary on the structures he has chosen to illustrate the progress made. The aim has been to provide something of interest to structural engineers, architects, and the interested layman. Some technical terms have, however, been unavoidable, and a glossary of these is given on page 193.

12 July 1982

# Introduction

Rowland Mainstone

R.J. Mainstone DEng, CEng, FIStructE, MICE, FRSA, FSA, Hon.FRIBA.

Rowland Mainstone was at the Building Research Establishment from 1948 to 1979, where he was responsible for both structural and architectural research. Since then he has been a consultant and Visiting Professor at the Bartlett School of Architecture and Planning, London University.

He is author of *Developments in Structural Form* (Allen Lane and Penguin) and numerous other publications on structural and architectural history and co-author with his late wife of a book on the art of the seventeenth century. As well as holding a Doctorate in Engineering Science, he is a Fellow of the Society of Antiquaries and an Honorary Fellow of the Royal Institute of British Architects.

## Why two centuries?

Why indeed? Why celebrate a 75th anniversary by looking back almost three times as far?

Part of the reason is that to look back only to 1908 would be to ignore much of what led to the formation then of a new professional body and all that made possible the achievements of structural engineers working at that time. Practical achievement in any art is rooted in long experience and in the lessons drawn from this experience. In structural engineering in 1908 it was rooted, also, in an understanding, built up over as long a period, of the ways in which structures behave and respond to the forces acting on them.

The more closely we look, the more aware we become of innumerable, interwoven threads of development stretching back even beyond recorded history to man's earliest attempts to build, perhaps some 10 000 years ago. Development was not always continuous. Hardwon lessons and skills might be lost, only to be learnt and mastered again, later, in some other place. But there was no significant break in Western Europe after the surge in building activity in about the 11th century. The design of the great Gothic cathedrals (*Figures 1* and *2*) developed out of that of the Romanesque or Norman churches that preceded them. And a detailed study of them still guided and inspired leading designers like Wren in 17th century England and Soufflot in 18th century France.

By the latter part of the 17th century, changes were, however, afoot in the understanding of structural behaviour, and they gained momentum during the 18th century. It is clear the Gothic master masons, responsible for the design of the great cathedrals, must have had a keen awareness of the way in which, for instance, the weights of the high vaults of these structures pressed downward and outward on their supports and of the action of the flying buttresses in countering the outward pressures. Yet all the evidence we have shows that it was primarily an intuitive understanding, akin to that which we have of the pushes and pulls acting on, and exerted by, our own bodies, and of the ways in which these are balanced. To build, it was necessary to quantify – to choose particular sizes and spacings of supports, particular shapes of vault and arch, and the particular materials of which they were to be built. This was done directly in terms of past experience with similar structures, rather than indirectly in terms of forces and strengths and abstract concepts of the conditions of balance between forces *(Figure 3)*.

The changes were the bringing to bear, in various ways, of abstract concepts of just this sort. In themselves, they had had a long history, seemingly almost wholly independent of practical construction, and stretching back at least to Archimedes who, in the 3rd century BC, first codified the laws of balance for vertically-acting

*Continued on page 9*

*Figure 1*
*Amiens Cathedral.*

Structural engineering has a long history, even though it has only recently become known by that name. These two fine examples of French and English Gothic were both begun in 1220 and largely completed over the next few decades. The spire at Salisbury was added a century later.

*Figure 2*
*Salisbury Cathedral.*

*Figure 3*
*Salisbury Cathedral; cross-section from Price,* A series of particular and useful observations . . . upon that admirable structure the Cathedral-Church of Salisbury, *1753*.

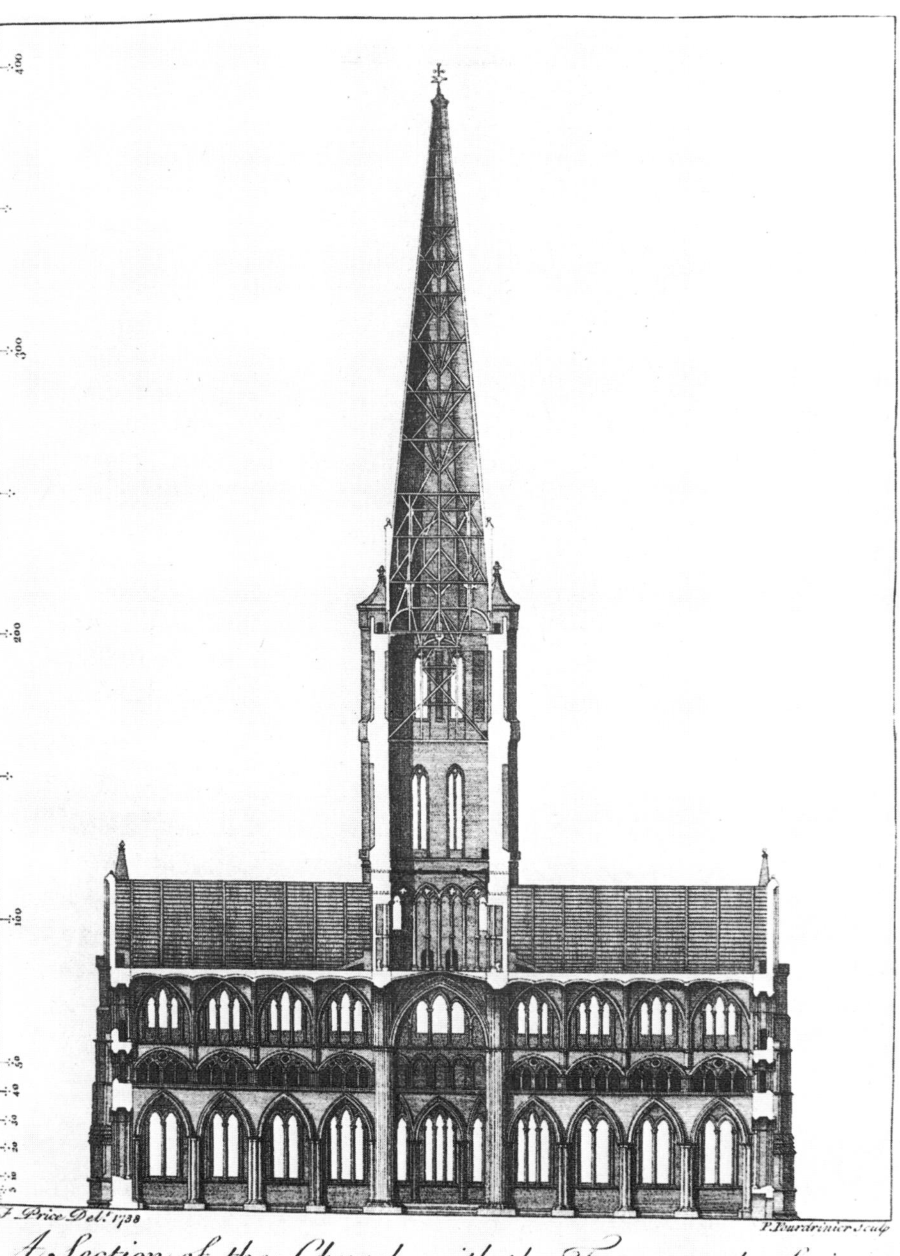


*Figure 4*
*The stability of an arch and a hanging chain from Poleni,* Memorie istoriche della gran cupola del Tempio Vaticano, *1748*.

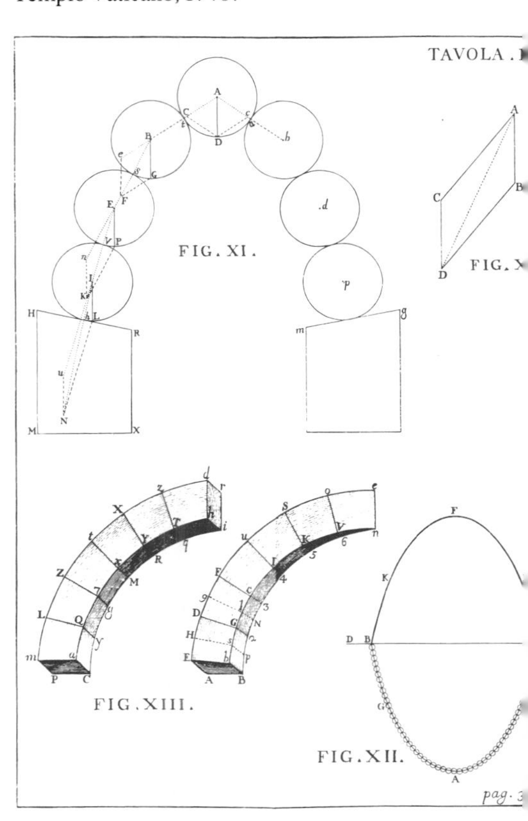


These two plates symbolise the old approach to structure and the new one that was taking its place in the mid-18th century. Price, like the Gothic designers, still saw the 'critical mechanism' essentially in terms of the visible form and its geometry. Poleni shows it, in his Figures X and XI, in terms of the weights of the balls and the pressures they exert on each other.

*Figure 5*
*The frontispiece to Belidor's* La science des ingénieurs, *1729.*

The first major text that attempted systemicatically to place structural design on a rational basis. It was probably written for use primarily by Belidor's students at the school of military engineering at La Fère. As the background indicates, it is concerned chiefly with the construction of fortifications.

weights. By the latter part of the 17th century, this sort of understanding was no longer limited to vertically-acting weights. Men like Robert Hooke turned their attention to such questions as the curve assumed by a hanging chain to maintain equilibrium between the tensions in the links and the weights of the links – and, by analogy, the ideal profile of an arch formed of smooth balls simply resting on one another. At the same time, Hooke and others began to measure the strengths of different materials and the extent to which some of them were (like a spring) stretched by an applied force.

Wren knew Hooke well, so it is probable that Hooke's ideas influenced Wren in, for instance, his final design for the dome of St Paul's. What is beyond doubt is that, around 1742, several analyses were made of the stability of the dome of St Peter's in Rome (then alarmingly cracked near the foot) as a guide to deciding on measures to ensure its future safety *(Figure 4)*. Broadly similar analyses were

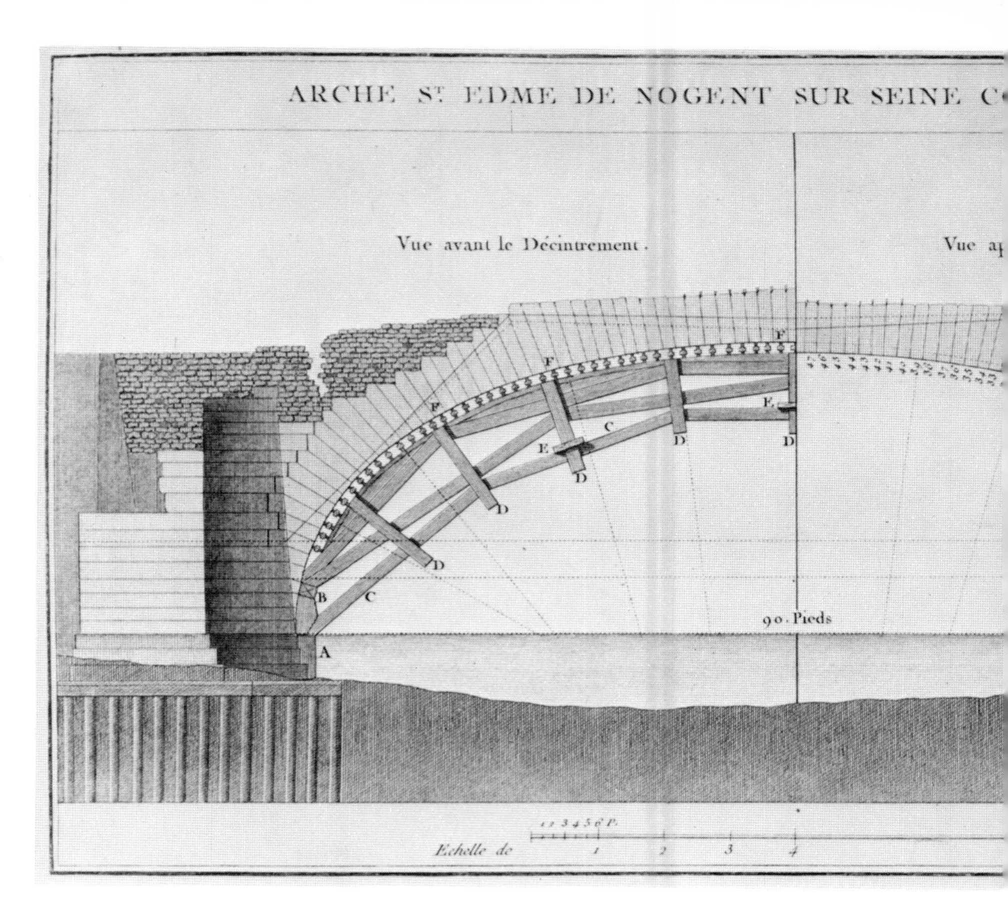


*Figure 6*
*Measured settlements on decentering an arch, 1768.*

Perronet, chief engineer for French bridges and roads from 1764 to 1794, made a careful study of all aspects of the construction of masonry arch bridges and applied the lessons learnt in the design of bridges like that at Neuilly. Very flat arches with splayed haunches were adopted there, carried on piers wide enough only to support their weights acting vertically downwards so as to offer the minimum resistance to the flow of water past them. All arches had therefore to be constructed together and their centres struck simultaneously so that the side-thrusts were always balanced on each side of a pier.

*Figure 7*
*Decentering the arches of Perronet's bridge at Neuilly, 1772 both from Perronet,* Description des projets et de la construction des Ponts de Neuilly . . . , *1782-89.*

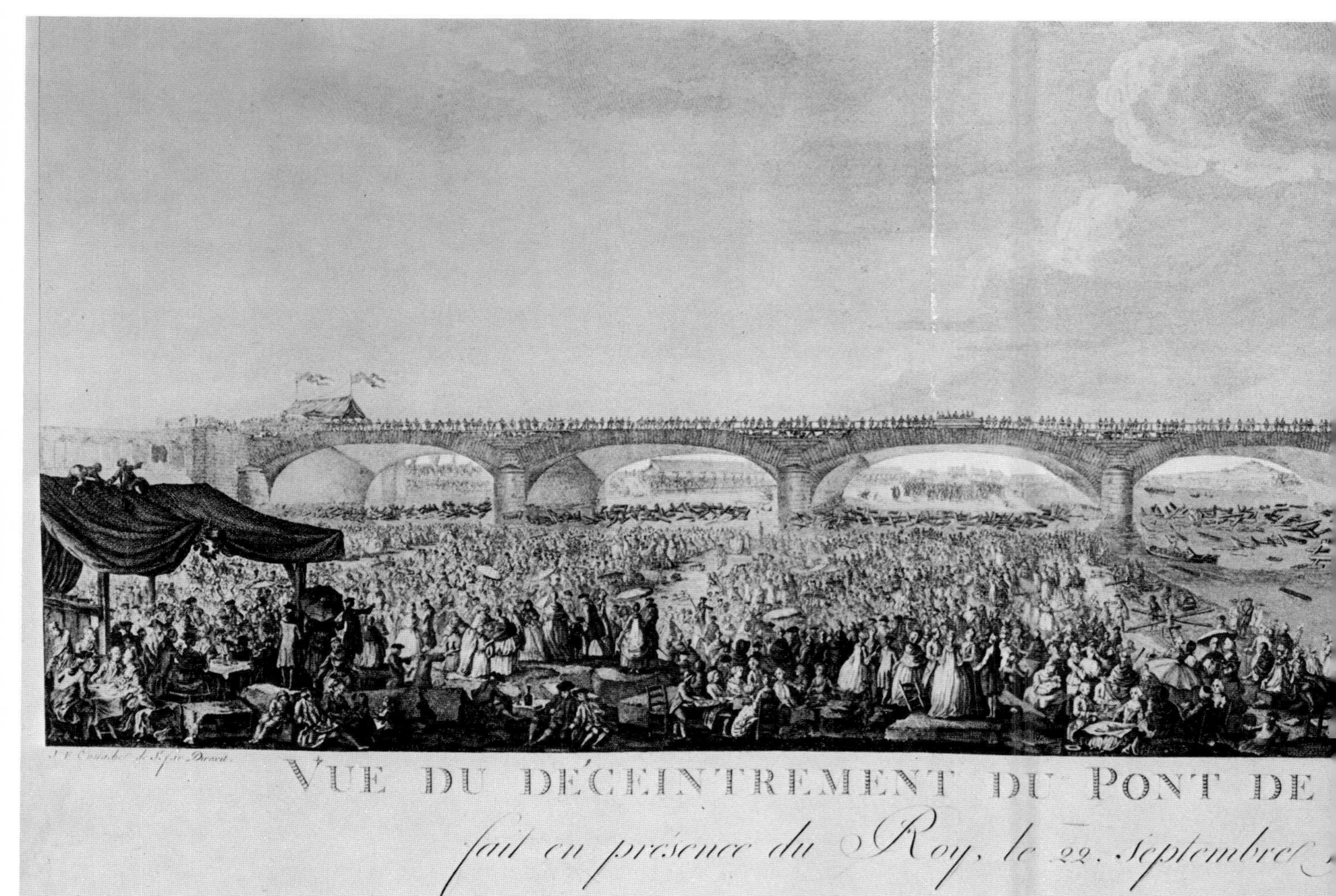

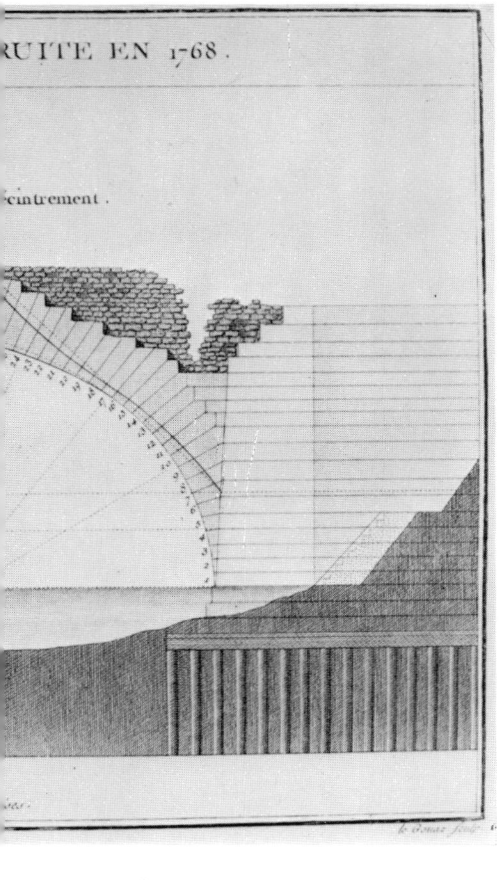

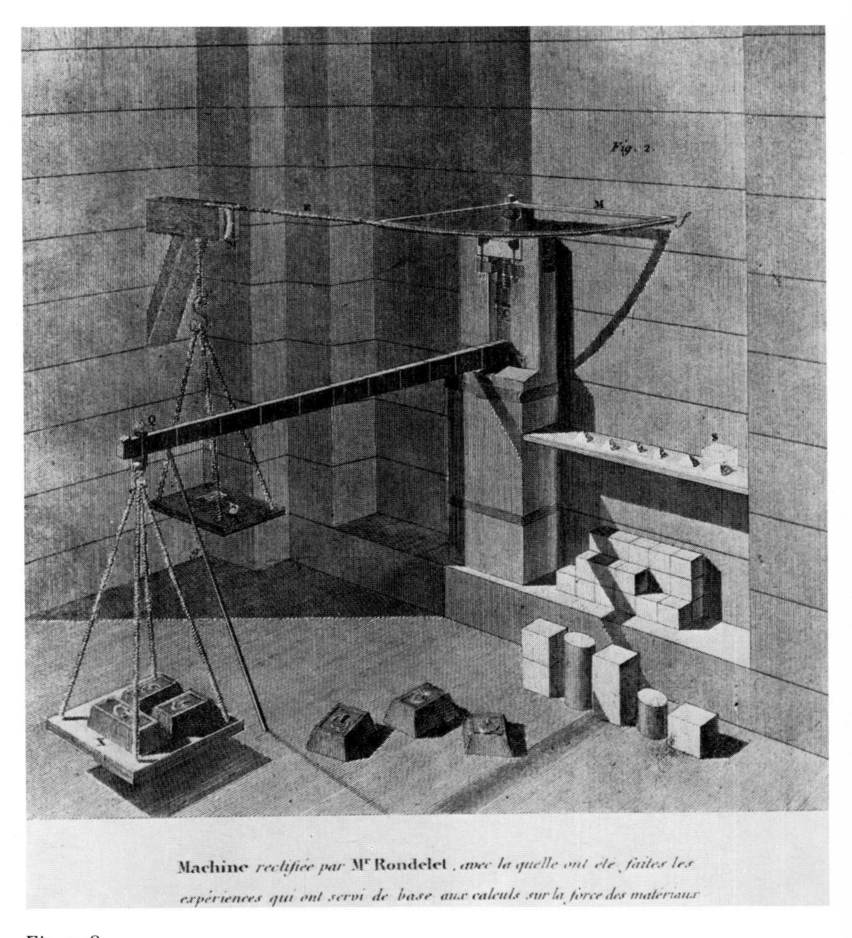

Fig. 2
Machine rectifiée par Mr Rondelet, avec la quelle ont été faites les expériences qui ont servi de base aux calculs sur la force des matériaux


*Figure 8*
*Machine to measure the crushing strength of stone from Rondelet,* Traité de l'art de Bâtir, *6th edition, 1820.*

Design in terms of the forces acting on a structure calls for a knowledge of the strengths of the materials where these may be critical. Several machines for measuring the crushing strength of stone were in use in Paris in the late 18th century and tests were made with them on the stone of the piers of Soufflot's Pantheon.

made a little later to support and guide Soufflot in his designs for what is now the Pantheon in Paris.

In parallel with these changes, the 18th century saw also the emergence of civil engineering as a distinct profession. From the Middle Ages onwards the term 'engineer' had been used intermittently (and sometimes almost interchangeably with 'architect') to denote someone engaged in the design of military engines and defence works. In late 17th century France the military engineer was given formal status by the creation of a *Corps des ingénieurs du Génie militaire*. This corps of military engineers was followed, in 1720, by a corps of bridge and road engineers – the *Corps des ingénieurs des ponts et chaussées*. Equally significantly, a systematic training based on the latest scientific knowledge and understanding was introduced *(Figure 5)*. Among the various schools that were founded was the highly influential *École des ponts et chaussées*. In this lively milieu, backed by the State, the greatest French engineer of the century, Perronet, carried the design of masonry arched bridges to a new and technically unsurpassed peak *(Figures 6 & 7)*.

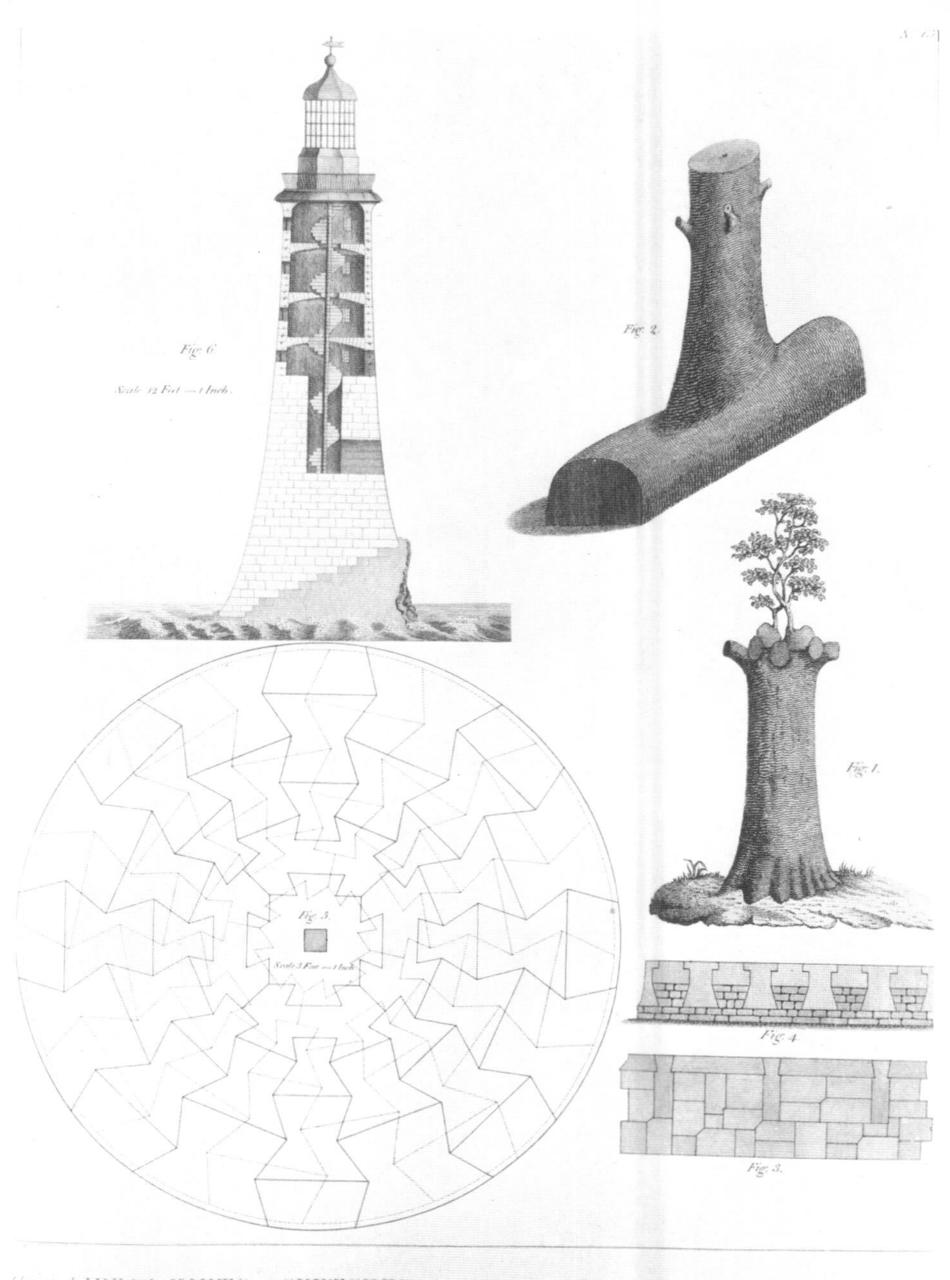


*Figure 9*
*Ideas for the Eddystone Lighthouse.*

*Figure 10*
*Construction of the lighthouse, showing arrangements for lifting and placing stone at different levels, both from Smeaton,* A narrative of the building and a description of the construction of the Eddystone lighthouse with stone, *1791*.

The third Eddystone Lighthouse, built between 1756 and 1759, was an achievement without precedent. Charged with its construction, Smeaton made careful inquiries into everything that could be relevant, including making extensive experiments on suitable mortars for use in a very exposed situation at sea. The profile was suggested by that of the trunk of an oak, well adapted to resist the wind and therefore, Smeaton argued, well adapted to resist the force of the sea. The interlocking of the blocks of stone, as seen in the plan view, was suggested by other types of interlocking illustrated by Belidor in his *Architecture Hydraulique* and reproduced at the bottom right of Figure 9.

And it was Perronet's successor as chief engineer, Gauthey, who acted as Soufflot's, and later Rondelet's, advisor on the Paris Pantheon.

In England, the profession may be said to have emerged in the person of one man, John Smeaton, who combined scientific interests with practical skill in design in much the same way as Perronet *(Figures 9* and *10)*. The only counterpart of the French *Corps* and *Écoles* was, however, a very different body, the Royal Society, founded in 1661. In spite of its royal patronage, this was essentially a group of individuals active in many fields but brought together by a shared scientific curiosity and (to a greater extent than today) a desire to turn new knowledge to useful ends. Both Wren and Hooke had been members. Smeaton was elected a fellow at the age of 28 in recognition of early work on, and with, scientific instruments. He also undertook notable research on the power of wind and water to drive mills and was recommended by the then President of the

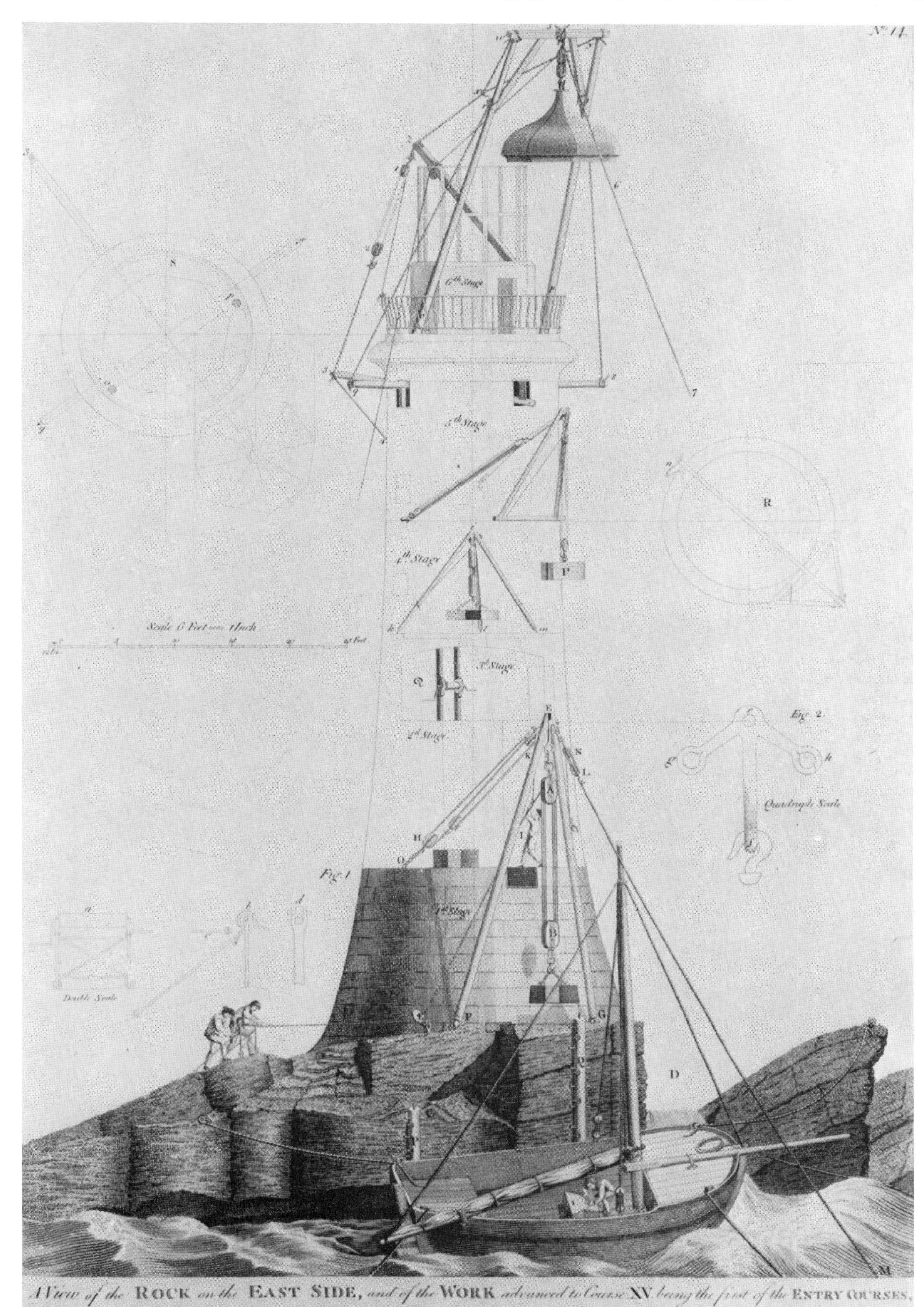


A View of the ROCK on the EAST SIDE, and of the WORK advanced to Course XV. being the first of the ENTRY COURSES, Shewing the manner of LANDING and HOISTING the STONES &c. in every Stage of the BUILDING.

*Figure 11*
*Detail of the iron bridge at Coalbrookdale, 1779.*

This bridge was the first major structure to employ cast iron. But it was essentially a stone bridge in its adoption of an arch of semicircular profile and it largely followed traditional timber practices in its detailing.

Society to prepare designs for the rebuilding of the Eddystone Lighthouse, the commission that really launched him on his civil engineering career. Fifteen years later, in 1771, a Society of Engineers was founded, with Smeaton as its leading light. Their interests ranged much more widely than those of the structural engineer today. But they included these as far as they were then relevant.

In the light of these changes, ought we not, however, to look back another century at least?

The chief justification for looking only as far back as 1780 is the introduction, around then, of the first major new construction material since Roman concrete. This material was cast iron. As James Sutherland points out, iron had long been used in small quantities in another form for such important structural members as tie-rods, just as materials with some of the characteristics of Roman concrete had been used well before the 2nd century BC. But, for the first time, the

*Figure 12*
*Timber framing of the Barley Barn, Cressing Temple, Essex, probably late 12th century.*

cast form became widely available, opening up new possibilities and calling for a fresh approach if they were to be fully exploited. The first large-scale uses slightly preceded 1780. But here there had been little more than a straight substitution of the new material for timber or masonry *(Figures 11* and *12)*. It was really in the 1790s that its full exploitation began in the hands of men like Telford *(Figure 13)*.

Another very significant factor in England at this time was the rapid growth of new industries, which both generated new requirements and provided the resources with which to meet them. Important among these requirements were those for bridges and for fireproof mill buildings. Both (and particularly those for bridges after the coming of the railways) called for much more consideration of the loads imposed on the structure in use, in addition to its ability to support its own weight. Previously, with more massive forms of construction and smaller imposed loads, there had been little need for this, and that had been a crucial factor in permitting the development of structures like the Gothic cathedral without any explicit consideration of the forces acting.

Thus it is in 1780 (without, however, attaching any very precise significance to this date) that the story is taken up in more detail in the following chapters. Each contributor has described what he sees as the most significant British achievements during a particular span of years, with the emphasis on what was actually built – the whole *raison d'être* of structural engineering – rather than on ideas, theories, and general backgrounds, which are less easy to deal with over short timespans. While these have not been ignored where they are particularly relevant to the period under discussion, it may be helpful to conclude this introduction with some wider-ranging comments on the developing relationship between science and engineering, on developments in professional practice including the relationship between architecture and engineering, and on relationships between British achievements and those elsewhere.

*Figure 13*
*Thomas Telford, frontispiece to the Atlas,* Life of Thomas Telford, *1838.*

This great British civil engineer of the late 18th and early 19th century, first President of the Institution of Civil Engineers in 1820, was one of the first to see the real structural potential of iron. He is seen here against the background of his Pont-y-Cysylte Aqueduct – an iron structure carried on tall masonry piers.

## Science and engineering

Structural engineering is concerned primarily with the activity of getting things built; science is concerned primarily with knowledge. Science is useful to the engineer both when it clarifies and extends his essential intuitive understanding of structural behaviour (without which he would be reduced to blindly following precedent in choosing what to do) and when it enables him to make quantitative analyses that draw more effectively on past experience for the purpose of selecting precise dimensions, cross-sections, materials, etc., to meet the given requirement. The chief branch of science with which we are concerned here is structural mechanics. At its most fundamental, this comprises theories about the action and balance of forces and theories about the ways in which materials deform under load and their limits of strength. At another level, these fundamental theories are applied to particular situations such as the bending of a beam or the behaviour of a complex framework. Usually, the theories are expressed in the language of mathematics, without which most of this application of the fundamental theories to increasingly complex situations would be virtually impossible. Such, indeed, is the importance of mathematics that much of the application has been largely a mathematical exercise. To relate the results to the real world, there has, however, been also a constant need for testing.

Some early developments of the fundamental theories have been referred to already, as have some of the first analyses of particular structures. Over the last two centuries the dependence of the engineer on the insights and possibilities of analysis furnished by the scientist has grown continually because of the increasingly wide and demanding range of needs that the engineer has sought to satisfy and the ever-broadening variety of materials, techniques, and forms, on which he has drawn to meet these needs. Almost anyone can design a structure for a small house, using bricks, mortar, and timber, in a traditional way, without any need for modern science. But to design an acceptable and economical structure for a very tall building, making the best use of the materials and techniques now available, can tax to the utmost both the skill of the engineer and the latest scientific knowledge and resources of theory and calculation.

As practical men, with the end always in view and time at a premium, engineers have never espoused science for its own sake, however, while acting as engineers. While they could get along nicely without a new theory, they have, typically, ignored it. On the other hand, when faced with a new and otherwise intractable problem, they have sometimes called in the scientist or mathematician and stimulated him to further effort. Thus there has been a very variable timelag between advances in science or theory and the use of these advances in design. In reviewing past achievements, we must also remember that knowledge can inhibit as well as help. Where it saves us from error it should, of course, be regarded as a help more than an inhibition. But it is rarely complete. It becomes an unfortunate inhibition when its incompleteness means that it instils an unnecessary caution – a consequence that is commoner now than it used to be because of the extent to which concerns for public safety have led to control of design by regulations.

Early British engineers were not wholly ignorant of scientific developments across the channel. Telford, for instance, like Smeaton before him, possessed an extensive library which included most of the major French publications of the time. But they always seem to have placed more trust on direct observation and test than on calculation, and they were less inhibited than any of their successors by an inability to calculate how a new structure would behave, by a fear of failure, or by a need to seek the approval of any academy or regulatory body. Remarkably little theory went into the development of the suspension bridge by Telford and Brown in relation to what we now know of the complexities of the problems it presents and even in relation to the analyses made by the French engineer Navier after his inspections of their bridges. On the other hand, Stephenson's venture into the unknown with his Conway and Britannia tubular bridges called for a major scientific investigation as described in the next chapter.

The one type of structure that was widely used in the 19th century, and that could not be designed efficiently without a clear theoretical understanding of the way in which the loads were carried, was the trussed railway bridge. In the earlier part of the century, large numbers were built, especially in North America, without this understanding. Some were wholly timber, some iron, and some part timber and part iron. All were highly inefficient, with an unnecessary multiplicity of members *(Figure 14)*. There were also many collapses. Once the behaviour was better understood, much simpler forms were adopted with just enough members to create a rigid assembly in each span. The forces could then be calculated in each member and the necessary strengths and stiffnesses provided. The calculation had to assume that, wherever several members met, they were

*Figure 14*
*Savage Bridge, Maryland, 1852.*

A Bollman truss, one of many types patented in the USA during the first half of the 19th century and built in large numbers on the new railways. A better understanding of the structural action permitted great simplification in later designs.

*Figure 15*
*An iron bridge from Verantius,* Machinae Novae, *c1616.*

Another illustration of the importance of the greater understanding of structural behaviour gained since the 17th century, allied in this case with the exploitation of new materials and techniques. In each bridge the deck is supported by diagonal stays descending from towers or pylons over the piers. In Verantius' proposal the linked short beams of the deck would, however, have been excessively flexible and there seems to be no clear recognition of their interaction with the deck. In the 19th century radiating stays (chains or cables) were often used as a secondary support in normal suspension bridges, chiefly to reduce sway and undulation of the deck. Only in the last few decades has their behaviour been understood sufficiently to permit the design of structures like the North Bridge.

*Figure 16*
*North Bridge, Düsseldorf, 1958.*

connected by means of a frictionless pin. Care was therefore taken to introduce such pins until it was realised that they were usually unnecessary and that a better structure might result from the use of simpler, more rigid joints.

The calculations in this case were purely 'statical' ones, i.e. they were based only on the simple conditions of balance of forces (the forces in the truss members plus any imposed loads) acting together at a joint. The calculations could be carried out entirely in terms of the imposed loads and the geometry of the proposed truss. Most subsequent structural design has called for more complex calculations because there have been alternative possibilities of balance in terms of just geometry and imposed loads, just as there were in the truss illustrated in Figure 14. The actual behaviour in such cases depends also on the relative stiffnesses of the alternative paths for each load – i.e. on the relative lengthening or shortening under load – and hence on the characteristics of the materials employed. It is said to be 'statically indeterminate'.

Statically indeterminate structures have many practical advantages, including the obvious one that the existence of alternative paths for loads makes sudden collapse less likely. Strictly speaking, moreover, they include all structures in which different materials are constrained to act in unison, as they are in reinforced concrete. Thus there are few 20th century structures that are not statically

*Figure 17*
*Cable-net canopies for the Munich Olympics, 1970.*

The form here had even earlier models in simple tent structures. But to construct it on this scale called for such complex calculations to determine the precise geometry to give a reasonably uniform loading of the cables, that a powerful computer was needed to make them.

indeterminate in some important respect, and the analysis of such structures has been a major concern of engineering science since the latter decades of the 19th century. It is inevitably more complex, mathematically, than purely statical analysis, so it is hardly surprising that designers have not infrequently fought shy of its full rigour and sought simplifications where they seemed to be justified by experiment or experience. All assumptions about the properties of the materials in an as-yet unbuilt structure, the loads that will, in future, act on it, etc., are, in any case, open to some doubt, and the engineer's objective is a safe and economical structure rather than an elegant and rigorously correct analysis.

It is impossible here to review all developments since the early solutions of the problem of the bending of a beam that is continuous over several supports. Major areas of interest, from the late 19th century onwards, were the behaviour of continuous frameworks with rigid joints and the behaviour of members and structures of reinforced (and later prestressed) concrete. In the past few decades, more attention has been given to fully 3-dimensional structural behaviour and to the general question of how to ensure, at the time of design, that a structure will be safe and serviceable. During this same period, powerful electronic computers have come to the engineer's aid. They have greatly reduced the need for the simplifications and the ingenious computational techniques that facilitated analysis in the middle part of the century. It is no exaggeration to say that they now make feasible the design and safe execution of structures that could scarcely be dreamt of before *(Figures 15* to *17)*. Yet it remains as true as ever that it is the engineer who must conceive the form and envisage clearly enough how it will carry its loads to decide what analyses need to be made and by what criteria the predicted performance should be judged acceptable. This is an onerous responsibility whenever new ground is being broken, as periodic failures during construction or in service continue to testify. The individual engineer is only partly relieved of it by the Codes of Practice devised by his peers to guide him and the regulations devised by legislators to safeguard the public.

## Engineer and architect

It was noted above that the terms 'engineer' and 'architect' were sometimes used almost interchangeably in the past. We are today struck by the structural invention to be seen in the Gothic cathedral. But most designers – whether of buildings or fortifications, bridges or harbour works – either stayed well within the limits of proven practice in construction or moved beyond it very circumspectly. The chief skill they were called on to display was the ability to conceive a form and convey their concept to others through drawings – a skill referred to in Renaissance Italy as *disegno*.

Engineering began to appear as a specialism within the wider ranks of designers as certain types of construction began to call for a more detailed knowledge and understanding of structural and mechanical matters. But Belidor could still follow his *Science des Ingénieurs (Figure 5)* with a longer work entitled *Architecture Hydraulique* which set out to place on a similarly scientific footing the design of canals, harbour works, underwater foundations, etc. And Telford, whose early work was certainly architectural in the modern sense, moved easily to the design of bridges and roads and canals, when opportunity arose and he recognised 'a stronger disposition for executing works of importance and magnitude than for the details of house architecture'.

By the mid-19th century the civil engineer had a virtual monopoly of these 'works of magnitude and importance', which now included all major works in iron and all that called for structural analysis or test. He was relatively unfettered by aesthetic precedent because there was little that was relevant, but his designs often showed considerable aesthetic sensibility and are often today valued as much for this as for their technical merit. This left to the other side of the construction design profession – to the architect, as he continued to be known – most buildings and anything of a more decorative or monumental, than utilitarian, character. He became, on the contrary, increasingly interested in the past and its aesthetic canons, as he saw them. Thus arose a sharp divergence of the two sides of the profession, nowhere better exemplified than by the juxtaposition of Scott's Gothic-style Midland Hotel at St. Pancras and Barlow's iron-roofed train shed – equally fine works on their own, very different, terms.

By this time the civil engineer had already largely dropped the earlier interest of men like Smeaton in machines, leaving these to the mechanical engineer. Further specialisation followed with the introduction of new materials and new structural forms and the need to master more and more theory. Some civil engineers continued to practise over the whole range of construction. Others limited themselves to reinforced concrete or steel structures, for instance, and became known, more precisely, as structural engineers. These soon found themselves entering into a new relationship with the architectural profession. The introduction of steel and reinforced concrete into buildings for the main loadbearing elements made their structural expertise necessary in design, while the architect remained the overall designer responsible for both planning and appearance. Hardly surprisingly, the results were not always happy, as is pointed out on page 90. It is difficult not to regard as the finest works of the early part of this century those – like the Swiss bridges of Robert Maillart – in which an engineer with a good eye remained in sole control.

From around 1910, some architects in continental Europe – first in Germany, later in France and the USSR and elsewhere – began, however, to see the architectural possibilities of some of the new structural forms, as indeed several Chicago architects had already done a few decades previously in the case of the multistorey steel frame. In the 1930s it was no longer necessary to speak chiefly of 'continental' Europe. Thanks partly to a number of architects and engineers who came over from the continent including Arup and Samuely, but also to men like Sir Owen Williams, a similar recognition appeared in Britain. Since 1945 that recognition, and the mutual understanding by architects and engineers of each others' roles and abilities, has become much more widespread, with wholly beneficial results. Many of the best works of these postwar decades illustrated in the last few chapters are the product of true professional collaboration. Yet one must also admit that there has been a tendency, on the part of some architects, to be seduced too easily by the novelty and excitement of new structural possibilities like the cantilever and some shell roofs, and too great a readiness, on the part of their engineer consultants, to give them what they ask for. In a large bridge, a dam, or an offshore oil rig, structural considerations may be dominant; in buildings, they should rarely be allowed to become so.

## Britain and elsewhere

No art has developed for long in complete geographic isolation. It seemed right to celebrate a British anniversary by concentrating on British achievements. But it will already have become clear that these have owed a good deal to achievements in other countries. British engineers have, in return, contributed to, and influenced, developments abroad, from the examples they set by early iron bridges onwards.

It would be out of place here to review all borrowings, leads, influences, and other interactions. The reader should merely bear in mind that the authors of the following chapters were left to choose for themselves the emphasis to be given to them in each period. That emphasis does not necessarily reflect the relative importance in different periods. Broadly speaking, the interactions become more numerous, and certainly more immediate in their effect, the nearer we come to the present. In recent years, there has, for instance, been far more contact, and more continuous contact, between both engineers and scientists on a worldwide basis than ever before.

We may, nevertheless, ask how, or why, there comes to be a British – or any other national – achievement that may be distinguished by more than mere location. Why was the development of the suspension bridge carried so far in Britain in the 1820s, only for the lead to pass, for over a century, to the USA and then to be taken up again in Britain around 1950? Why did the pioneering development of the iron-framed building in Britain lead nowhere after 1860,

*Figure 18*
*Lever Building, New York, 1952.*

*Figure 19*
*Moscow University, 1952.*

*Figure 20*
*York University, 1963.*

All these buildings have a steel frame as the basic structural support. The very large differences between them probably stem more from differences in what the architects and engineers were asked to do than from anything else. The Lever Building might, as one of the most successful buildings of its time in the spirit of the pioneering modern architecture of the 1920s and 1930s, be regarded as the product of enlightened private patronage. It was also a commercial slogan skilfully exploiting a recent change in planning legislation as well as new construction techniques. Moscow University was more a slogan of the state and put into effect a very different concept of state planners for that city. York University was also, in effect, state sponsored, and employed a structural system developed for use in state schools during the 1950s. Its unassertive character stems from a primary concern, on the part of both its architect and the state, for its educational role.

leaving it to a few architects and engineers in Chicago to demonstrate the real potential? Why do we then find the frame apparently exploited so very differently in the postwar decades in the USA, the USSR, and Britain *(Figures 18 to 20)*. And why, at this time, was a novel shell form taken up so enthusiastically in Central America when, across the border in the USA, the chief focus of similar enthusiasm was the very different framed geodesic dome *(Figure 22)*.

There is never a single simple answer. Obviously, the skill and knowledge of the designer, and sometimes the testing and analytical support available to him, are important factors. But at least as important are the opportunities presented to him, the resources of men, money, and materials, and the whole situation in which he works. Unlike the proverbial artist in a garret, he cannot do as he pleases but must do as some client, and ultimately the society in which he lives, asks him and allows him. Major advances have been made in response to new needs and challenges and their direction and pace determined partly by when and where these have arisen.

Thus each major advance in suspension-bridge design was a response to a challenge at a particular place and time and against a different background of resources, prior experience, knowledge, and restraints on venturing into the unknown. Similar challenges were at least partly responsible for the fact that it was in Chicago rather than, say, London that the tall steel-framed building first appeared in essentially its present form, and for rapid developments in steel-bridge design in Germany in the 1950s *(Figure 16)*. The differences seen in

*Figure 21*
*Church of the Miraculous Virgin, Mexico City, 1954.*

In the 1950s Candela made extensive use of the hyperbolic paraboloid form of thin reinforced concrete shell, sometimes to great architectural effect, as in this church. Nowhere else was it used to the same extent. It uses little material to cover a given area, but much labour is required to construct the formwork on which the reinforcement and concrete are placed. In Mexico, this labour was relatively cheap. In Europe, where the form was first used, it became too expensive, and the daring of some of Candela's structures might have been unacceptable to the watchdogs of public safety.

Figures 18 to 20 stem chiefly from different social priorities and values, while the different approaches to roofing a large single space seen in Figures 21 and 22 reflect not only different visions on the part of the designers but also very different national economies, construction industries, and building costs.

In late 18th and early 19th century Britain, the conditions under which engineers worked must have been close to ideal for fruitful innovation. There was every encouragement to try something new and few restraints, a new material in plentiful supply and ample labour, and the designer was able to specify and control the whole process of construction if he wished. By the end of the 19th century, and in the early 20th century, there were fewer challenges and considerably more restraint in the form of regulations, so that there was more scope for initiative in the USA and on the continent. In recent years, there have been fresh challenges both at home and abroad and stimuli to innovate, both to meet new requirements and to achieve more with limited resources. The engineer's task has not, however, been an easy one. Concern for public safety has grown rather than diminished and still tends to be expressed through regulations that are too restrictive and costly to comply with. The easy route to economy

*Figure 22*
*Climatron, St Louis, Missouri, 1960.*

Fuller's development of the geodesic dome, used on a large scale in the Climatron, stemmed from a desire to enclose space with minimum resources in the very different economy of a highly developed country. The dome was therefore designed for easy assembly on site from prefabricated components as near identical with one another as possible.

through large-scale repetitive production that has been followed in the USSR and some other Eastern European countries for mass housing, is denied by a justifiable desire for greater choice and variety. And the organisation of the building industry, with its clear separation of responsibilities for design and construction, has deprived the designer of the advantage enjoyed by many designer/contractors abroad of being able, like his 19th century predecessors, to specify the construction process and take full advantage of it.

What of the future? The possibilities are now so wide in terms of the engineer's skills and the materials and techniques available to him that the answer seems to turn less on these than on what he is asked to do and with what means. Professor Happold foresees a greater use of organic materials, modelled, perhaps, on forms in nature with their characteristic initially compliant response to load. Will this sort of response be acceptable? Or shall we continue to require most of our structures to give way as little as possible when loaded? Natural structures have innate powers of regeneration to cope with ageing or damage. In the absence of similar powers in their manmade counterparts, what limitations on lifespan shall we accept?

It is on the answers to questions such as these, and more generally on the nature of the demands made of him and the conditions under which he will work, that the nature of the engineer's future achievements will now surely chiefly depend.

# 1780-1850

James Sutherland

R.J.M. Sutherland BA, FIStructE, FICE, FIHE, MConsE.

James Sutherland gained experience for his career as a consulting Civil and Structural engineer with Sir William Halcrow & Partners.

He has been a partner in Harris & Sutherland since 1958 and closely associated with the Institution of Structural Engineers over a number of years (a Vice-President 1980-82). Currently he is Vice-Chairman of the Literature Committee and Convenor of the Institution's History Study Group.

Apart from a fairly wide responsibility for the design of many types of engineering works (urban roads and bridges, universities, industrial, civic and residential buildings) he has a strong interest in architecture, in the evolution of towns and in particular in engineering history. He has written and lectured quite widely on engineering and historical matters both in Britain and abroad.

To a large extent the period 1780-1850 was the new iron age. It was a period of rapid change in building and one when iron developed from a secondary material used only occasionally for cramps, tie-rods, and hinges, to becoming the dominant component of many bridges and some complete buildings.

Unlike the small castings and blacksmith's iron of earlier centuries, the engineering irons of the early 1800s (first cast iron and then wrought) were effectively new materials, mass-produced on an industrial scale. It was primarily the successful smelting of iron with coke in place of charcoal by Abraham Darby in 1709 that made big structural castings possible and Henry Cort's twin inventions of the puddling furnace and of grooved rollers in 1784 that paved the way for large rolled sections of wrought iron. Exploitation seldom follows hard on invention, and it took nearly 100 years in the case of cast iron and 40-50 years with wrought iron, for the possibilities to become both highly desirable and feasible on a large scale. These were not just years of improving technology but times when many influences were at work. The growth of the manufacturing industries, the introduction of steam power, improved transport, and radical changes in men's thinking, all played a part in creating the demand for mass-produced iron and in making its production progressively cheaper.

Such was the impact of this 'new' material that it is easy to forget that right up to 1850 – and beyond – most buildings contained no more iron than those of the 18th or earlier centuries. Walls were mostly of brick even when faced in stone and, above the level of basement vaults, timber beams and the occasional timber trussed partition supported the floors, while simple pitched trusses, again in timber, carried the roofs. These were the materials with which architects felt happy and which builders knew how to detail. Not only did masonry walls provide vertical support but they divided space, kept out the weather and, by their massiveness, ensured lateral stability without the designer needing to consider this.

Even in engineering structures, masonry and timber still remained the most common materials for bridges, aqueducts, and viaducts, of moderate span, with masonry dominating all harbour works. The continued use of masonry and wood did not necessarily mean that the methods of design in these materials remained unaltered. In most domestic buildings the changes were slight, but when engineers of a new breed turned their minds to more critical structures the changes in thinking were often startling. Smeaton's careful interlocking of the blocks in the Eddystone Lighthouse (1757-9) was well ahead of its time and could not have been further from the earlier tradition of two visually neat skins of brick or stone filled virtually with rubble. Later, Telford's insistence on hollow masonry for ease of inspection, as in the case of the slender piers of Pont Cysylte Aqueduct (*Figure 1*), followed the same trend. On a more theoretical level the analysis of lines of thrust in this period and the geometrical treatment of oblique arches, although at first uncertain, went far beyond anything considered in the earlier craft period. What is more, the spans of masonry arches had been creeping up and, by the 1830s, had reached 60 m.

The new breed of engineers of the late 18th and early 19th centuries knew few boundaries. Largely self-taught, always learning but often brash and self-seeking, they were ever eager to grasp anything new or to exploit any opportunity. There was no specialisation; all engineering, whether we would now call it civil, structural, mechanical or marine, was one discipline. It was part of the strength of these engineers, as well as a weakness, that they lacked the theoretical education of their counterparts on the Continent and that they were so little aware of the limits of their understanding.

It was perhaps these new engineers who caused the revolution in construction as much as any new material, but they did not do it on their own. In the same way that the development of the iron industry was not due to a single cause, so with construction the industrialists created the demand for new types of building and better means of transport, while they also made these possible. Behind them all was ample risk capital to support the new developments. All of these influences were interlocked, and there was no clear line of cause and effect. The one fact that is certain is that the greatest advances flowed from the right combination of need (or desire), the entrepreneurial will and skill of certain engineers, adequate funds, and new materials, notably iron.

One may well ask what the architects were doing in this period. While some, e.g. John Nash, exploited new materials, they did so more as users of components than as creators of new forms. Stone could be artificial but was used like the real thing; cast-iron beams were simply stronger than wooden ones; cast-iron columns could be more slender than equivalent masonry piers. Most architects did not even go as far as this and turned their backs on the new technologies, thus limiting the range of their works or becoming increasingly dependent on others.

Towards the middle of the 19th century, three major changes took place. Cast iron, always brittle and in beams liable to sudden and catastrophic failure, was eclipsed by the increasing availability of the much more resilient wrought iron. At the same time the need for higher technical education and a scientific understanding comparable to that on the Continent was recognised, but as the understanding grew some of the wild daring of the early engineers was lost. The third change, and perhaps another loss, was in the universality of engineering. By 1850 knowledge was accumulating fast and specialisation was becoming inevitable. The founding of the Institution of Mechanical Engineers in 1847, 29 years after the Institution of Civil Engineers, was perhaps the first formal acknowledgement of this.

The period 1780-1850 was in many ways a 'golden age' of scientific awakening and great engineering progress. Six types of construction each symbolised by one structure, three bridges and three buildings, have been chosen as giving the flavour of the most advanced engineering in the period. All of these incorporated iron and all but one was dominated by it.

*Figure 1*
*Pont Cysylte Aqueduct 1795-1805 Hollow stone piers up to 39 m high supporting canal in cast-iron trough.*

## BRIDGES: 1780-1850

Three new structural forms each dependent on iron revolutionised long-span bridge construction during this period (and to a large extent made it possible)

- the cast-iron arch;
- the level deck suspension bridge;
- the riveted wrought-iron beam or girder.

Of these, the riveted wrought-iron girder emerged only in the mid 1840s, but its development and immediate large-scale application in the Britannia Bridge had the greatest effect of all and established new thinking with new techniques that remained virtually unchanged until well into the present century.

The cast-iron arch

### Mythe Bridge, Tewkesbury, 1823-6

'. . . I deem this to be a good specimen of the cast-iron arch'. Thomas Telford.

Designer: Thomas Telford
Span: 52 m
Width between railings: 7·3 m
Structure: Six braced cast iron arch ribs spanning between masonry abutments on timber piles.
Iron founder: William Hazeltine of Shrewsbury.
Contractor for masonry: Hugh McIntosh

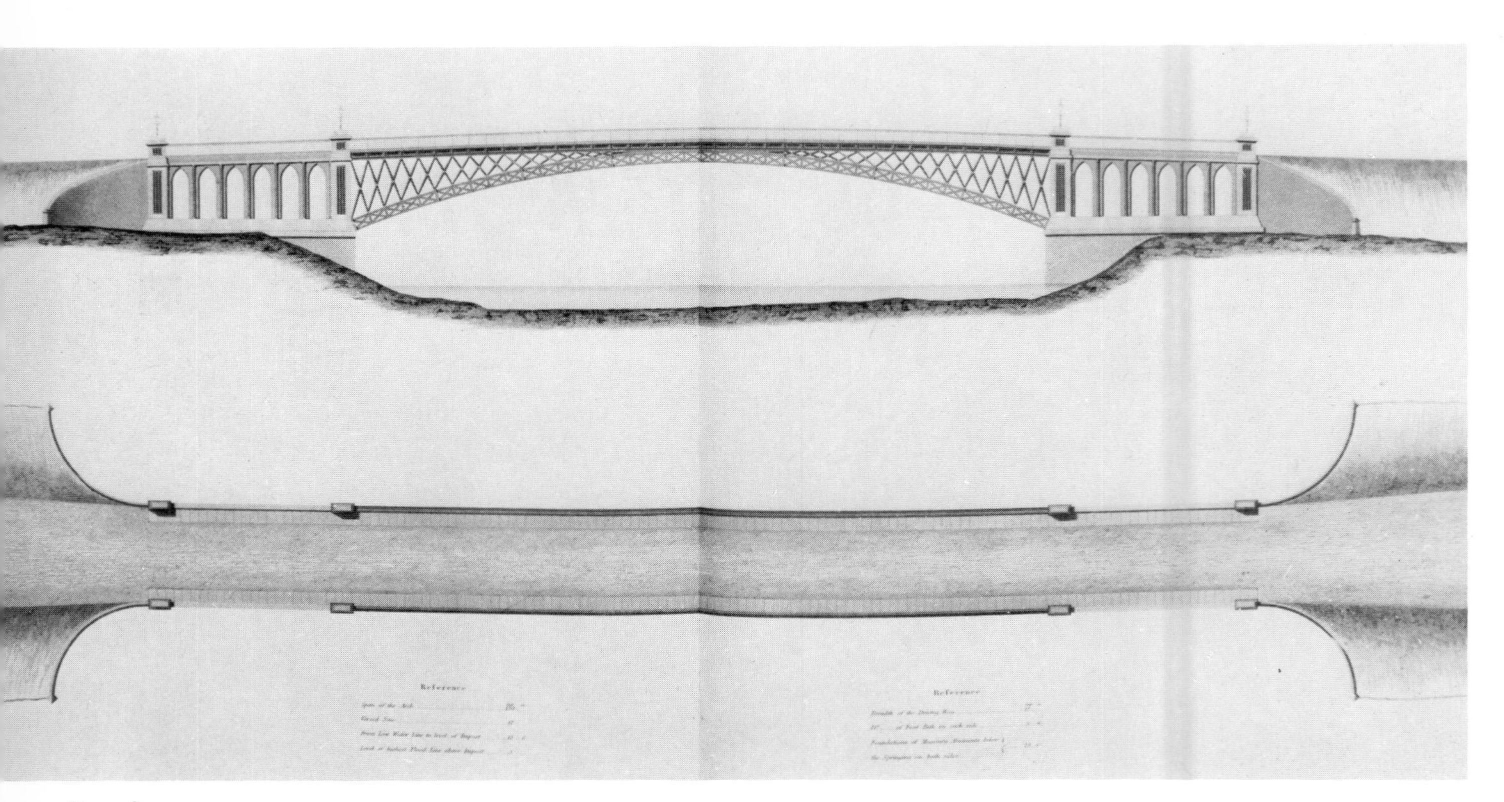

*Figure 2*
*Elevation of Mythe Bridge 1823-6; as illustrated in the* Life of Thomas Telford.

Mythe Bridge was far from being the first cast-iron arch bridge. Starting with the famous Ironbridge at Coalbrookdale of 1777-1779 (*Figure 5*) more than 50 cast-iron arches preceded it, mostly in Britain, including several designed by Telford.

Mythe Bridge never had any claim to have the longest span. Wilson's Wear Bridge of 1792-6 (72 m) and Rennie's Southwark Bridge completed in 1819 (73 m) were longer.

Mythe Bridge does have a strong claim to the title of 'most elegant' cast-iron bridge. It is elegant in three senses. Visually, it is undoubtedly very beautiful. Intellectually, it represents the climax in the evolution of the cast-iron arch; moving away from the heavy earth-filled masonry arch imposing large lateral forces on the abutments, through the confused carpenter's detailing at Ironbridge and the uncertain mutual action of the double arches at Buildwas, Telford arrived at a clear statement of the philosophy of economy through minimum weight, minimum quantities of expensive material, and great simplicity. Finally, the detailing of the ironwork shows a mature mastery of prefabrication for which the ironfounder, William Hazeltine of Shrewsbury, probably deserves as much credit as Telford.

In all, Mythe has been a successful bridge, still surviving with little change and still carrying two lanes of modern road traffic.

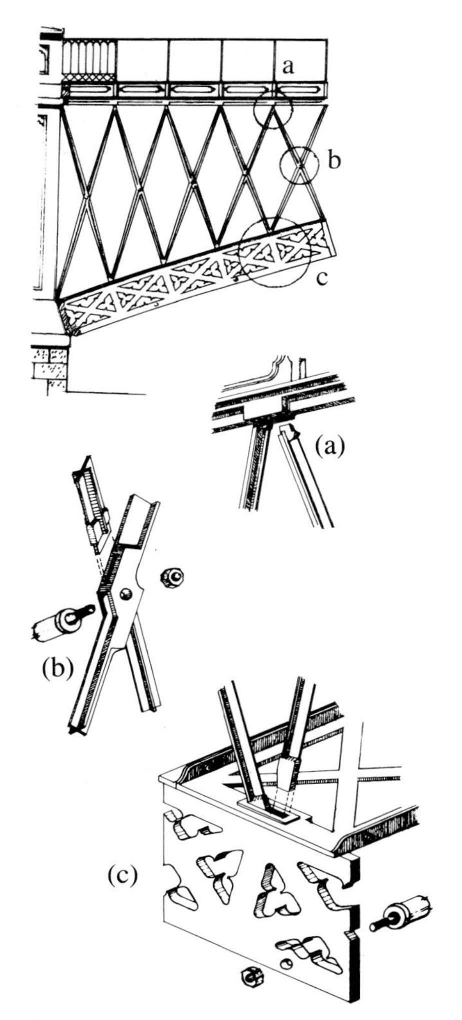


*Figure 3*
*The prefabrication system for the ironwork to Mythe Bridge.*

*Figure 4*
*Buildwas Bridge 1796.*

*Figure 5*
*Ironbridge at Coalbrookdale 1779.*

*Figure 6*
*Mythe Bridge today.*

The level deck suspension bridge

## Menai Straits Bridge, 1819-26

The longest span in its day and in many ways the climax of suspension-bridge building in the first half of the 19th century.

Designer: Thomas Telford
Span: 177 m
Primary structure: Timber decking suspended from eye-bar link chains of wrought iron with masonry towers and arched approaches in masonry.
Iron founder: William Hazeltine

Just as Mythe Bridge may be seen as the peak in the development of the cast-iron arch bridge, so the Menai Suspension Bridge, built roughly at the same time and by the same engineer, could be considered the climax of suspension-bridge building in the first half of the 19th century.

The important distinction between 19th century or later suspension bridges and the primitive 'jungle' type is that the former have level decks suitable for wheeled traffic rather than steeply curved decking laid on top of the supporting cables. Credit for the level deck suspension bridge is normally given to James Finley of Pennsylvania who built several from 1801 onwards and patented his system in 1808. Finley's idea may well have been all his own but there is evidence that others had the same idea several centuries earlier; for instance, Verantius published a very plausible design in *Machinae Novae* in 1595 (*Figure 7*) although there is no evidence that it was built.

In Britain the main credit for the development of the suspension bridge in the early 19th century must be shared between Telford and Captain Sam Brown, both following on chronologically from Finley but apparently little influenced by him.

In 1814 Telford embarked on an extremely adventurous project for a suspension bridge of 305 m span at Runcorn, using multiple wire cables similar to those used today. It was perhaps good for his reputation that neither his proposed single span arch for London Bridge nor his Runcorn Bridge scheme got beyond the drawing board. The safe stresses that Telford calculated from experiments for Runcorn were notably too high and the dip of his cables (1/20 span) too small by later standards.

At the time when Telford was working on his proposal for Runcorn, Captain Sam Brown was developing the eye-bar link for the cables of suspension bridges. He patented this in 1817 and built a number of bridges with eye-bar chains, including his 133 m Union Bridge over the Tweed (1819-20).

The two suspension bridges by Telford, which followed on from the Runcorn scheme and which were actually built, are those at Menai and Conway. For these, Telford used an adaptation of Brown's eye-bar links (*Figure 9*) and showed a real mastery of all but one of the problems of the suspension bridge.

Designed largely from direct experiment rather than mathematical theory, with each link of the cables proof-loaded and meticulous safeguards against corrosion, no apparent precautions were omitted in Telford's struggle to make the performance of the Menai and Conway Bridges perfect. The word 'apparent' is significant because Telford failed to foresee the problem of aerodynamic instability which plagued many 19th century suspension bridges and, even as late as 1940, led to the dramatic collapse of the Tacoma Narrows Bridge.

The Menai Bridge was damaged by wind within a few days of its opening, again in 1836 and more severely in 1839. It was progressively stiffened throughout the 19th and early 20th centuries and finally widened between 1938 and 1940 with new chains and substantial stiffening trusses. No one but a specialist would notice the difference, and even the specialist can still see the original chains at Conway.

In spite of its aerodynamic problems, succeeding generations of engineers have all been loath to criticise its performance. They

*Figure 7*
*Suspension bridge proposed by Verantius 1595.*

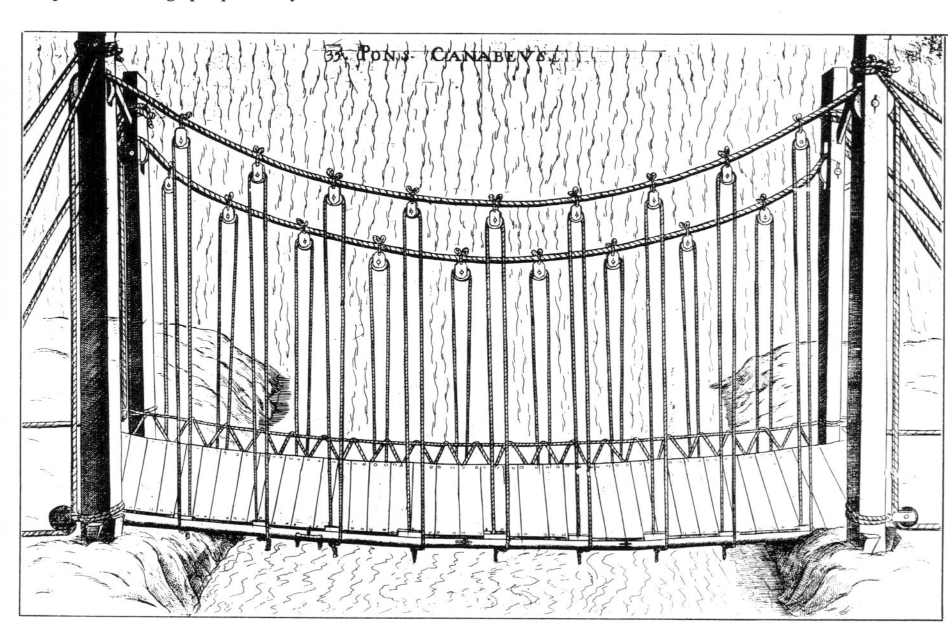

have recognised it, rightly, as a masterpiece on the border of current knowledge and have always striven to keep it as close to the original as possible.

The influence of the Menai Bridge was considerable, on Navier in France in particular and from France back to America in the 1830s where the suspension bridge seems to have been forgotten after Finley's work before 1820.

In 1834 the record for the world's longest span passed from the Menai Bridge to Chailey's Fribourg suspension bridge of 265 m and the initiative with suspension bridges gradually slipped away from Britain not to return until the triumph of the Severn Bridge in the 1960s.

*Figure 8*
*Elevation of bridge.*

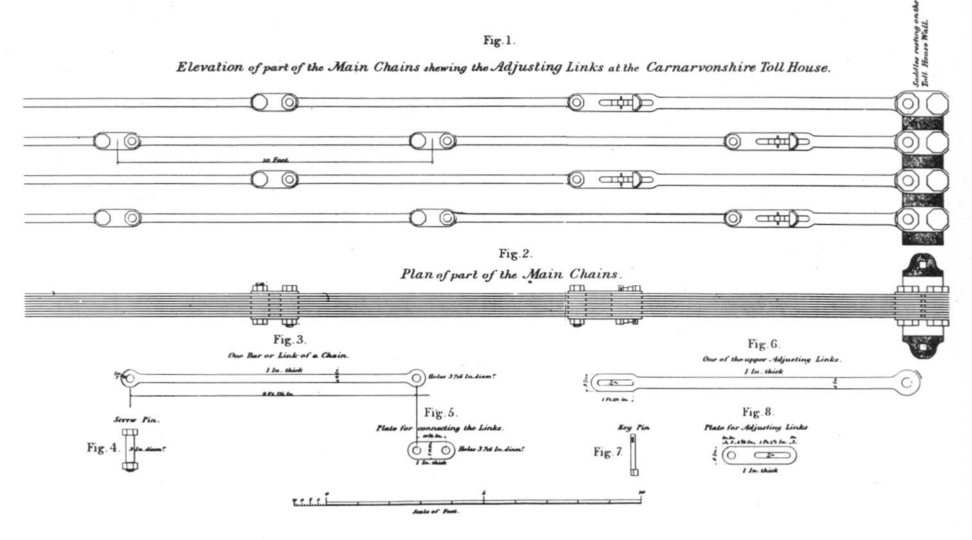


*Figure 9*
*Eye-bar links for chains of Menai Bridge. The form was adapted by Telford from that developed and patented by Captain Sam Brown.*

The wrought-iron girder

## Britannia Bridge: 1845-50

Represents perhaps the greatest step forward in structural understanding and practice in the last 200 years.

Designer: Robert Stephenson assisted by William Fairbairn and Eaton Hodgkinson
Clear spans: 70 m, 140 m, 140 m, 70 m
Structure: Twin tubes in riveted wrought iron large enough for trains to pass through and each continuous over four spans
Contractors (iron works): Charles Mare of Blackwall and Messrs Garforth of Duckinfield
Contractor (masonry): Nowell, Hemingway & Pearson

The Britannia Bridge was built to carry the Chester and Holyhead Railway across the Menai Straits and thus improve the route to Ireland. The minimum span needed was of the order of 130 to 140 m, well within the proven capabilities of suspension bridges of the time. However, in the 1830s, Captain Sam Brown's unhappy experience with the Stockton Bridge had shown that conventional suspension bridges were too flexible for rail traffic.

The only alternative to a suspension bridge was a cast-iron arch. The actual arch spans then built were 73 m or less but doubling this would have been feasible structurally by the 1840s if this form had been acceptable on other grounds. It was not. The shipping interests demanded full vertical clearance over the whole span.

Thus in 1845 Robert Stephenson was faced with a commitment to build a massive bridge in a very short time with no known method of meeting the requirement. The sequence of ideas leading to a solution to the problem is complex and not without dispute. Riveted wrought-iron plate as used in ships was seen as the most likely material from the start. Stephenson consulted Fairbairn because of his experience with iron ships, and Fairbairn brought in the eminent theorist Eaton Hodgkingson. From the earliest concept of circular or elliptical tubes, with the trains running through them, and some support from suspension cables, the design developed to the final continuous box girder of rectangular section with cellular flanges and no cables.

The long-term significance of the Britannia Bridge lies not so much in the successful completion of an extremely difficult and original design but in the effect the massive theoretical and testing programme had on our understanding of the behaviour not only of iron bridges but of all types of structure.

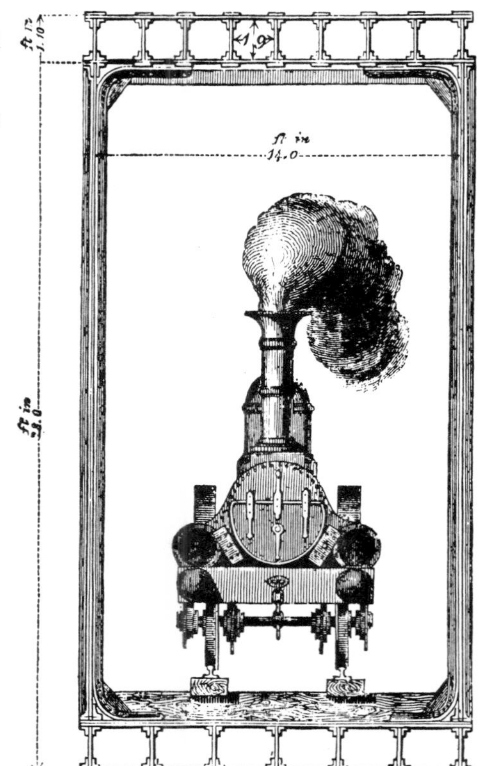

*Figure 10*
*Cross-sectional view of one of the pair of tubes as finally built, showing the cellular flanges and stiffened webs found necessary by experiment to prevent plate buckling.*

*Figure 11*
*Mr Stephenson putting in the last rivet.*

*Figure 12*
*Isometric projection (not to scale).*

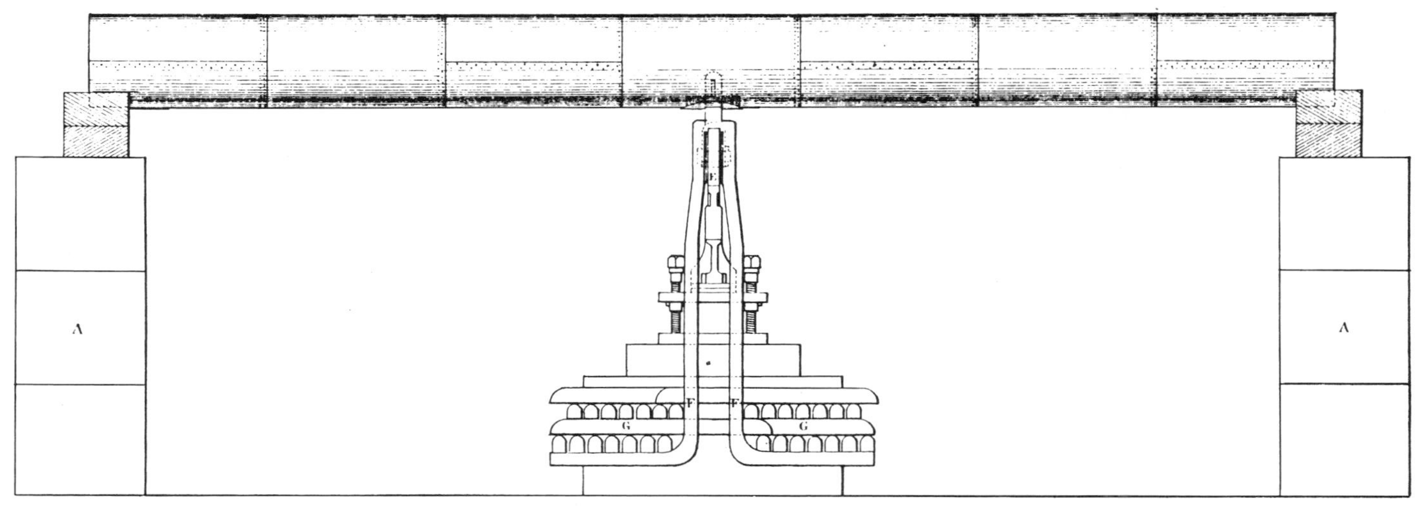


*Test rig with circular or elliptical tube in place for load test loading.*

*Figure 13*
*Loading tests on large-scale models.*

By test, the problem of plate buckling was isolated from the earlier belief that wrought-iron was inherently weaker in compression than in tension. Rivets were analysed and found to act as much by clamping as by dowel action. Temperature movements were analysed, allowed for, and measured. Wind forces were fully provided for.

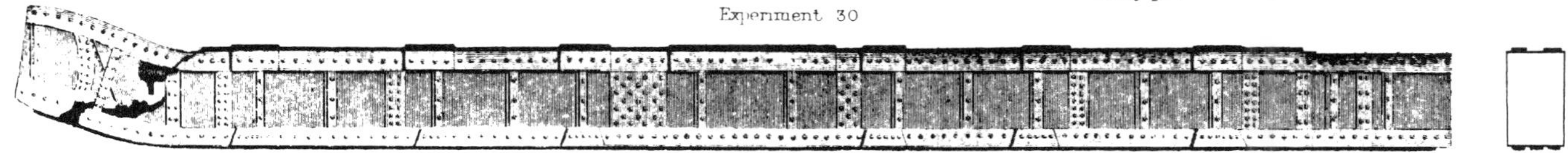


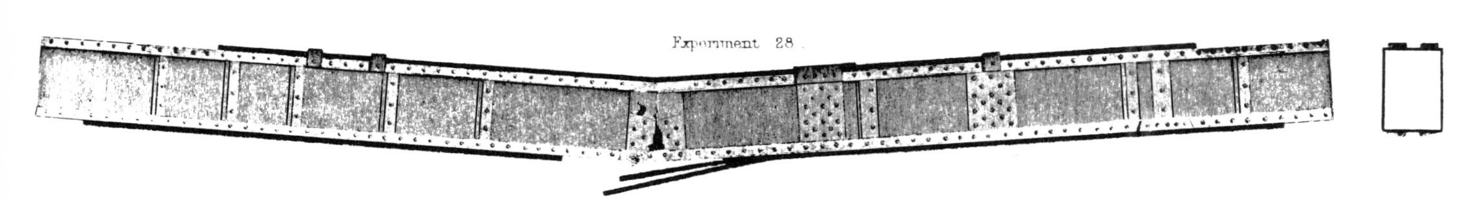


*Typical results of load tests on rectangular tubes with stiffened webs.*

| | | | | | | | | | | | | |
|---|---|---|---|---|---|---|---|---|---|---|---|---|
| 15 | Sept. 18 | 26·25 | 24· | 21·25 | 14·125 | ·1594 | ·1455 | 3·823 | ·379<br>·772<br>1·152<br>1·534<br>1·915<br>2·297<br>2·672<br>3·050<br>3·444 | ·04<br>·09<br>·13<br>·17<br>·22<br>·28<br>·34<br>·42<br>·45 | Barely perceptible. | Failed at top, before the whole of the last weight came on it. Breaking-weight probably 3·246 tons.<br>Minor diameter diminished before failure by 1·9 inch. |
| | | | | | | | Thickness of Plate, ·0688 inch. | | | | | |
| 16 | Sept. 18 | 19·66 | 18·5 | 12· | 7·5 | ·1035 | ·0977 | 2·038 | ·379<br>·770<br>1·161<br>1·548<br>1·930<br>2·311<br>2·499<br>2·685<br>2·875<br>3·065 | ·125<br>·2<br>·3<br>·4<br>·51<br>·625<br>·71<br>·78<br>·87<br>·95 | <br><br><br><br><br>·04<br>·08<br>·1<br>·14 | Tube with a cell or fin on top; which, however, soon became distorted, doubling up for some inches on each side of centre. |
| | | | | | | | Thickness of Plate, ·071 inch. | | Not broken, but shewing much distress on top side. | | | |

*Typical results of loading test on elliptical tubes.*

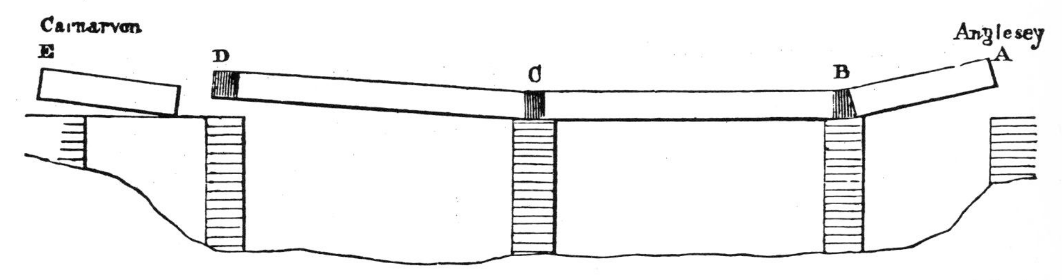


*Figure 14*
*Method of building in fixity when jointing the tubes.*

Not only was each tube analysed as a continuous beam over the intermediate supports but the benefit of continuity even for the self-weight was ensured by raising one end of each tube by a calculated amount and lowering it after jointing.

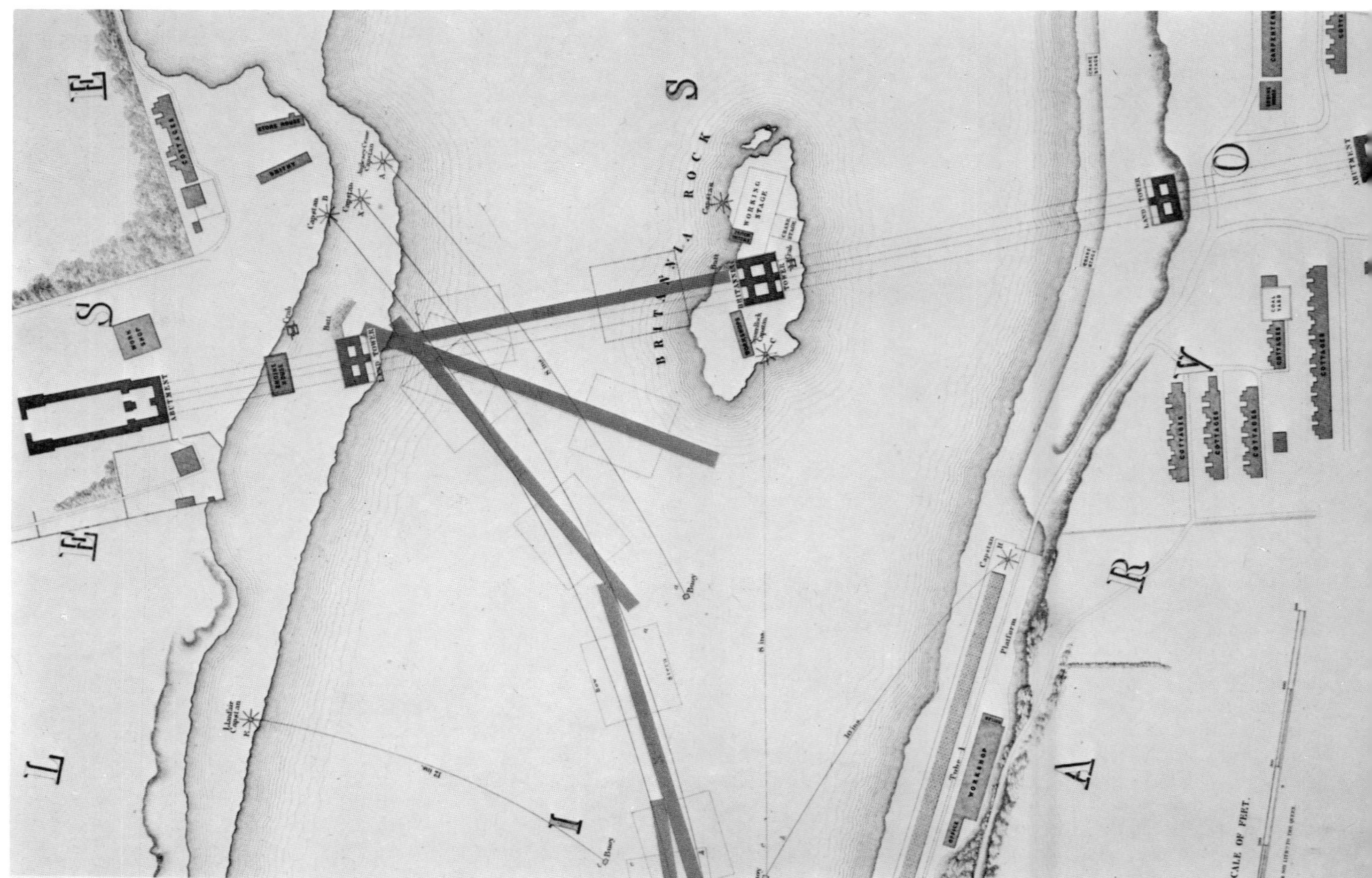
BRITANNIA ROCK
WORKING STAGE
LAND TOWER
ABUTMENT
COTTAGES
WORKSHOP
Platform
Tube 1
SCALE OF FEET.

*Figure 15*
*Elevation of the bridge.*

The 140 m central spans were fabricated on the shore, floated out, and raised by hydraulic jacks.

*Figure 16 (left)*
*Plan showing stages in the floating out of one of the 140 m tubes.*

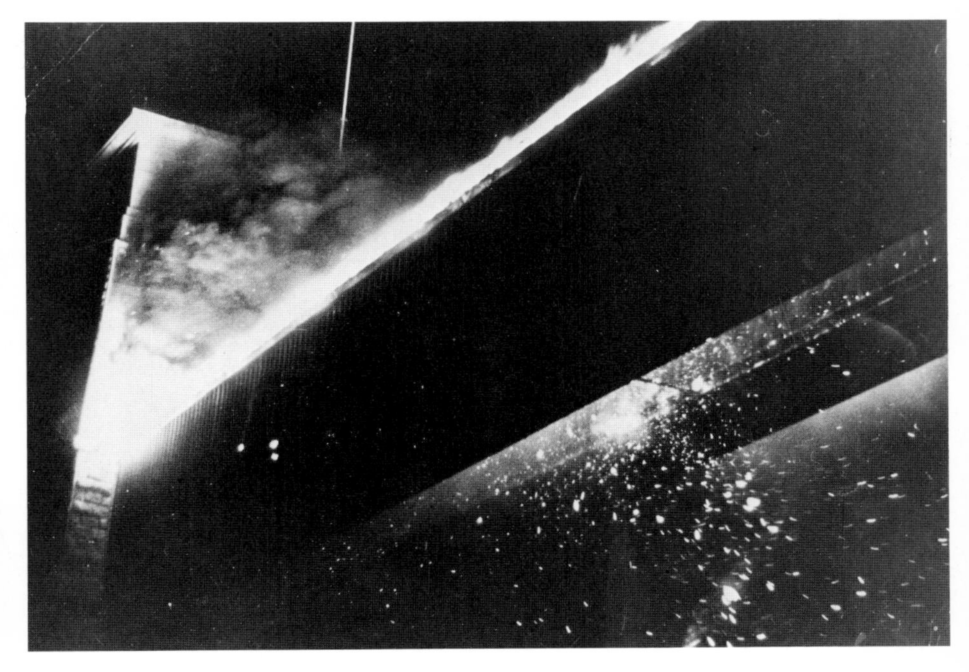

*Figure 18*
*The fire May 1970.*

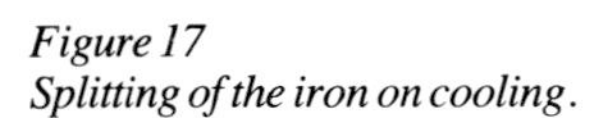

*Figure 17*
*Splitting of the iron on cooling.*

The Britannia Bridge gave good service for 120 years, but in May 1970, soon after a major appraisal had given it a clean bill of health, it was damaged by fire. Ironically, it was the burning of a lightweight 'roof' provided to save the tubes from rust that caused their destruction. Structural continuity was lost in the heat and when the iron cooled the distortion and splitting were such that there was no alternative to complete replacement. However, the slightly smaller Conway Tubular Bridge built at the same time remains, like Telford's suspension bridge alongside, in the form in which it was first built.

## NEW FORMS OF BUILDING: 1780-1850

Iron was the main new influence in this period but its use in buildings was usually less obvious and less dramatic than in the major bridges just described. However, there were two types of building, neither generally dominated by architects, where structural forms were revolutionised largely, but not entirely, by the use of iron as a structural material. These were:

- mills, where fire was the dominant factor;
- glasshouses, where unrestricted light was all important.

Fire-resistant mill buildings

### Belper North Mill: 1803-4

A completely incombustible structure of masonry and cast iron.

| | |
|---|---|
| Designer: | William Strutt |
| Max. floor span: | 2·7 m |
| Structure: | Masonry external walls cast-iron columns on a grid of 2·7 m × 2·1 m or 2·4 m brick jack arches. Cast-iron roof framing |

In the 18th or early 19th century fire was the main hazard with the textile mills – or factories as they would be called today. These were nearly always multistorey buildings planned around a system of shafts and belts which transmitted power to the individual machines from a central prime mover, either a waterwheel or possibly later a steam engine. The arrangement in the case of Belper North Mill is shown in Figure 21.

Traditionally, these buildings had massive masonry walls which contained and stabilised a simple framework of boarding, beams, and closely spaced columns, all in timber. It was this highly combustible interior that was gradually transformed around the turn of the century into a much more robust and incombustible assembly of cast-iron columns and beams supporting masonry jack arches or occasionally stone slabs.

The event that probably gave the greatest impetus to the change was the dramatic burning of John Rennie's newly completed Albion Mills in 1791 (*Figure 19*).

The main figures in the development of fireproof mills were William Strutt of Derby (1756-1830) and Charles Bage of Shrewsbury (1752-1822), although Boulton & Watt and others contributed.

*Figure 19*
*Albion Mills on fire, Wednesday morning March 2nd 1791.*

Strutt's first essay in fireproof building, at Milford 1792-3, had brick jack arches spanning between heavy timber cross-beams supported by cast-iron columns, the exposed soffits of the beams being protected against fire by plaster. Bage went one step further by introducing cast-iron beams, albeit of limited span, in 1796, and thereafter cast-iron beams became almost standard. Figure 20(a) shows a transitional stage and Figures 20(b) and 20(c) show comparable forms of fully incombustible construction.

Belper North Mill was advanced for its time with even the roof member in cast iron. Following this era the evolution of mill and warehouse buildings was slow with the brittle cast-iron beams gradually replaced by riveted wrought iron but the stabilising walls of masonry remaining throughout the 19th century. A notable exception was the Boat Store at Sheerness described in the next chapter.

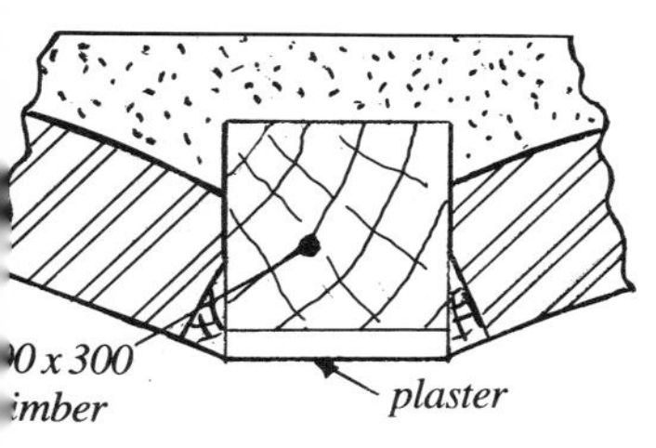


*(a) Strutt 1792*
*Cast-iron columns*
*Protected timber beams*
*Tied brick jack arches*
*2·7 m beam span*
*2·7 m arch span*

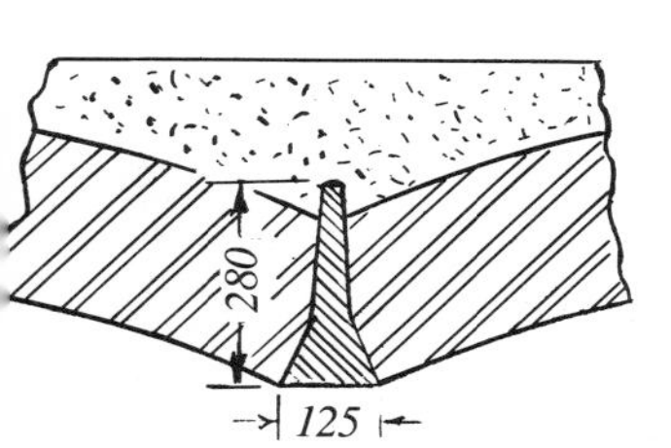


*(b) Bage 1796*
*Cast-iron columns*
*Heavy cast-iron beams*
*Tied brick jack arches*
*2·9 m beam span*
*3·2 m arch span*

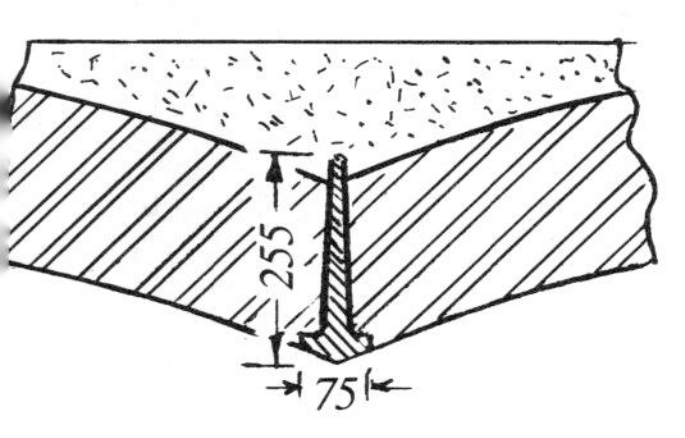


*(c) Strutt 1803*
*(as at Belper North Mill)*
*Cast-iron columns*
*Lighter cast-iron beams*
*Tied brick jack arches*
*2·7 m beam span*
*2·1 m arch span*

*Figure 20*
*Cross-sections of fire-resistant mill floor constructions.*

*Figure 21*
*Cross-sections through Belper North Mill.*

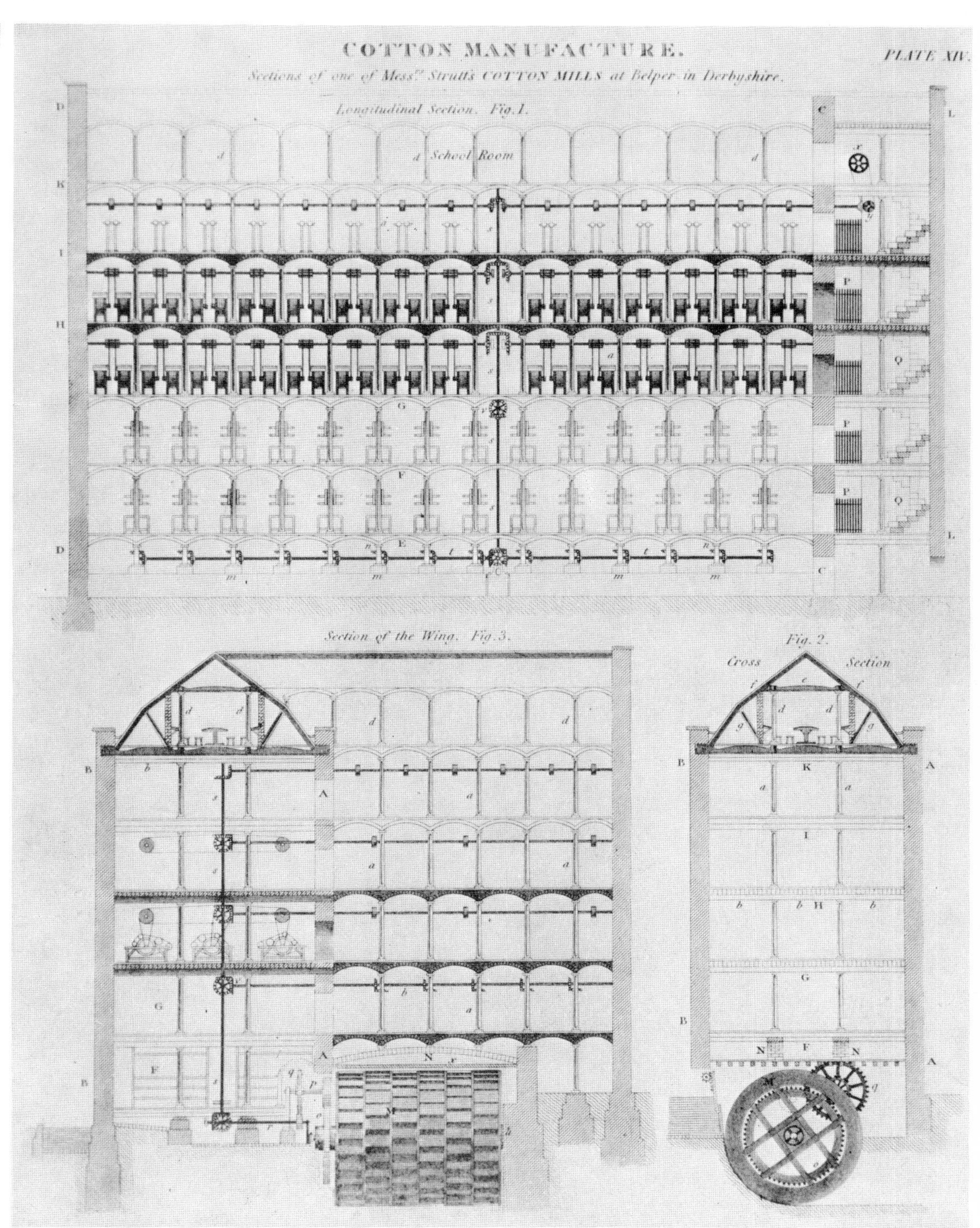

## A CONTRAST IN GLASSHOUSE DESIGN

It was a difference of thinking, rather than of time, that separated two masterpieces – The Great Stove, Chatsworth, and The Palm House, Kew.

Apart from mills of the type just described, it was in glasshouses or conservatories that the new structural ideas were most fruitful. Three men were dominant in this field: J. C. Loudon (1783-1843), Joseph Paxton (1803-1865), and Richard Turner (1798-1881). The first two were primarily gardeners and the third an ironfounder. All three were natural engineers and major innovators. Two of these, Loudon and Turner, were 'men of iron' while the third, Paxton, was, in spite of a reputation as a master of iron, really a master of timber construction with only a minimal understanding of iron.

### J. C. Loudon

Loudon was first in the field with a slender wrought-iron glazing bar (*Figure 22*) which he 'invented' in 1816 and which was designed to give the minimum restriction to light. This bar was easily bent to form curvilinear or ideally domed glasshouses in which Loudon and his contemporaries had a strong belief. The theory was that the benefit of the sun's rays would not pass through a sheet of glass unless the rays struck it almost at right angles; thus as one writer put it you should 'make the surface of your greenhouse roof parallel to the vaulted surface of the heavens', the idea being that some part of the surface was always perpendicular to the sun's rays. An alternative, also proposed by Loudon, was to use ridge and furrow glazing at an optimum slope with which part of the glass would be at right- angles to the sun's rays twice each day and thus twice as much light would get in.

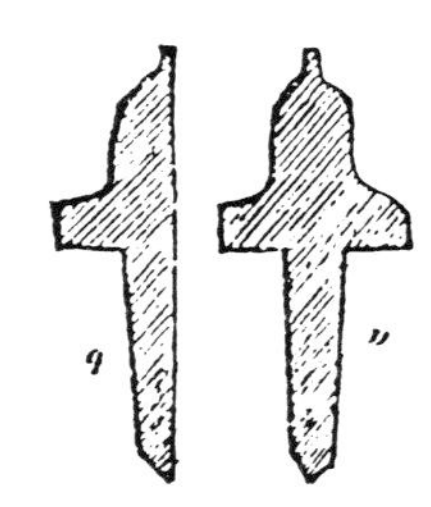

*Figure 22*
*Loudon's wrought-iron glazing bar.*

*Figure 23*
*Bretton Hall glasshouse built by W. & D. Bailey in 1827 using Loudon's glazing bars spaced at 175 mm with short lengths of straight glass between them. It seems that a clear central span to the dome of more than 16 m was at least intended.*

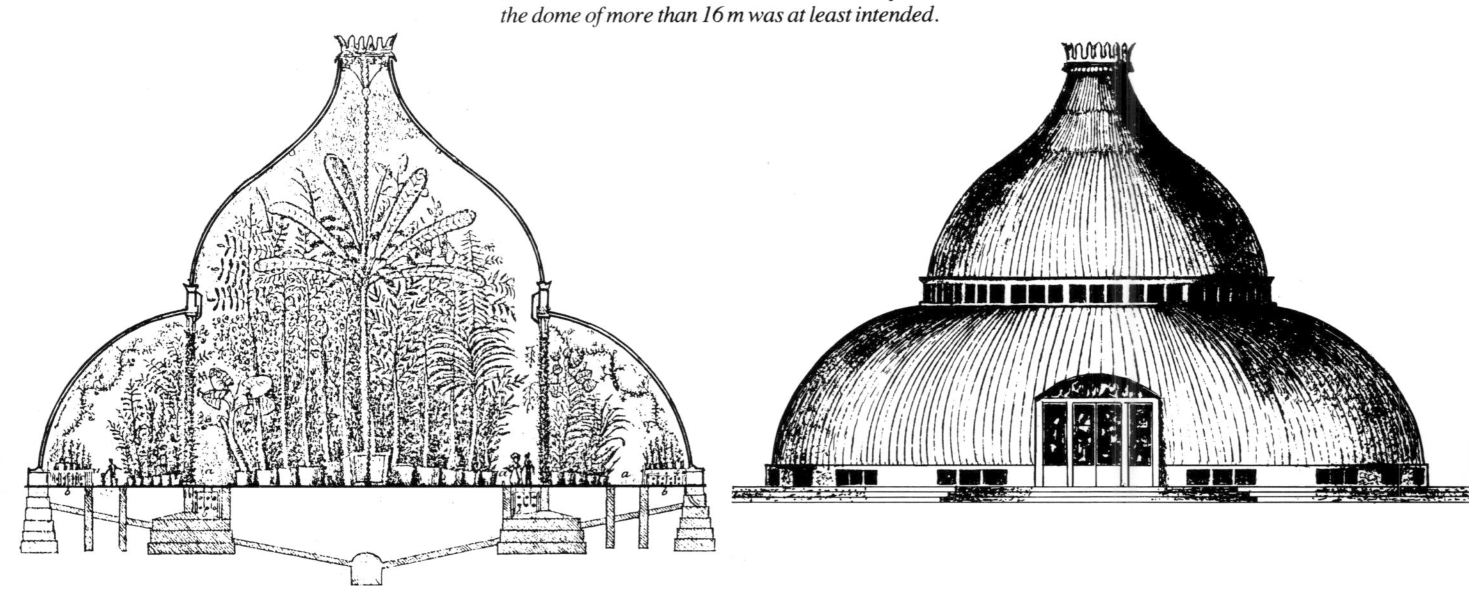

Gardening was becoming very scientific and although these theories on light have been discredited they are important for the effect they had on the structural forms of glasshouses.

There is no record of Loudon building a ridge and furrow glasshouse, but he must have found that, when he curved his glazing bars to satisfy his ideas on light, they would arch and thus span considerable distances without intermediate supports. The result was a number of very elegant curvilinear glasshouses built by a contractor W. & D. Bailey with whom Loudon worked and to whom he made over the rights to his glazing bar. One of the boldest of these was at Bretton Hall, Yorkshire, built in 1827 (*Figure 23*).

This glasshouse was 30 m in diameter with a ring of columns at the change of curvature but 'no rafters or principal ribs'. Thus the glazing bars must have spanned about 7·0 to 7·5 m. The question whether there was a central support in its final construction is still unanswered, but Figure 23 indicates that the intention was to have a dome spanning more than 16 m. Loudon records that before the structure was glazed 'the slightest wind put the whole of it in motion' but that once the glass was in place it was absolutely firm. Clearly, they had built a membrane structure in which the glass and the ribs acted together.

Regrettably, this glasshouse was dismantled soon after its owner died. A slightly later, but smaller, example of the type – one of a handful that survive – is shown in Figure 24.

*Figure 24*
*Bicton Park Palm House. Probably built in the 1830s by D. & E. Bailey who succeeded W. & D. Bailey. Incorporates Loudon-type glazing as at Bretton Hall.*

# Joseph Paxton and the Great Stove at Chatsworth 1836-40

| | |
|---|---|
| Designer: | Joseph Paxton (with Decimus Burton) |
| Max. span: | 21·3 m |
| Max. height: | 20·4 m |
| Overall plan dimensions: | 84·5 m × 37·5 m |
| Floor area: | 3169 m$^2$ |
| Main structure: | 'Laminated' timber arch ribs and cast-iron columns. |
| Glazing: | Ridge and furrow with long straight 'cylinder' glass in timber glazing bars the whole laid to the curve to the laminated ribs. |

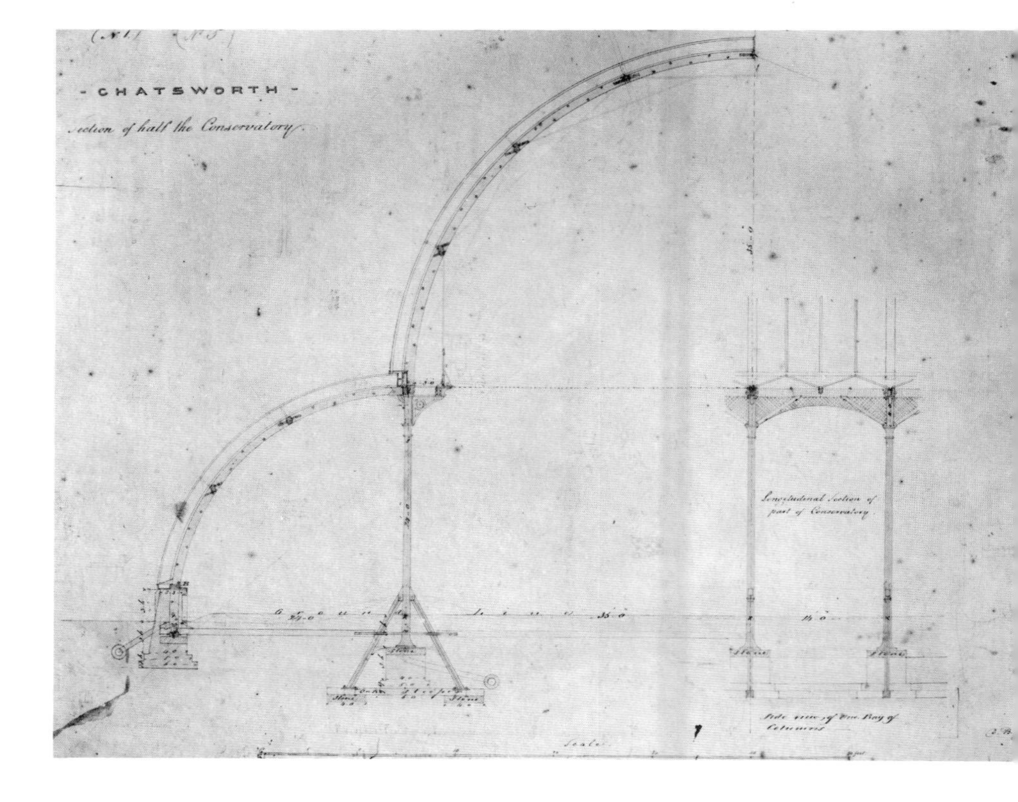


*Figure 25*
*One of the drawings at Chatsworth signed by Decimus Burton. Because the building was demolished in 1920 it is now impossible to compare these drawings in detail with the final construction.*

The first glasshouses designed by Paxton at Chatsworth date from about 1832 when he was 29 years old and had been head gardener there for 6 years. Paxton used ridge and furrow roofs because he believed, as did Loudon, that they would let in more light than roofs in one plane. However, unlike Loudon, Paxton favoured timber for his glazing bars and for almost all the rest of his structures, where only the columns were free standing in cast iron.

Paxton's developing mastery of timber and glass construction, and of labour-saving ways of machining and assembling it, reached a climax in his work on the Great Exhibition Building in 1851 which is described in the next chapter. However, in the late 1830s he was already able to demonstrate this on a colossal scale in the Great Stove House at Chatsworth, a building whose size, for a private greenhouse, is hard to comprehend; its floor area and its clear span were 40% larger than those of the Palm House at Kew and its height no less.

In this vast building, Paxton combined both a curvilinear shape and ridge and furrow glazing (*Figure 26*) taking advantage of the full spanning potential of each. Further, he persuaded the glass makers, Chance Brothers, to supply the newly introduced cylinder glass in 1·2 m lengths, so that each pane could be not only broader than previously but unjoined between ridge and furrow.

There has been some debate on the position of the architect Decimus Burton on this building. The only existing drawings are signed by Burton but dates and all other evidence point to Paxton as the originator of the design and as being the man who was in control technically from beginning to end. It seems that Paxton's employer, the 6th Duke of Devonshire, may have been persuaded of the need for a second opinion or possibly had doubts himself on the wisdom of leaving so large a project solely to the judgment of a 34-year-old gardener, however able. If, at this stage, the Duke had any doubts about Paxton, these must have been dispelled more than amply by the events that followed.

*Figure 26*
*Each valley was a gutter into which rain water was directed by the slope of the glazing bars. This picture shows work during restoration.*

*Figure 27:*
*The Great Stove at Chatsworth.*

# Richard Turner and the Palm House at Kew 1844-48

Figure 28
*The Palm House as it is today.*

| | |
|---|---|
| Designer: | Richard Turner (with Decimus Burton) |
| Max. span: | 15·2 m |
| Max. height: | Approx. 20 m |
| Overall plan dimensions: | 110·5 m × 15·2 m (wings) 30·4 m (centre) |
| Floor area: | 2274 m$^2$ |
| Main structure: | Wrought-iron arch ribs (and cast-iron columns in central section). |
| Glazing: | Curved panes of long cylinder glass fixed in wrought iron glazing bars at approx. 250 mm centres. |

Richard Turner was in no sense a gardener but an ironfounder associated, to varying extents, with many famous glasshouses, including those at Belfast and Dublin, the Winter Garden in Regents Park, and, above all, the magnificent Palm House at Kew. He also built numerous smaller glasshouses, mostly in Ireland, and the world's first really long-span railway roof, at Lime Street Station, Liverpool (see page 59). He submitted an entry based on iron for the Great Exhibition Building Competition which was well before Paxton's blotting paper sketch and was 'highly commended' but, as he felt rather bitterly, he was out-manouvred by Paxton and others.

The influences on Turner are uncertain, as are most aspects of his life. Many of his ideas were highly original, at least in relation to glasshouses, but were clearly opposed to those of Paxton.

Turner's originality reached a peak at the Kew Palm House (*Figures 28-30*). For the main arch-ribs he used Vernon & Kennedy's rolled wrought-iron ships deck-beams, which were probably the first rolled I-beams (5 years ahead of Zorés in France). These were made in lengths of only 3·8 m and to provide the 12 m lengths necessary for each half of his tall 15 m arched spans, Turner invented a form of thermic welding, the details of which, regrettably are lost. Also, for longitudinal stability, he employed tie-rods 'stressed' onto hollow cast-iron tubes between the ribs by tightening nuts at the ends (*Figure 30*). All this was patented. The glazing bars were made of wrought iron, similar in section to Loudon's, but more widely spaced, as now possible with large-pane cylinder glass.

Perhaps almost more interesting than the advanced technical details of this building is Turner's relationship with the architect Decimus Burton over the evolution of them.

For a long period, Burton and Turner sparred with each other, submitting rival schemes to the Director, Sir William Hooker, and openly criticising each other's proposals. Eventually, in order to get the job, Turner had to put in a tender for a cast-iron structure designed by Burton, certain in his own mind that he would be able to change this later. He did so and the result was a spectacular success, Turner's

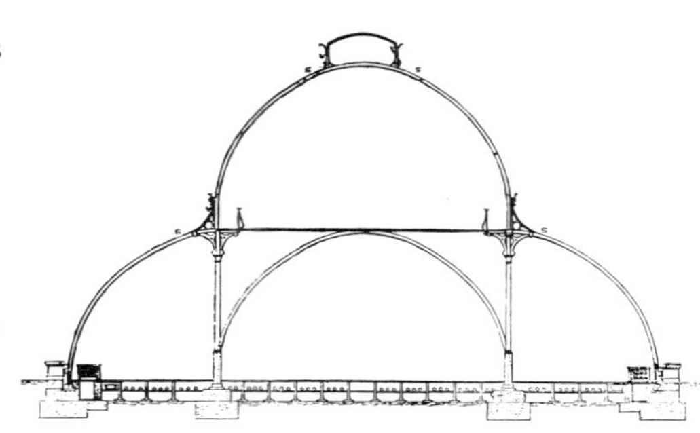

Figure 29
*Cross-section and plan of the Palm House.*

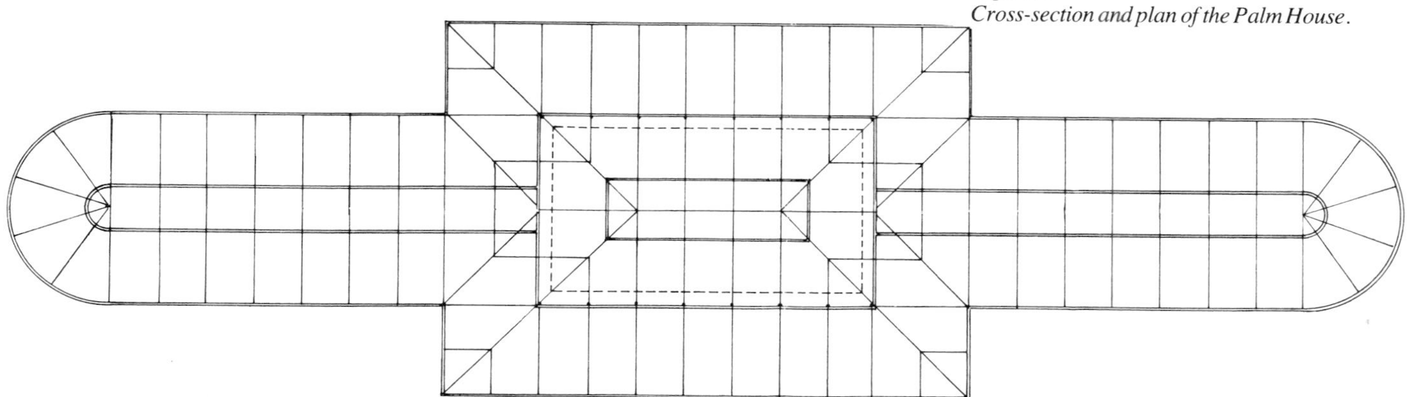

revolutionary wrought-iron structure being a quarter the weight of Burton's and letting in correspondingly more light.

While some may criticise Turner's tactics, there is no doubt that technologically his thinking was far ahead of Decimus Burton's, as Paxton's had been at Chatsworth. No longer was the architect wholly in command of his materials and his methods of construction. Structural engineering had arrived in all but the name.

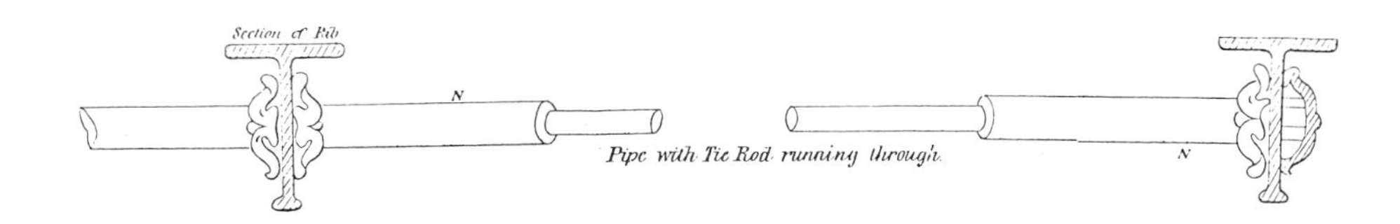


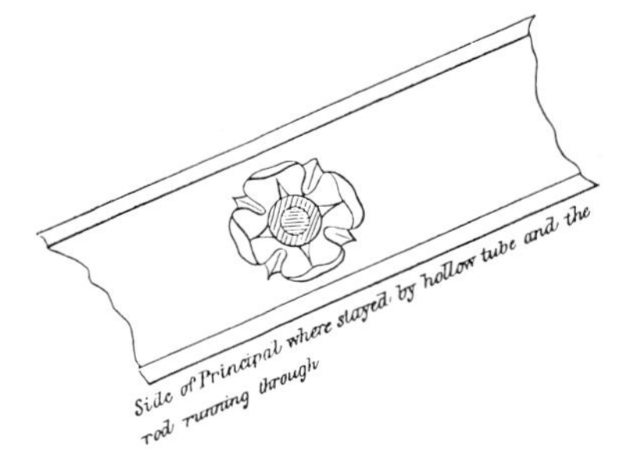


*Figure 30*
*Details of construction of the Palm House at Kew.*
*(Above & right) method of tying the wrought iron ribs together (Turner Patent No. 11496 of 15th December 1846) as seen today.*
*(Left) detail connection to ribs.*
*(Below) section of pioneer wrought iron I-beam (Vernon & Kennedy) as actually used in the ribs.*

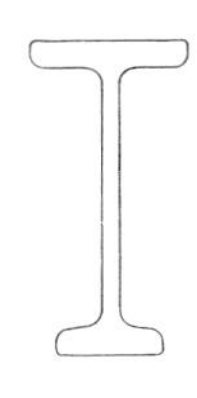

## Epilogue on 1780-1850

The influences from this period on structural engineering in the following decades were mixed. Cast-iron beams virtually died after 1850 and cast-iron arches gradually gave way to wrought iron. In spite of the technical brilliance of the Palm House at Kew, glasshouses reverted largely to timber without curvature. The fallacy of Loudon and Paxton's thinking on light angles was exposed, although it is not quite clear when this was. Paxton's greatest triumph on the glazing of the International Exhibition Building belongs to the next chapter, as does the first total structural frame, unbraced by masonry.

The one big influence from this period was the understanding of riveted wrought-iron achieved on the Britannia Bridge and the ensuing revolution in all structural thinking.

# 1850-1890

James Sutherland

R.J.M. Sutherland BA, FIStructE, FICE, FIHE, MConsE.

James Sutherland gained experience for his career as a consulting Civil and Structural engineer with Sir William Halcrow & Partners.

He has been a partner in Harris & Sutherland since 1958 and closely associated with the Institution of Structural Engineers over a number of years (a Vice-President 1980-82). Currently he is Vice-Chairman of the Literature Committee and Convenor of the Institution's History Study Group.

Apart from a fairly wide responsibility for the design of many types of engineering works (urban roads and bridges, universities, industrial, civic and residential buildings) he has a strong interest in architecture, in the evolution of towns and in particular in engineering history. He has written and lectured quite widely on engineering and historical matters both in Britain and abroad.

While 1780-1850 was an era of innovation in structural engineering, 1850 to 1890 were years of successful execution and great confidence, the latter only occasionally misplaced. Many notable structures in Britain date from this period and it is gratifying how many of these still survive today. At this time British engineering was penetrating to almost every part of the world, taking with it British skills and British products, above all bringing railways.

By the 1850s engineering education at university level had become quite well established. University College and King's College in London had been providing lectures on engineering since their foundation in the late 1820s and the first professor of engineering was appointed in 1840, at Glasgow University, with professorships in London soon after. Later the pioneering Glasgow chair passed to the great W.J.M. Rankine who held it from 1855 until his death in 1872.

Engineers had now become at least junior members of the Establishment and were no longer the admired but, in some ways, rough race of men that they had been. Robert Stephenson and Joseph Locke were both Members of Parliament from 1847 until they died in 1859 and 1860, respectively. Several engineers were knighted (no higher honours) and in fiction, Trollope, writing in 1867, had only slight doubts about the suitability of engineering as a profession for the younger son of a well-connected country squire.

In spite of the improved status of engineers, some may say because of it, there was an air of complacency, with little new thinking on structural matters in Britain between 1850 and 1890. When new ideas did emerge, they tended not to lead anywhere as there was no real demand for them. With wrought iron, now well entrenched, and masonry, available as always, everything that needed to be done could be done, or so it must have appeared. This may be the reason why Wilkinson's promising reinforced concrete system, patented in 1854, never took hold. Doubtless it was seen as just one of many 'fireproof' flooring systems but it contained the basis of a complete form of construction of unprecedented versatility. This then lay dormant until, quite independently, it was imported fully developed from France in the 1890s.

The same lack of demand may explain why Godfrey Greene's revolutionary four-storey boat store at Sheerness had no direct descendants. This structure, which is described on pages 56-58, has a good claim to be the world's first multistorey iron- or steel-framed building depending for its stability only on stiff connections between the members. It has neither iron diagonals nor bracing walls, thus antedating the development of such frames in America by 20-30 years. Apparently, it was not noticed, and designers in Britain, whether architects or engineers, went on using masonry walls for stability until we imported steel-framed construction from the USA at the turn of the century.

One advantage of a long period without major changes in structural practice was a steady increase in understanding of how each material could best be used. Cast iron found its proper place in columns and in secondary components like baseplates and brackets but less and less in beams. Riveted wrought iron either in plate girders, trusses or rolled I-sections took over for beams. Masonry remained the staple material for walls, bridge piers, and even for complete viaducts.

The construction of most buildings changed little in this period. Iron beams were often introduced into timber floors to increase clear open spaces, possibly with one or two cast iron columns, and sometimes, especially in public or commercial buildings, the timber was replaced completely by filler joist floors or other fire-resistant construction, although these features were seldom visible. Stability, as already mentioned, continued to depend on masonry walls.

It was in the long-span iron roofs for railway stations and exhibition buildings that the new structural techniques took over with most effect and, of course, in bridges. It was here, also, that the various forms of iron truss found most favour. Compared with the heavy plated construction of the Britannia Bridge, open trusses, once mastered, used iron, an expensive material, much more efficiently. Hence their popularity.

The history of the structural truss is long, complicated, and uncertain, full of ingenious ideas and curious misconceptions. There were many parallel paths of development but much of the credit in the later stages must go to the Americans for their work with timber and iron rods. All that need be said here is that the full analysis of anything other than the simplest trusses was not achieved until about

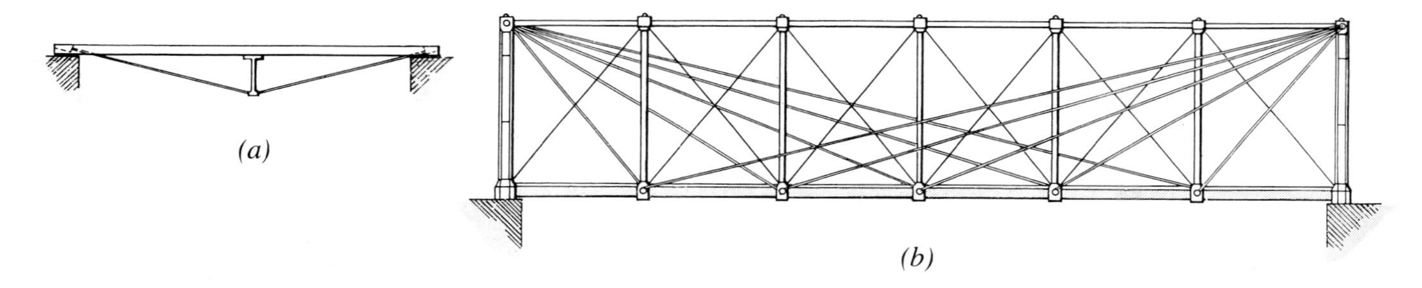


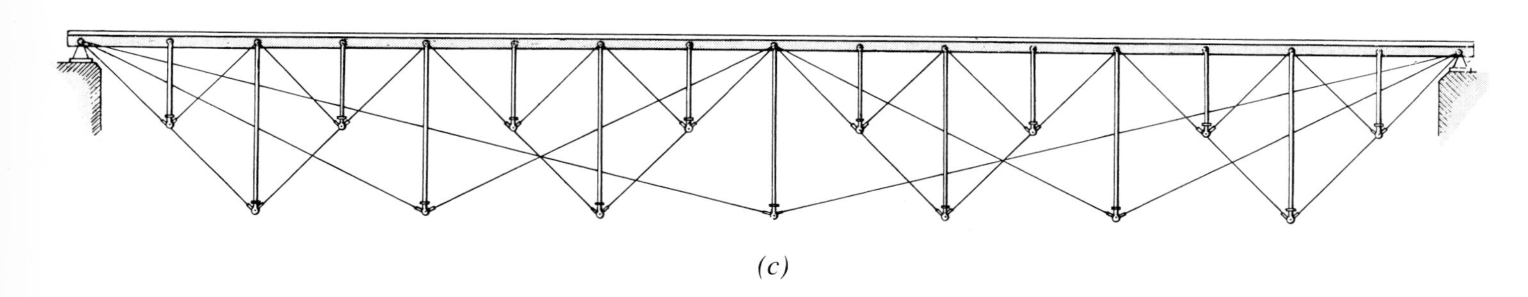


*Figure 1*
*Early intuitive types of truss.*

Both the Bollman and Fink trusses appear to derive from multiple superimposition of this simple (type a) truss form.
a) The simplest form of trussed beam.
b) The Bollman truss.
c) The Fink truss.

1850 and that this may explain the complexity of some of the early forms. Some were highly redundant, with duplicated support systems, often part truss and part arch, the arching members possibly added as much to increase stiffness as strength. Others (as *Figures 1b* and *c*) derived from complex superimpositions of the simplest truss form (*Figure 1a*). Their appearance was often bizarre.

In the second half of the 19th century, with better understanding and the stronger joints possible with iron, the forms could be clarified and the duplication dropped, leaving several accepted types of 'pin-jointed' truss, the forces in which could be calculated with precision (*Figure 2*). However, even after 1850 it is not certain that some of the greatest engineers, notably I.K. Brunel, really understood how their trusses behaved. This is discussed further on pages 63-65.

It would be wrong to end these introductory remarks without mentioning the one major development in materials that took place in the period 1850-90. This is the introduction of steel which gradually replaced wrought iron. The change was essentially metallurgical. Although ultimately it affected stress levels and costs, it had no visible effect on structural form.

This last point is best understood if one remembers that the Forth Bridge of 1882-90 is made of steel, while the Eiffel Tower of 1887-89 is of wrought iron. Visually, it would be difficult to say which is made of which. In fact, there has been considerable confusion over this.

In the following pages, four individual structures and Brunel's timber bridges are selected as symbols of the achievements of the period to illustrate the diversity of forms that still existed, especially at the beginning of the period.

*Figure 2*
*Mathematically rational trusses (as still used).*

a) The Pratt truss.
b) The Warren truss.

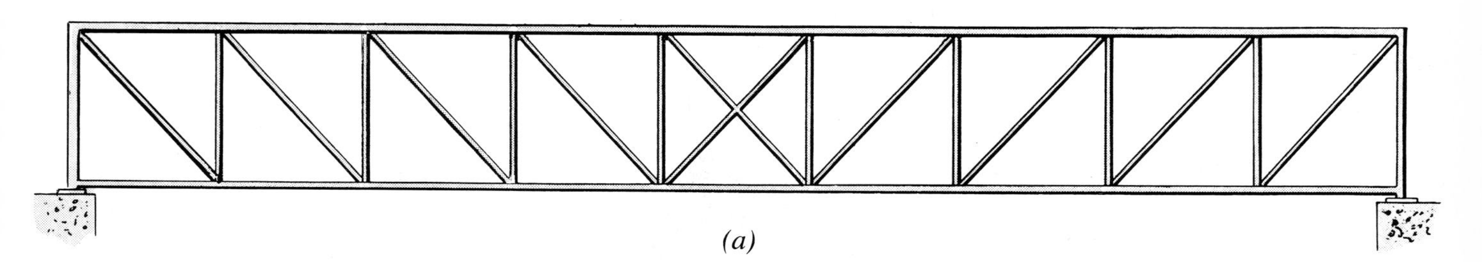

*(a)*

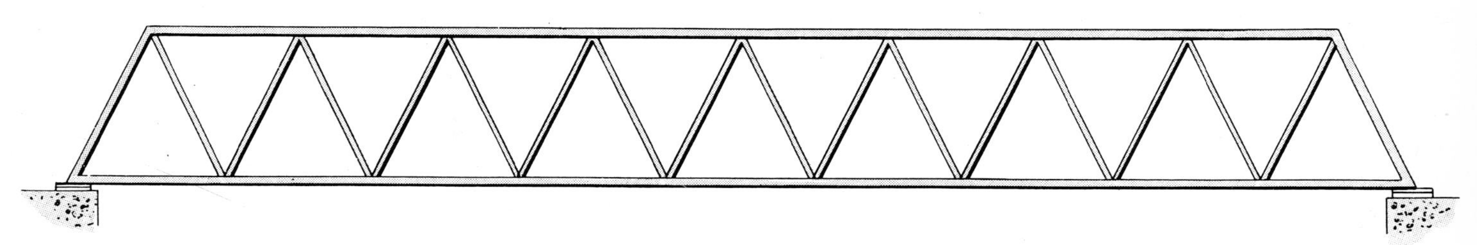

*(b)*

## The Great Exhibition building – 1851

A mastery of prefabrication unprecedented in its time and hardly matched since.

| | |
|---|---|
| Designers: | Sir Joseph Paxton and Sir Charles Fox |
| Max span: | 22 m |
| Structure: | Main beams and columns, in wrought or cast iron. Timber floors and timber and glass cladding and roofs. |
| Contractor: | Fox Henderson & Co. |

The importance of the Great Exhibition building does not lie, as has been variously suggested, in the width of its spans, or in Paxton's bravery in pioneering the use of iron and glass, or in the influence of the building on railway roofs later in the 19th century.

The spans were quite modest, at most less than half those achieved by Richard Turner at Lime Street Station in Liverpool a year or two before.

No new iron technology was used, the design

*Figure 3*
*Aeronautic view of the Palace of Industry for all Nations, from Kensington Gardens.*

being based on theoretical principles and practical techniques established several years earlier. Further, the design of the ironwork owed little to Paxton, virtually all credit for this being due to Charles Fox of Fox Henderson and his assistants.

Much less of the building was in iron than is generally supposed. The columns and the main girders were iron but the whole of the upper floors and the roof, including the arches over the transepts, were of timber, as was the external cladding, apart from some iron trimmings.

The direct influence on iron construction appears to have been very small although, because of its success and prominence, the building must have done something towards making ironwork more generally accepted.

Having disposed of the commoner myths, one can say that the building contains brilliantly creative detailing in timber and glass – all due to and patented by Paxton – together with an approach to standardisation and prefabrication, probably attributable jointly to Paxton and to Fox, that was wholly unprecedented and has hardly been matched since. Without this, the building could never have been completed within what must have seemed an almost hopelessly unrealistic programme.

92 000 $m^2$ of building on three floor levels completed in 9 months, including design and the development of all standard components, is no small achievement, even allowing for the absence of today's complex building services.

*Figure 4*
*Cross-section through part of building, construction programme and schedule of components and materials used.*

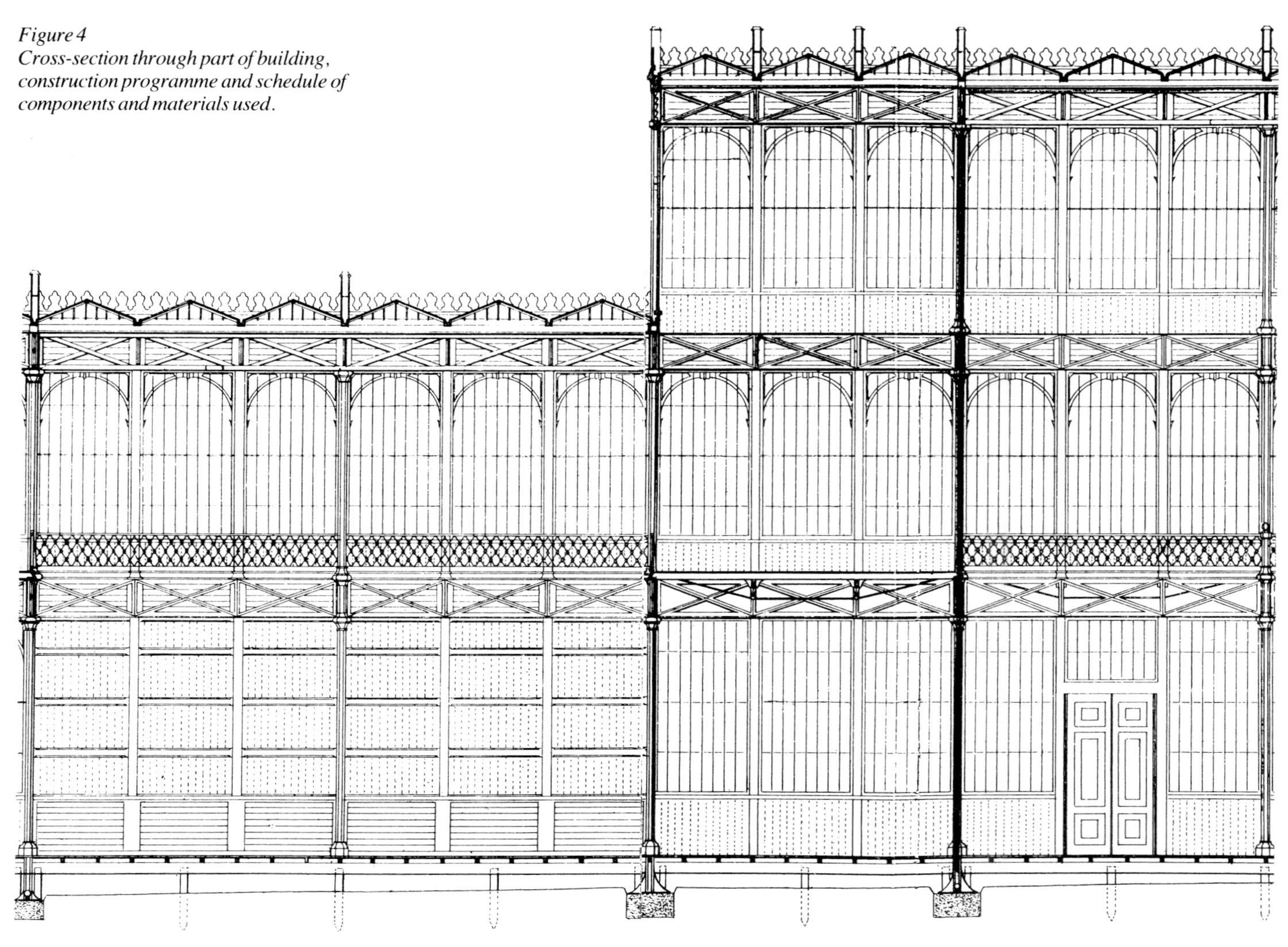

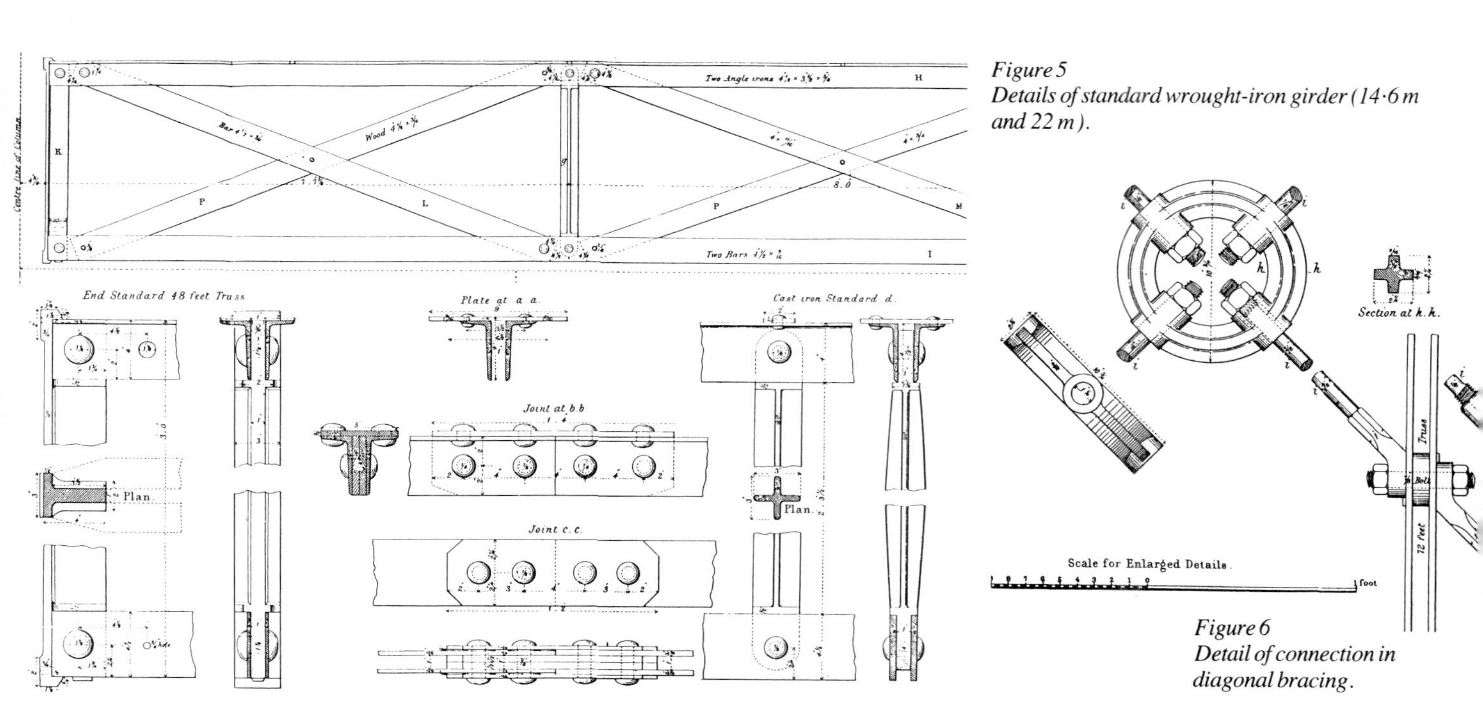


*Figure 5*
*Details of standard wrought-iron girder (14·6 m and 22 m).*

*Figure 6*
*Detail of connection in diagonal bracing.*

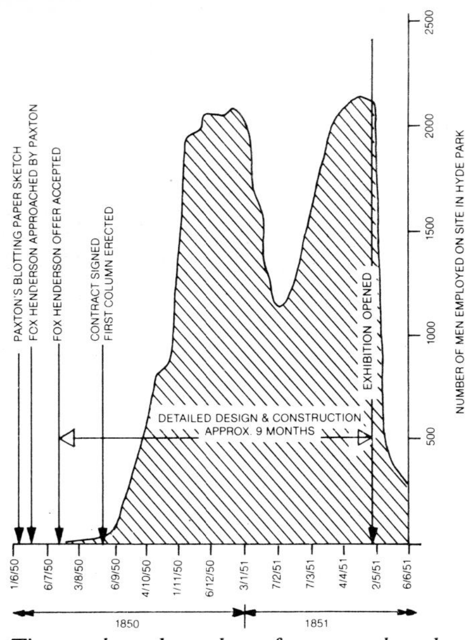


*Time scale and number of men employed*

**Principal components & materials supplied**

| QUANTITY | ITEM |
|---|---|
| 1107 | Column base castings |
| 2494 | Column shaft castings |
| 2500 | Column connection castings |
| 2357 | Cast-iron girders |
| 128207 | Other cast-iron pieces |
| 400417 | Wrought-iron pieces |
| 293655 | Panes of glass |
| 264972 | Pieces of wrought timber |
| 412634 | $ft^3$ of rough timber |

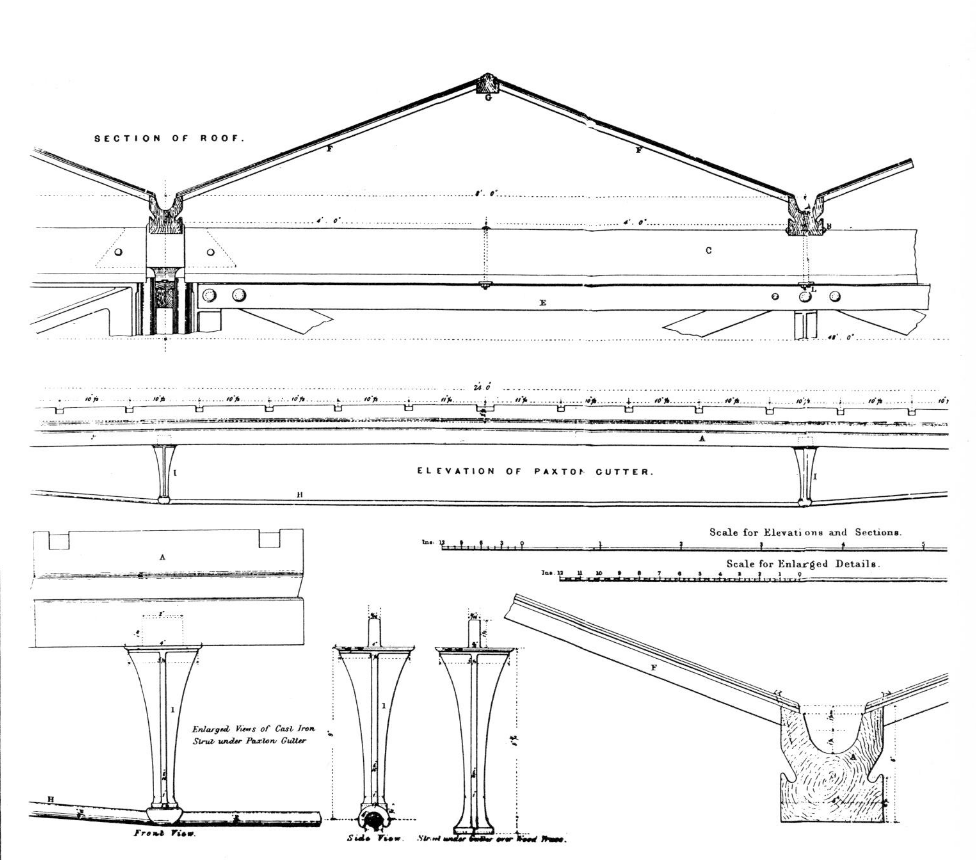


*Figure 8*
*Detail of Paxton's gutter and glazing system.*

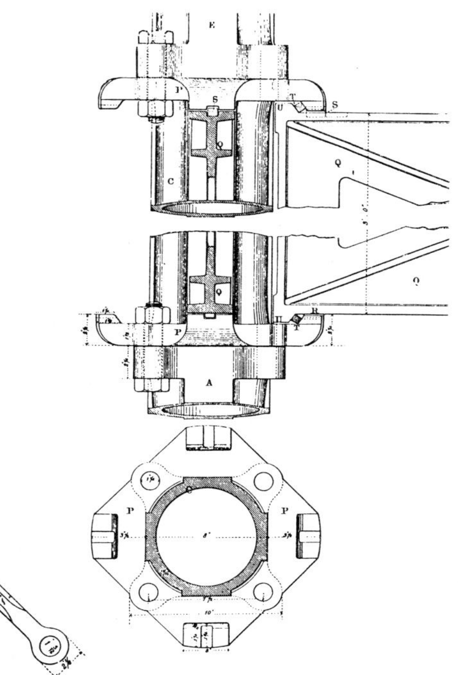

*Figure 7*
*Detail of beam-to-column connection.*

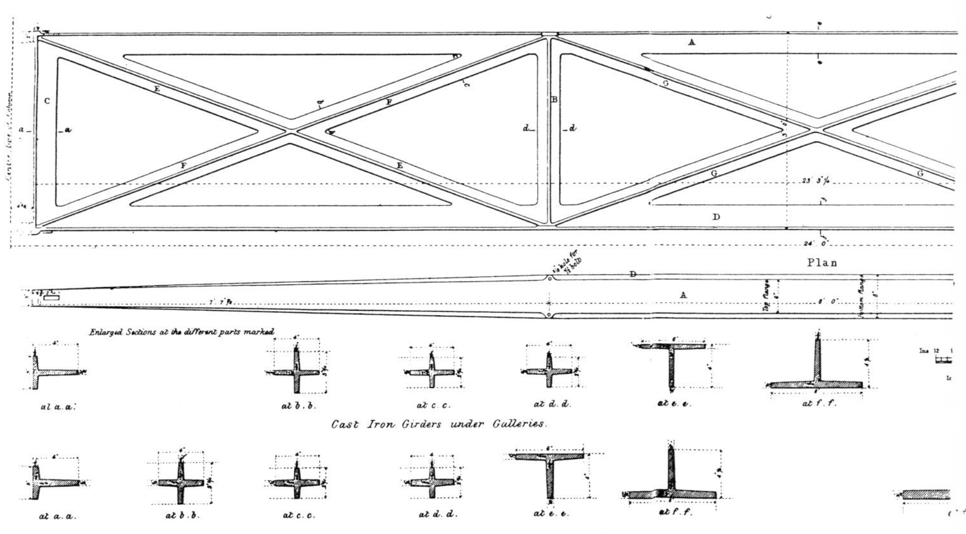


*Figure 9*
*Detail of standard cast-iron beam (all 7·3 m span).*

20th century framing in the 1850s.

## The boat store, Sheerness: 1858–60

A strong claim to be considered the world's first multistorey framed building stabilised by portal action.

Designer: G. T. Greene
Max floor span: 9 m
Structure: Beam and column construction in wrought and cast iron with moment connections at each junction. Timber upper floors. Galvanised corrugated iron cladding and glass.
Ironwork contractor: Henry Grissell

*Figure 10*
*Elevation of the boat store today.*

Whatever may have been the original thinking on the beam-to-column connections in the Great Exhibition Building, in the form in which it was built it depended for stability on diagonal bracing bars (see *Figure 6*). In contrast, the simple, but elegant, four-storey boat store in Sheerness dockyard has true portal framing, and relies for stability wholly on the stiffness and strength of the joints.

The principle of achieving stability through stiffened joints had been applied earlier to the roofs of markets and stations, usually with arch-shaped beams so as to ensure the maximum stiffness within a minimum depth.

There is nothing accidental about this framing, no question of getting the best answer for an irrelevant reason. The action of the beam-to-column joints was fully and consciously worked out.

Here is the complete embodiment of the modern steel frame. If the short cross-beams and the columns had not been of cast iron but had been detailed in wrought iron like the longitudinal beams, it would have been hard to distinguish the boat store from a 20th century structure of the era just before welding.

The two significant questions relating to this structure are, who designed it and what was its influence?

It was designed by Godfrey Greene (1807-86), one of the most distinguished of many military engineers who carried out important and original engineering works in the mid-19th century. After nearly 25 years in India, Greene became Director of Engineering and Architectural works, Admiralty, in 1849 and remained in that post until 1864. The boat store at Sheerness is just one, but undoubtedly the most important, of his works and, as Professor A. W. Skempton has shown (*Figure 11*), they really were his work and not just carried out under his name.

It seems that the boat store had no influence, but it remains today, listed Grade I, as a single event in time. The almost identical framing that we imported from America at the end of the century almost certainly evolved quite independently. Two possible reasons for the absence of any direct follow-on are that utilitarian buildings in naval dockyards were hardly in the public eye, however large and original, and that there was no need for complete framing; most people preferred masonry walls to corrugated iron sheeting.

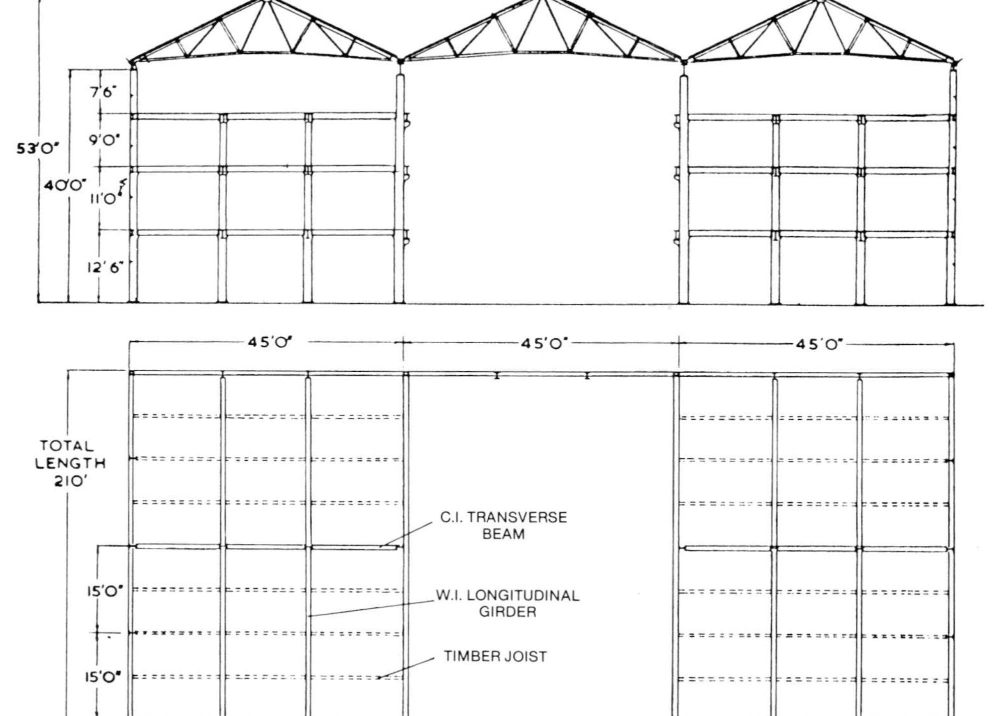


*Figure 11*
*Part plan and cross-section.*
*Drawing by Prof. Skempton in his paper in Newcomen Society Transaction XXXII 1959-60.*

*Figure 12*
*Details of the moment connections in the frame.*

Railway climax (1).

## St. Pancras Station roof: 1868

The absolute climax of the railway roof in Britain, unmatched for 25 years and then exceeded in span only by Joseph Wilson's big three-pinned arches in Philadelphia in the 1890s.

Engineer: W. M. Barlow (with R. M. Ordish)
Span: 73·2 m
Primary structure: 24 riveted wrought-iron arches at 8·9 m centres with ties below railway tracks.
Secondary structure: Timber boarding with slates and glass on wrought-iron purlins.
Ironwork contractor: The Butterley Company.

The first really long-span iron roof anywhere in the world was designed and built in 1846-9 by Richard Turner (of glasshouse fame) for Lime Street Station in Liverpool. This consisted of a set of light crescent-shaped trusses spanning 47 m and covered with glass and galvanised corrugated sheeting. The trusses were made up of slender rolled iron ribs of I-section, similar to those in the Palm House at Kew (see page 46), but tied and braced as shown in Figure 14.

This pioneer roof was followed in 1854 by one of similar form over New Street Station in Birmingham but this time tapering in plan with spans up to 65 m.

These two roofs and others in the 1850s were built as design-and-supply packages by specialist contractors and each was subjected to severe test loads to satisfy the engineer to the railway company and its directors. Three of the trusses for Turner's roof were erected in his works in Dublin and test loaded to the equivalent of 2kN/m$^2$ before delivery, including eccentric loading. The same testing was required from Fox Henderson for the New Street roof but with the additional requirement of a proof load of 139N/m$^2$ for all tensile members.

Apart from these two early long spans, most of the station roofs of the 1850s, for instance Paddington and Kings Cross, had roofs spanning little more than 30 m.

By the 1860s, station roofs were becoming more robust, with boarding and slates in place of the largely discredited galvanised iron and, at the same time, they were getting bigger and correspondingly more expensive. Hawkshaw's crescent trusses of 50 m at Charing Cross (1864) and of 58 m at Cannon Street (1866) were topped, in 1868, by W. H. Barlow's soaring 73 m tied arches at St. Pancras, the largest and most substantial roof of all.

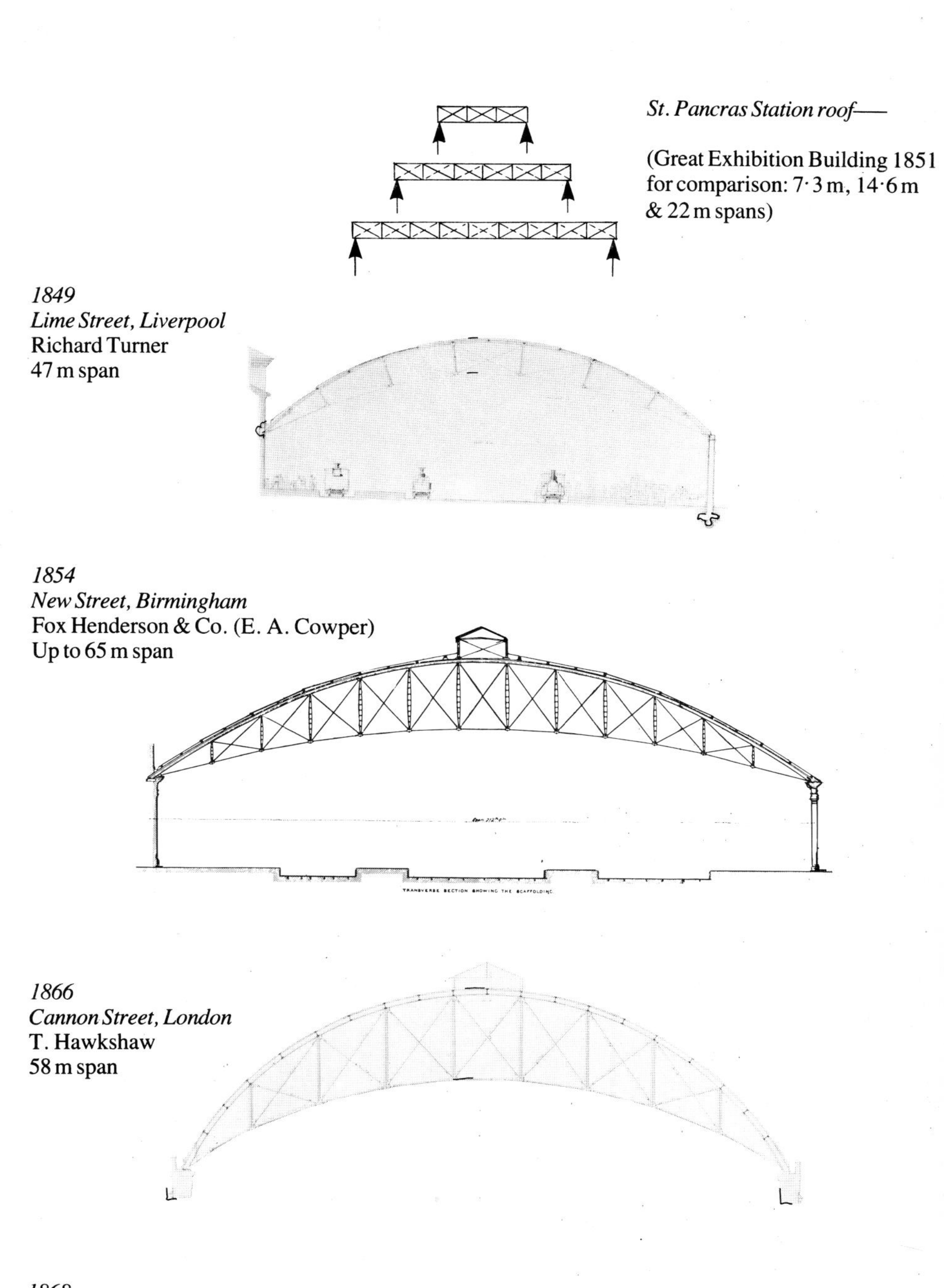


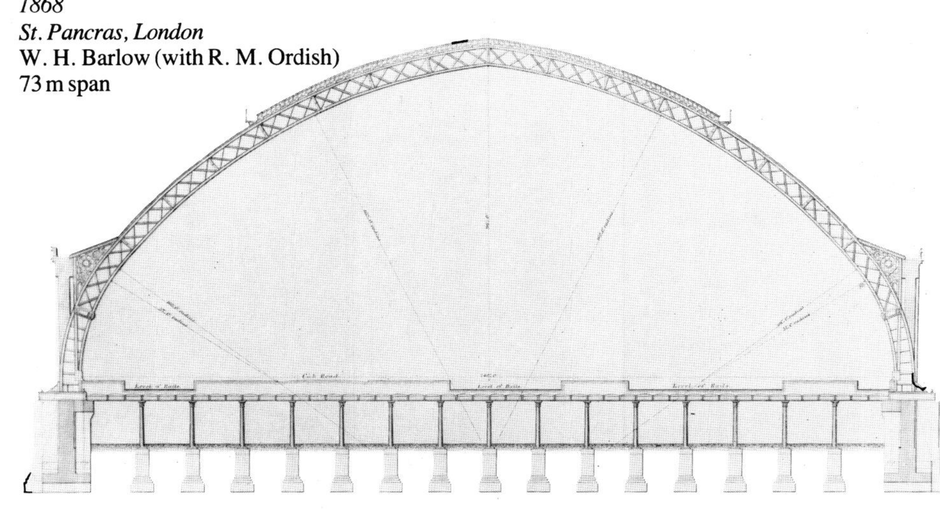


*Figure 13*
*The arches at St. Pancras compared with earlier long span-roofs for railway stations.*

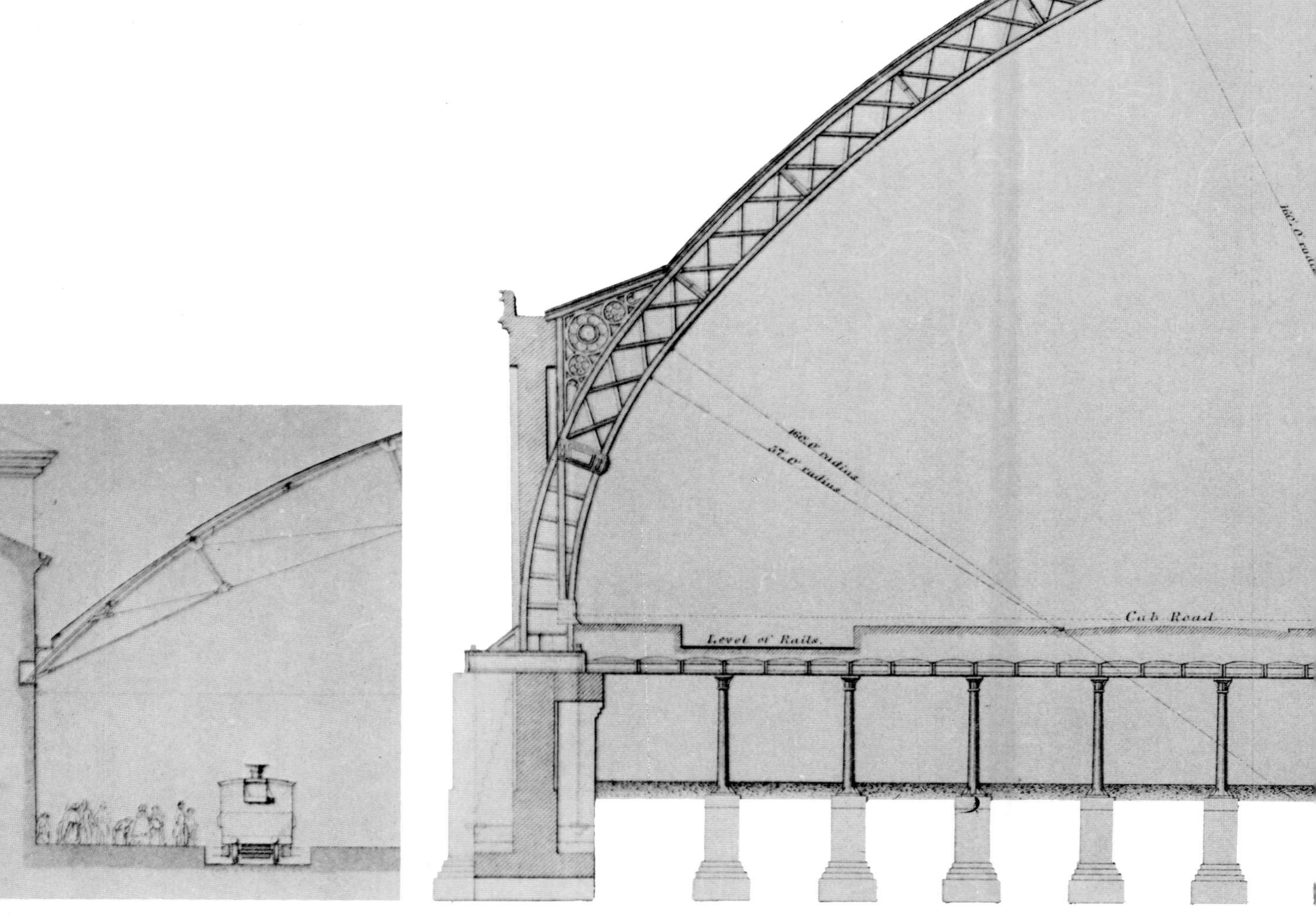


*Figure 14*
*Detail of Lime Street Station roof.*

*Figure 15*
*Cross-section showing roof, rail tracks, and vaults.*

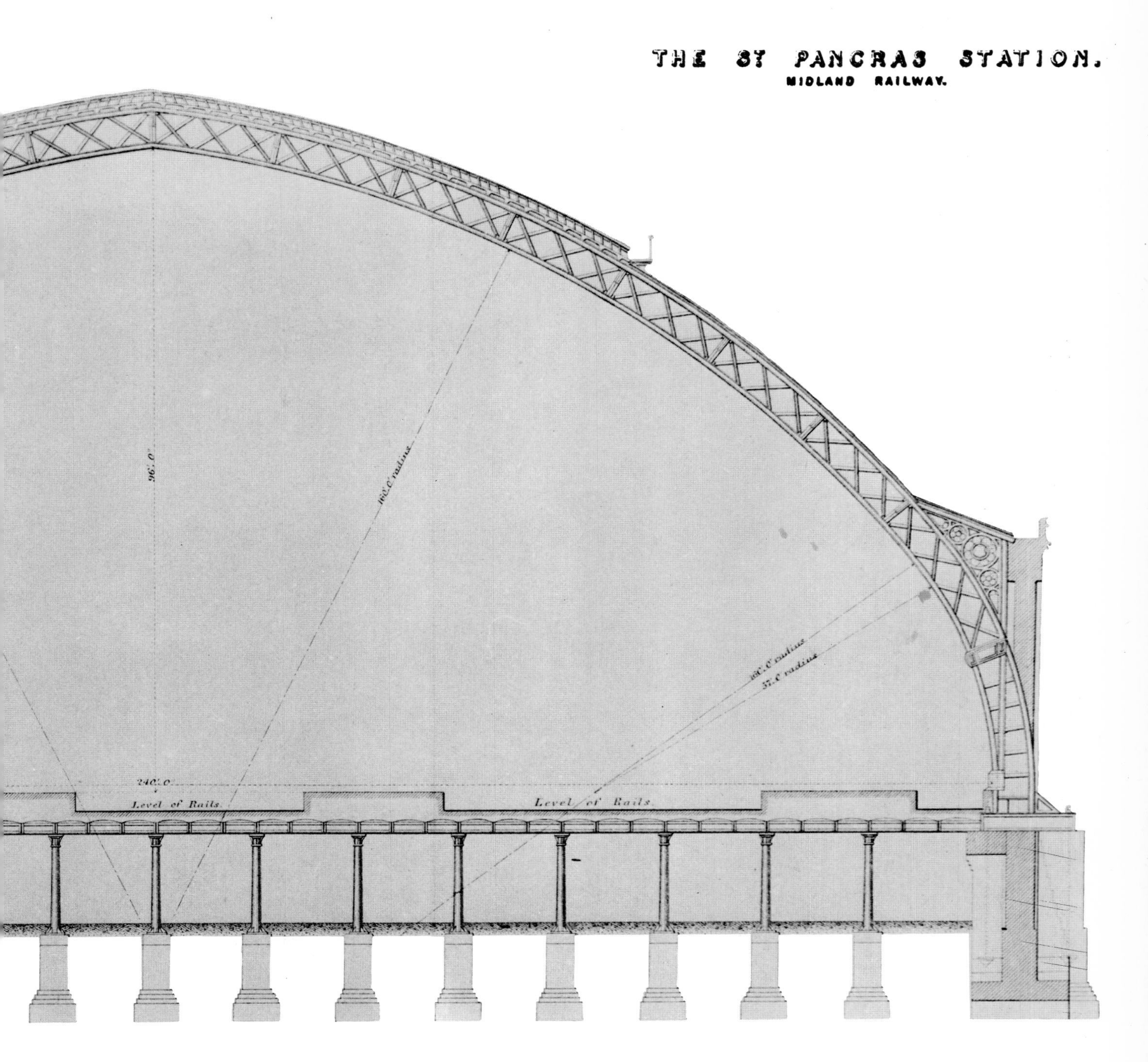


The case for a clear span over all tracks, platforms, and the roadway, was argued, perhaps rather speciously, on the grounds of foundation costs, saving the space occupied by the columns, and the need for freedom to alter the track layout. One cannot help thinking that, beneath these arguments, Barlow and the Midland Railway Company just wanted the biggest span in the world.

The tracks today are still in exactly the positions shown on the drawings of the 1860s.

At St. Pancras the roof was not only the world's largest but was unlike previous long-span ones in having arch ribs that were currently described as 'naked', i.e. with no external braces, as in the crescent truss, to maintain their shape. There are many uncertainties about the design of these arches which were still being analysed by theoreticians many years after their completion. Not least of the doubts is how much of the credit is due to R. M. Ordish, whose contribution Barlow acknowledged, and how much to Barlow himself.

Because of lingering doubts, load testing was allowed for in the contract but this was never carried out. By this time the days of such tests were really over.

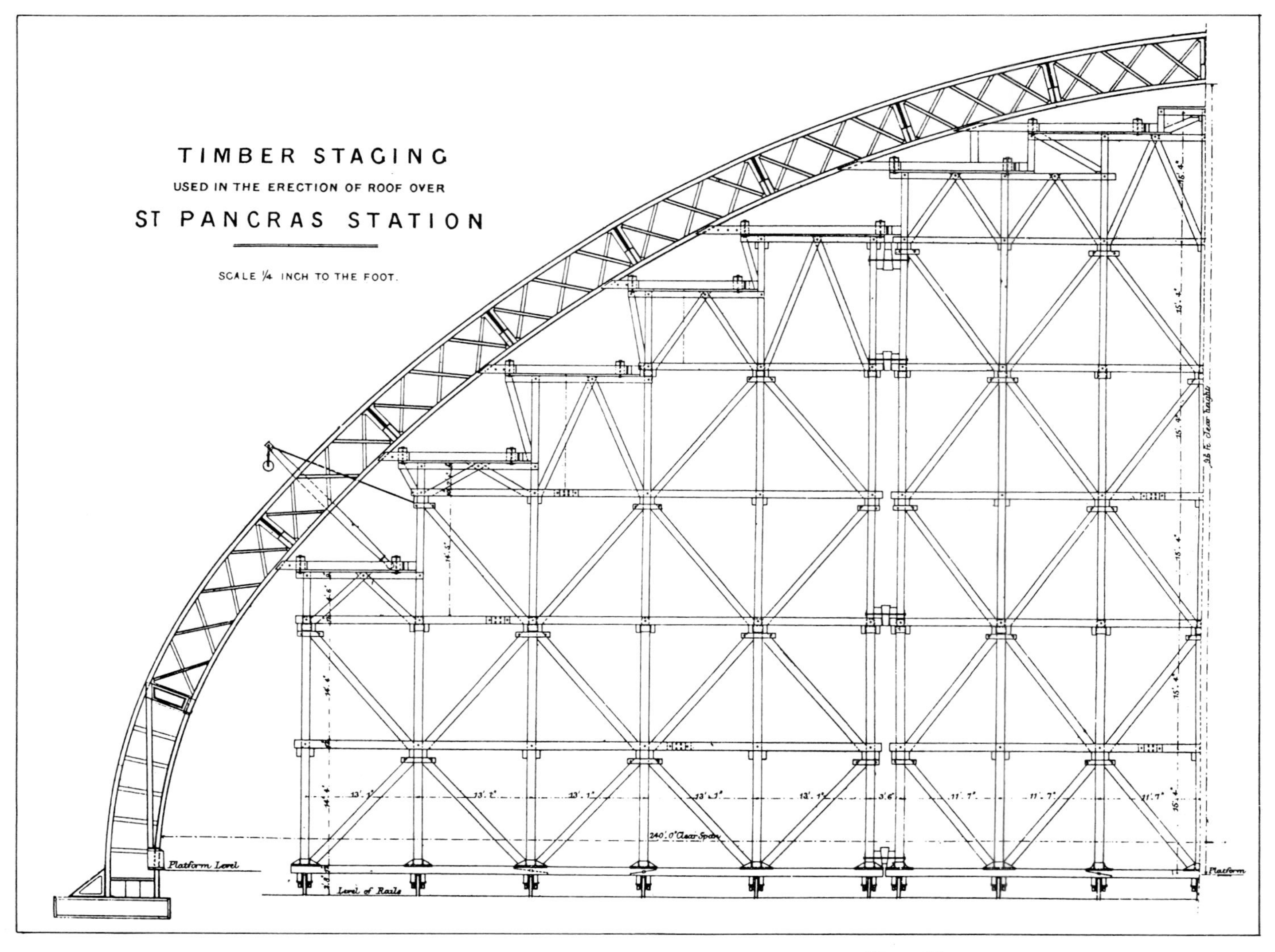


*Figure 16*
*The temporary works for the erection of the arch ribs at St. Pancras.*

The travelling staging on which the Butterley Company assembled the arch ribs was a major structure in itself. It weighed 580 tons, supported two ribs at a time, and moved along on rails in three separate sections. With this advanced piece of falsework the roof was erected, after some initial delays, at a rate of just over 1 week per arch rib.

## A structural sideline.
# Brunel's timber viaducts: 1849-1863

South Devon Railway
Cornwall Railway
West Cornwall Railway

| | |
|---|---|
| Designer: | I. K. Brunel |
| Spans: | Generally 12 m to 20 m |
| Height: | Up to 45 m |
| Structure: | Timber with wrought-iron tie-rods (some with masonry piers). |

Between 1849 and 1863, more than 60 timber railway viaducts were built in Devon and Cornwall to the designs of I. K. Brunel. Put together, they would add up to over 7 miles of continuous bridge decking.

The choice of timber as the structural material may seem curious because, by the middle of the 19th century, wrought iron had established itself as the paramount bridging material and, in other places, Brunel was a pioneer of wrought iron and one of its most notable advocates.

The reason for choosing timber was partly economic – a low initial outlay with acceptance of high maintenance costs, and probably partly a desire for speed in building – but added to these rational factors must be Brunel's undoubted love for timber as a material. Unlike Switzerland in the 18th century, or America in the 19th, there was never a strong tradition of timber bridge building in Britain. There was a scattering of timber bridges in the 1830s and 1840s, most notably the laminated (but not glued) arches by John and Benjamin Green, but that is all.

Perhaps the most interesting feature of these viaducts is not the choice of material but the doubts that their form seemed to cast on Brunel's belief in truss action, or even his understanding of it. This point has already been touched on in the introductory section of this chapter.

The majority of these West Country viaducts consist not of trusses in the sense that the word 'truss' is used today but of beams propped by raking timber struts fanning out from bases or tops of piers. Why didn't Brunel use continuous trusses which, by then, could readily be analysed mathematically? Had Brunel's understanding slipped behind that of some of his contemporaries?

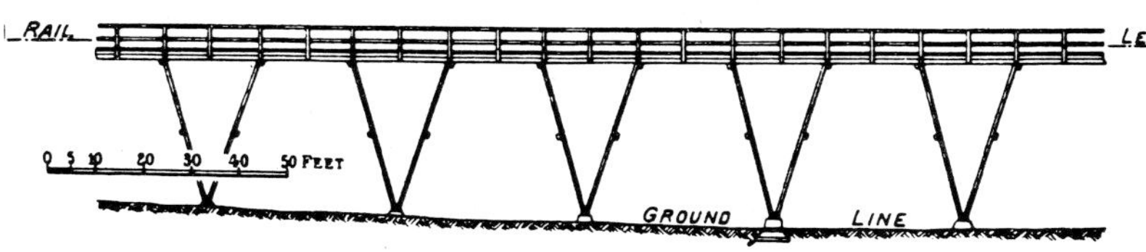


CORNWALL RAILWAY
*Pendalake viaduct* 12 m spans Opened 1859 Replaced 1877

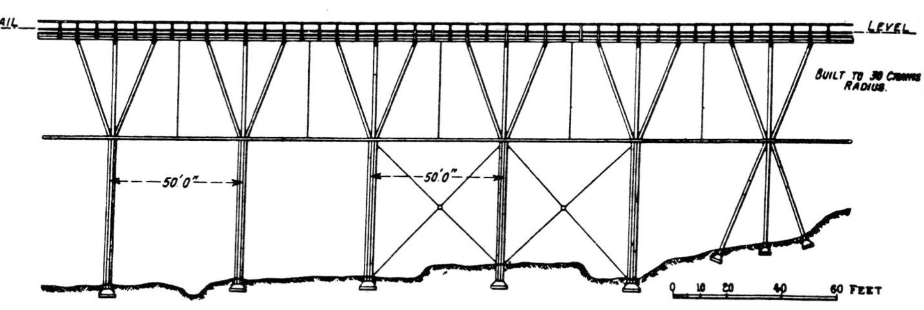


WEST CORNWALL RAILWAY
*Angarrack viaduct* 15 m spans Opened 1852 Replaced 1885

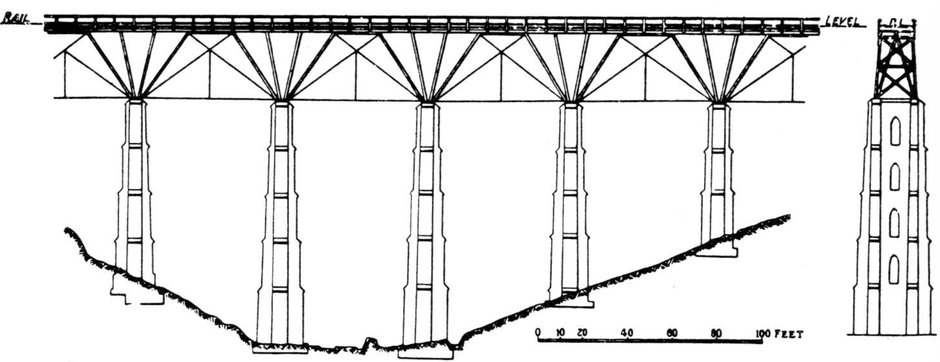


CORNWALL RAILWAY
*St. Pinnock viaduct* 20 m spans Opened 1859 Replaced 1882

*Figure 17*
*Typical timber viaducts by Brunel 1849-1863. In each case, radiating timber struts prop timber beams, the iron tie-rods resisting only any out-of-balance forces and providing general stability.*

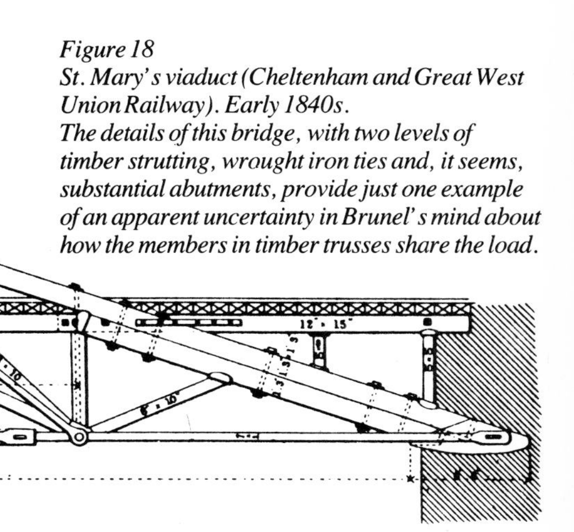


*Figure 18*
*St. Mary's viaduct (Cheltenham and Great West Union Railway). Early 1840s.*
*The details of this bridge, with two levels of timber strutting, wrought iron ties and, it seems, substantial abutments, provide just one example of an apparent uncertainty in Brunel's mind about how the members in timber trusses share the load.*

Not all of Brunel's earlier timber structures demonstrate a clear understanding of where the forces go (*Figure 18*) but, by 1852, his great 90 m railway bridge over the Wye at Chepstow (*Figure 19*) showed a complete mastery of truss action when using iron.

The real reason for using propped beams in the viaducts with iron ties essentially for stability, was probably not in any way connected with structural analysis but due to a deep feeling of how timber actually behaves. Timber can readily be used for struts, and within limits for beams, but the formation of efficient joints that will remain both stiff and strong is much less easy – then even more than now. By

*Figure 19*
*Chepstow Railway Bridge of 1852.*
*With vertical struts and diagonal ties, including counterbracing in the central bay, this structure demonstrates Brunel's apparently full understanding of truss action – with wrought iron – before 1852.*

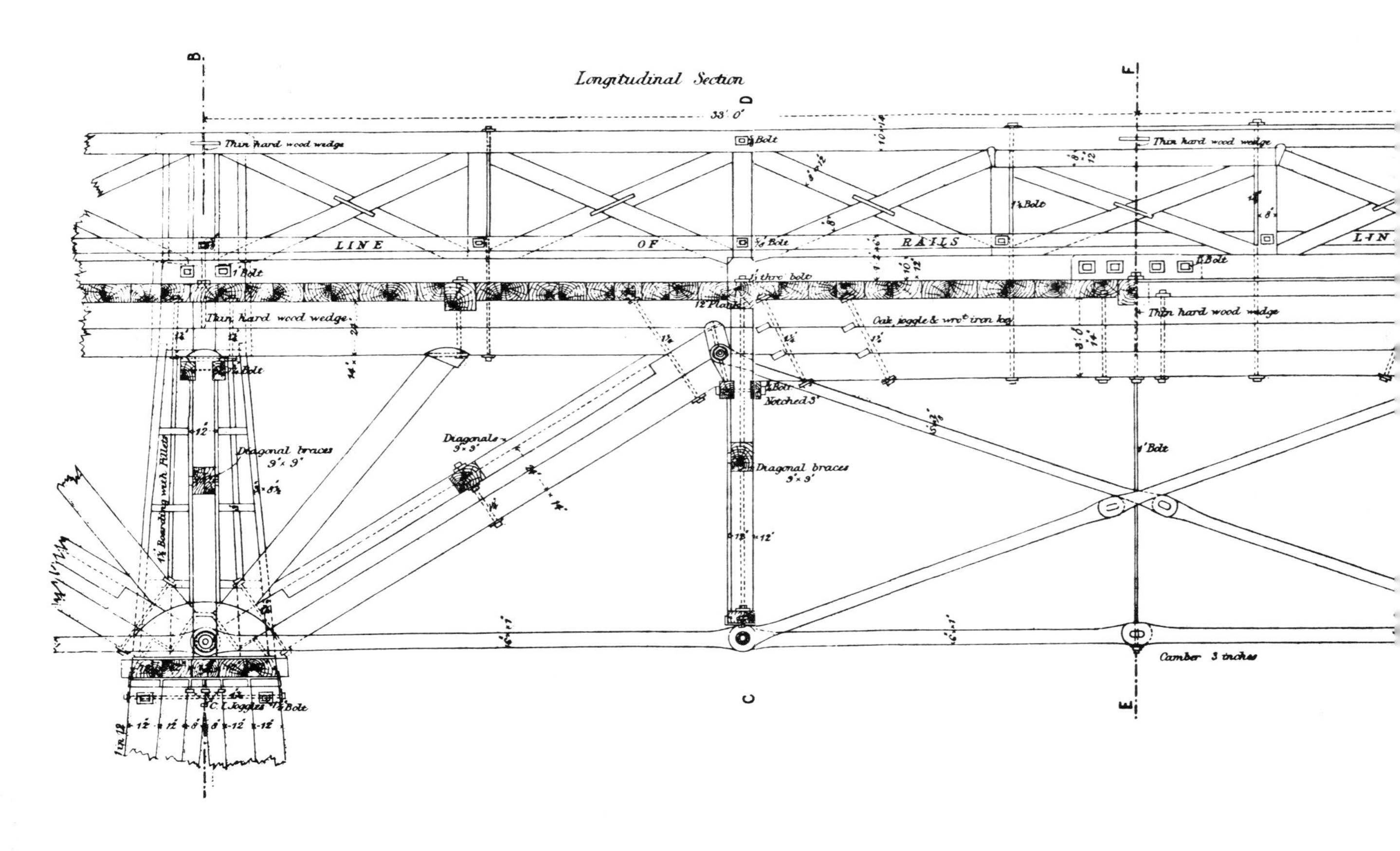


*Figure 20*
*Details of St Germans Viaduct, Cornwall Railway, opened 1859, replaced 1908.*

In an age when structural timber is either glued and laminated or used in sizes seldom exceeding those of a domestic floor joist, it is difficult to remember that 19th century engineers were habitually working with long solid sections often 350 to 400 mm square. Protected by kyanising (chloride of mercury), these simple structures, with solid timber members, lasted up to 70 years – not without considerable maintenance – the last one being replaced in 1934.

the 1850s Brunel may well have realised only too clearly that what he could do in wrought iron was unpractical in timber.

It is interesting to note that, in the roofs of his prefabricated hospital for the Crimea of 1855, he used simple propping (*Figure 21*) rather than the uncertain truss action of some of his earlier roofs.

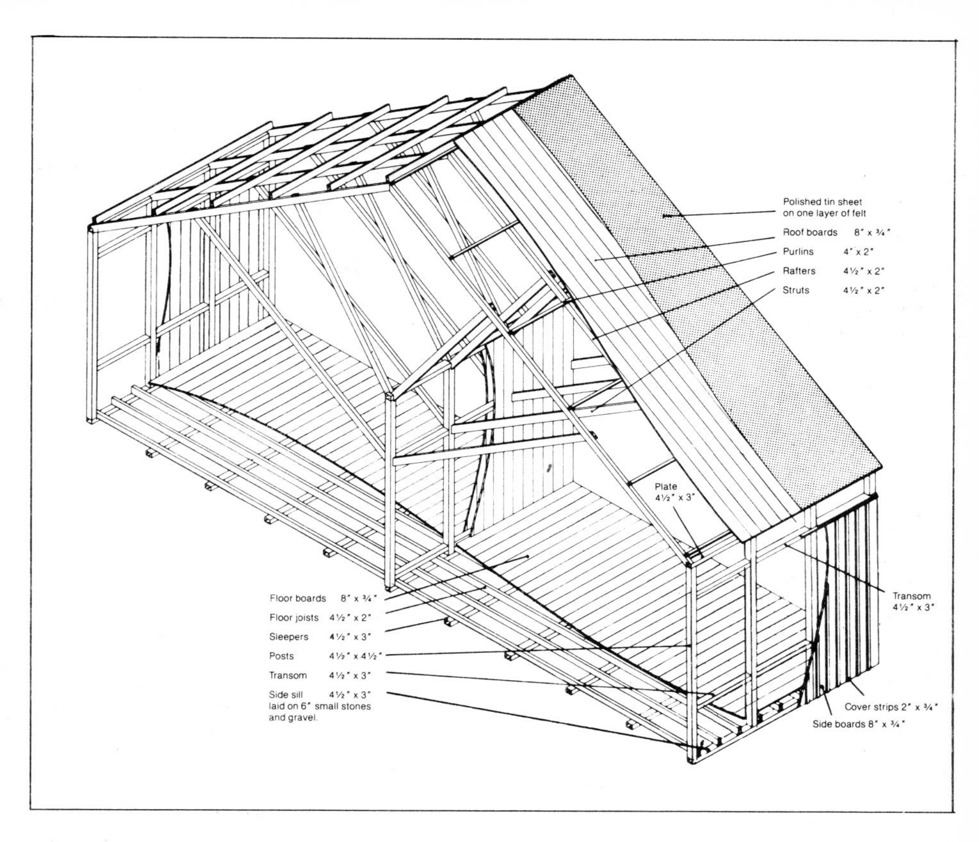


*Figure 21*
*Ward block for hospital Renkioi 1855.*
*In this prefabricated hospital system, built during the Crimean War, Brunel used simple propping, as in the West Country viaducts, rather than any of the long-established trussing systems for such roofs.*

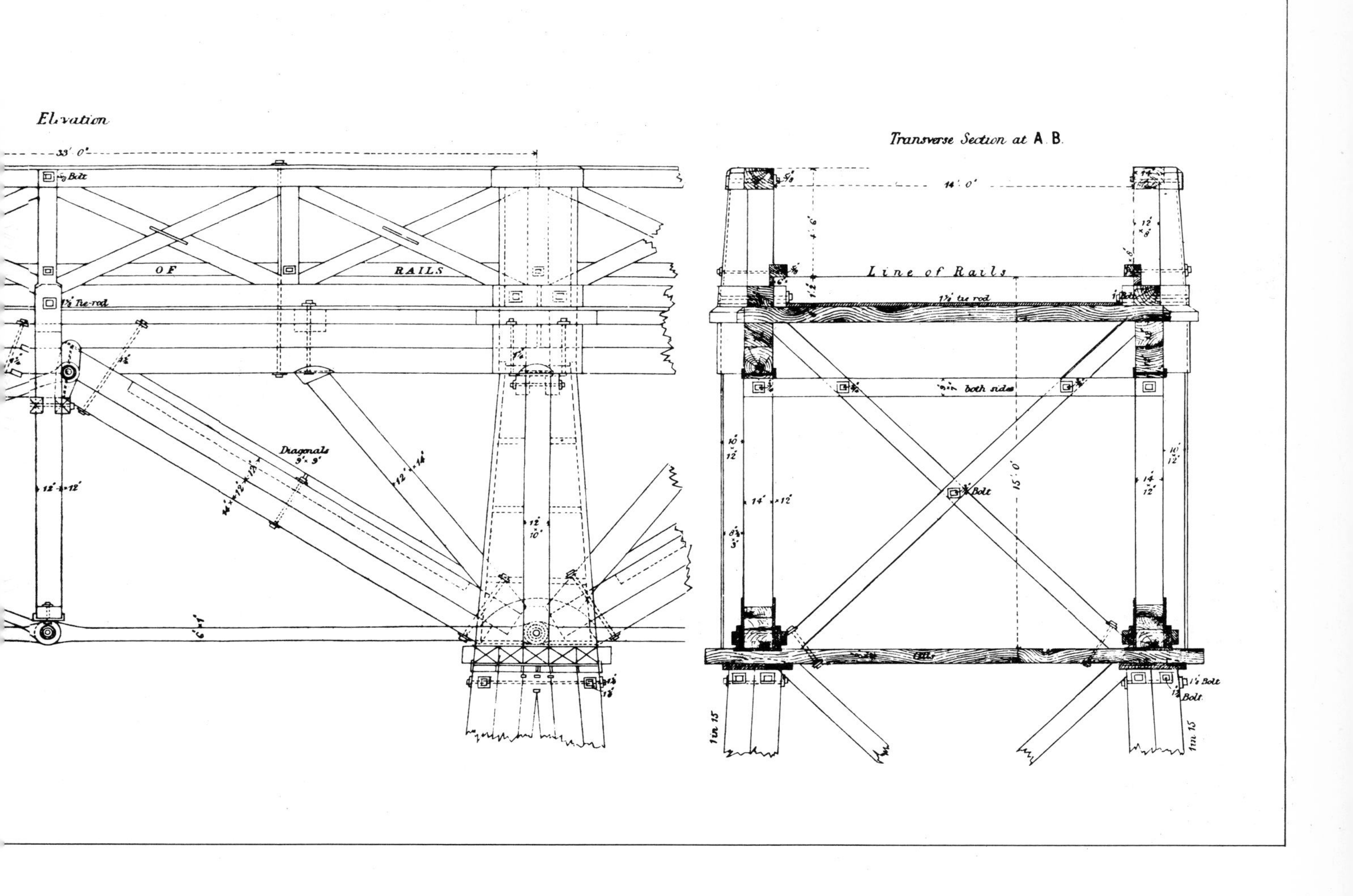

Railway climax (2).

## The Forth Bridge: 1882-1890

Bridge construction on a scale not matched for 30 years or more.

| | |
|---|---|
| Designers: | Sir John Fowler and Sir Benjamin Baker (principally Baker) |
| Contractor: | Tancred, Arrol & Co. Ltd. |
| Max span: | 521 m |
| Overall length: | 2465 m (1·53 miles) |
| Structure: | Three large balanced cantilevers with simple lattice connecting spans; all in steel (58 000 tons) |
| Labour force: | 4600 (max) |
| Casualties: | 57 killed |

Earlier schemes for a crossing of the Firth of Forth included road bridges and tunnels. One of the most notable was for a multispan suspension bridge published in 1818 by James Anderson. Like Telford's proposed Runcorn Bridge of the same period, it was well ahead of the technology of its time, with spans of over 600 m and, by present standards, far too shallow a dip to the cables.

*Figure 22*
*Sir Thomas Bouch's Forth Railway Bridge. This slightly curious-looking bridge was under construction when the Tay Bridge failed. The stump of one of its piers still remains alongside the present bridge.*

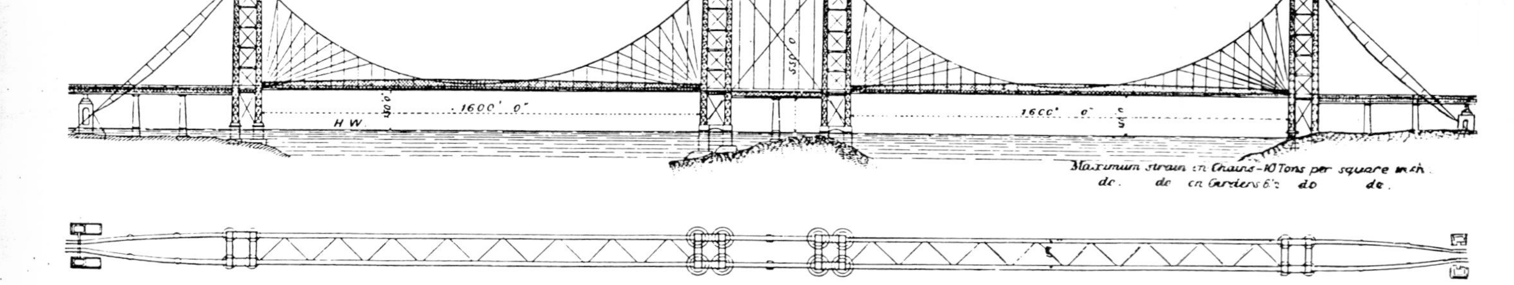

*Figure 23*
*Elevation and plan.*

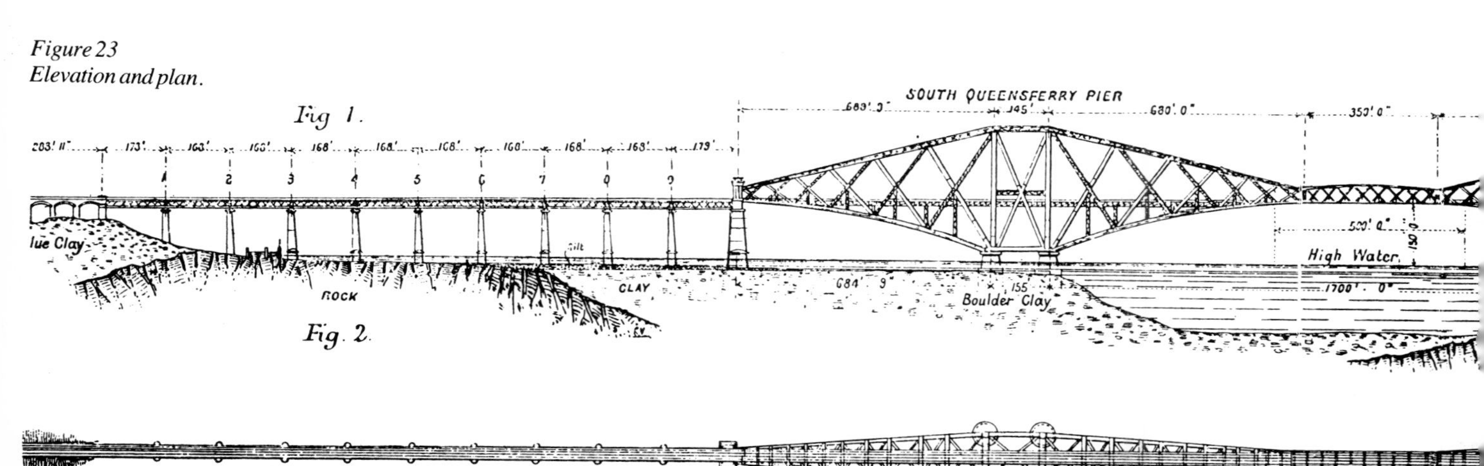

The most immediately remarkable feature of Benjamin Baker's Forth Railway Bridge is its size. Even by today's standards, it is an immense structure.

Not only is it a very long bridge – more than a mile-and-half – but, when built, it had the largest single span in the world – a record it held for nearly 30 years, having convincingly outstripped the 486 m of the newly-completed Brooklyn Bridge. Not only was the span greater but, unlike the Brooklyn Bridge designed for horse-drawn road traffic, the Forth Bridge had to meet the much more demanding needs of the railways.

The structural form of the Forth Bridge, with massive balanced cantilevers, was not new in concept, but it had hardly been used before and certainly not on anything approaching this scale.

The method of fabrication, using large, riveted tubes for the compression members, was not new either. I. K. Brunel had used big riveted tubes at Chepstow and Saltash 30 years earlier. The two arched tubes at Saltash are marginally larger than the biggest (3·7 m diameter) in the Forth Bridge, but one needs to remember that, whereas at Saltash the tubes are effectively the bridge, in the case of the Forth, these vast tubes are only individual units in a much larger structural frame.

It has been said the Forth Bridge was over-massive in its design – the result of a conservative reaction to the failure of Sir Thomas Bouch's Tay Bridge in 1879. This

*Figure 24*
*General view of the bridge: south central girder connected; north central girder not completed.*

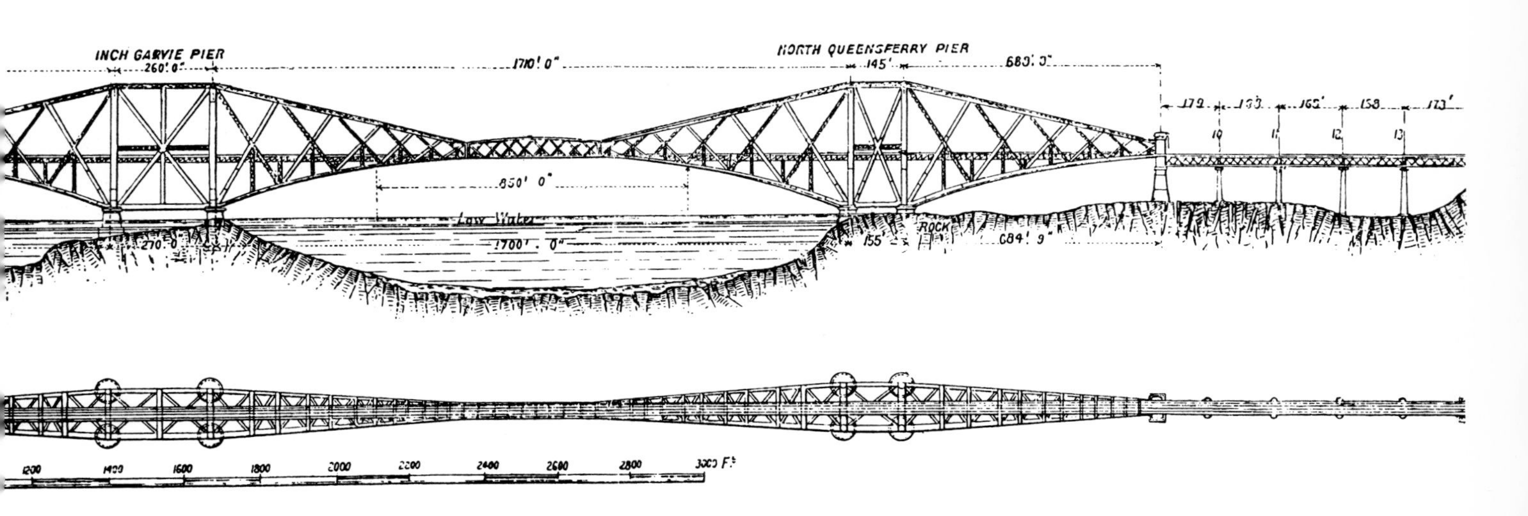

judgment is too facile, although the thought of what happened on the Tay could never have been far from Baker's mind. It certainly stirred him to a careful study of wind forces with numerous pressure measurements on the site of the bridge. It is also worth remembering that Bouch's Forth Bridge was actually being built at the time of the Tay disaster and abandoned only after Bouch had been discredited. Deserted temporary works and the stump of one uncompleted pier on Inchgarvie rock, were clear reminders of the price of failure.

Whatever its detractors may say, Baker's Forth Bridge was a major achievement in both design and construction, exploiting the technology of the day to the full, not the least in the part the public never sees, the caisson foundations sunk in compressed air in conditions that were far from easy. In terms of structural innovation, the Forth Bridge may not be able to match the Britannia Tubular Bridge but it does have the distinction of being built wholly in steel instead of wrought iron and being probably the first major railway bridge built in the new material.

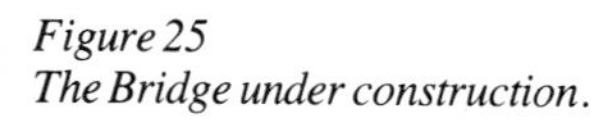

*Figure 25*
*The Bridge under construction.*

The work was carried out by Tancred, Arrol & Co. Ltd. under the supervision of William Arrol. It took 8 years and, in all, some 4600 men were employed on it, of whom 57 were killed in accidents.

As with other large bridges, one of the most difficult problems was to make the final connections, bearing in mind the extent of thermal movements from day to day.

## Epilogue on the period 1850-1890

The Forth Bridge was, in many ways, the peak of all structural engineering in Britain in the 19th century. It captured the world span record from America. No bridge so vast in every sense had been built before. Public acclaim was unbounded. Confidence in engineers, only temporarily dented by the Tay Bridge collapse, could not have been higher.

At the same time, the opening of the Forth Bridge marked the end of an age, the end of 40 unquestioning years, exploiting the inventiveness of British engineers in the 1830s and 1840s. The time had come for new ideas. These came in the 1890s and succeeding decades but, regrettably, not from inside Britain. Reinforced concrete, tall building frames, welding, prestressing, and the understanding of how soils behave, were all effectively born in other countries, but each was seized by British designers and developed with our particular native skill. These, more than the riveted iron of the 1840s, have been the techniques behind the achievements described in the following chapters.

# 1890-1910

Peter Campbell

P. Campbell JP, DIC, CEng, FIStructE, MSocIS(France), MASCE, ACIArb, MConsE.

Peter Campbell was educated at Purley Grammar School, Brixton School of Building and the Imperial College of Science and Technology, and was trained by Ove Arup & Partners from 1951 to 1962. He was a founder of Campbell Reith & Partners, Chartered Structural, Civil and Marine Engineers in 1962 and remains a senior partner to the present.

He has had a close association with the Institution and he was elected a Member of the Council in 1979 and was Chairman of the Education and Examinations Committee for 1982-84. He is Secretary of the Institution's History Study Group and founded the Museum of Concrete at Amberley, Sussex.

It is perhaps remarkable that the inventive genius of a limited number of 18th and 19th century craftsmen reached its climax during this short period in history, straddling the turn of the 19th century, and, in so doing, laid the foundations of the art and science of structural engineering as we know them today.

The medieval tradition of building in masonry and timber still persisted then, as it does today, but the pressures and demands brought about by the Industrial Revolution, and the consequent social changes that ensued, produced not only an escalation in the rate of building and the introduction of new building types, but also the need to make them larger, stronger, and more fire resistant. Moreover, since specialised development usually takes place in established areas, increased construction invariably places demands on land, providing an incentive to make buildings taller.

The resulting need for more sophisticated construction techniques had been apparent for some time, and the means to achieve these objectives had been developing slowly since the advent of the use of iron in construction, made possible by Abraham Darby (1720); the concept of the framed structure, demonstrated by William Strutt (1792); the invention of Portland Cement by Joseph Aspdin (1824); the idea that concrete could be substantially strengthened with iron, and therefore improved as a structural material, put forward by William Wilkinson (1854); and finally, the invention, by Henry Bessemer (1855), of the converter that first produced malleable iron, a process that heralded the introduction of mild-steel as a construction material. The reader will no doubt have learnt already, from previous chapters, of the creative ability of these early pioneers – men who can be properly regarded not only as great innovators but as the fathers of modern structural engineering.

While the means of modern construction, in terms of materials, were being developed, methods of analysis, design, and the regulation of construction procedures, were well in hand. Designers, especially in France, were concerned with, and deeply involved in, the systematic application of mathematics to the design of structures, and, despite the fact that the theoretical bases for the analyses had been accepted by the end of the 18th century, it was not until about 1900 that the main framework of the theory of structures, as we know it today, was defined.

By this time, the elastic analysis of all the principal types of truss, arch, suspension bridge, 2- and 3-dimensional braced roof structures, retaining walls and gravity dams, was perfectly possible, but the emphasis in reinforced concrete design was on the simple elements, the beam, column, and slab. With the introduction of structural steelwork sections, it became clear that it was possible to contemplate a fully loadbearing skeletal structure, using structural steelwork, that would then support the weather-resisting cladding envelope. In tandem with these developments, reinforced concrete was being developed as an alternative material for the construction of structures.

With few, at this time, being particularly interested in or able to comprehend these new developments, it became essential that guidelines for general use should be formulated. In 1894, therefore, the newly established London County Council introduced the most comprehensive Building Act since the Rebuilding Act of 1667, following the Great Fire of London one year earlier. It was not, however, until 1909, when the Amendment Act to the London Building Act was passed, that considerable progress could be made in structural design, especially in the use of steel and concrete.

The drafting of this legislation was undoubtedly assisted by the work of the British Fire Prevention Committee, a body of architects, surveyors, and others interested in preventing fire damage to buildings, who had, since 1897, been testing the fire resistance of building elements, particularly floors constructed in reinforced concrete. In 1902 the British Engineering Standards Committee was established which, in 1929, became the British Standards Institution, and in 1906 a Special Commission on Concrete Aggregates was established. These groups brought together men professionally qualified and commercially orientated, who were aware of the value of reliable information and its effective application.

A prerequisite for all these developments was a greater knowledge of soil mechanics and foundation engineering. Continuous strip foundations supporting loadbearing walls, transmitted relatively light loads on the subsoil, but the appearance of the framed structure produced the need to support high concentrations of loads from the stanchions and columns. Soil mechanics was, at this time, an almost entirely empirical science, and its application to foundation engineering was concerned very much with piled foundations, the potential of which had been rapidly grasped by engineers. Piles made of timber had been used by the Romans and, from then onwards, piled foundations were systematically developed. In 1887, the first precast concrete piles were introduced in Europe and, in 1908, the *in situ* concrete bored pile was perfected.

In conjunction with this work, methods of excavation and sheet piling were being developed, together with reinforced concrete rafts, reinforced concrete column foundations, and concrete encased steel grillage foundations.

As has happened often in the past (and indeed in more recent times), having established the means for a revolution in construction techniques by inventing modern reinforced concrete and structural steelwork, we failed to appreciate the technical and commercial value of these inventions and, as a result, left others to provide the impetus for their development and exploitation.

The Americans worked in both fields with an emphasis on steel-framed construction but, with the French, the emphasis was reversed, resulting in both systems being developed rapidly. The first multistorey building in Europe to be designed as a steel-framed structure, was the Menier Chocolate Factory, near Paris, built in 1871-2. This building anticipated modern structural steel skeletal frameworks by using the best traditions of medieval timber-framed construction, suitably stiffened and braced to cope with its inherent stability requirements, a critical factor in high-rise building design.

About a decade later, the exploitation of the mineral resources of America's

*Figure 1*
*A concrete encased iron/steel foundation grillage, used at the beginning of the 20th century (1900-1908).*

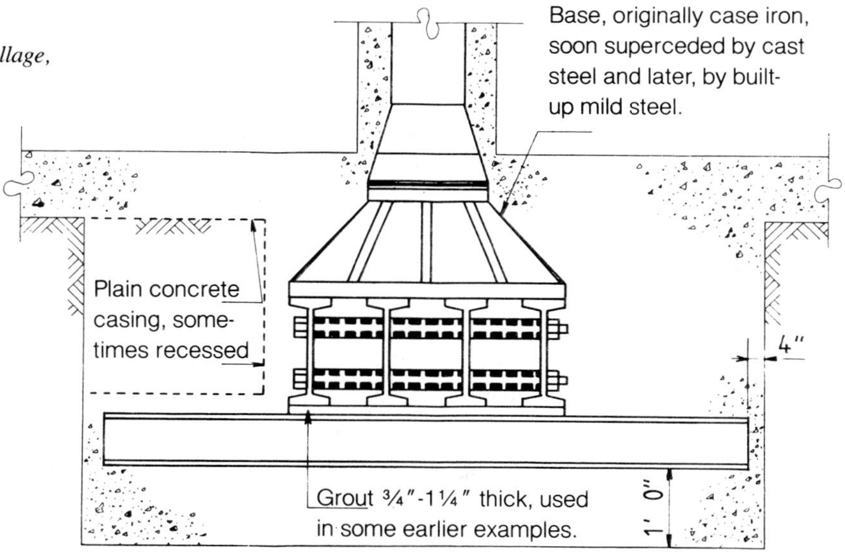

Base, originally case iron, soon superceded by cast steel and later, by built-up mild steel.
Plain concrete casing, sometimes recessed
4"
Grout ¾"-1¼" thick, used in some earlier examples.
1' 0"

*Figure 2*
*The type of precast reinforced concrete pile used by Hennebique at the turn of the century (1900) has changed very little in the last 80 years.*

Wire transverse ties (in sets of four), spaced at close centres in top and bottom of pile.
Solid steel driving point.

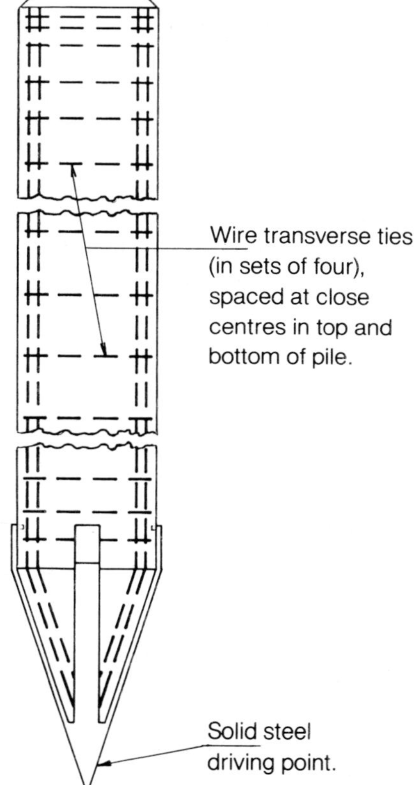

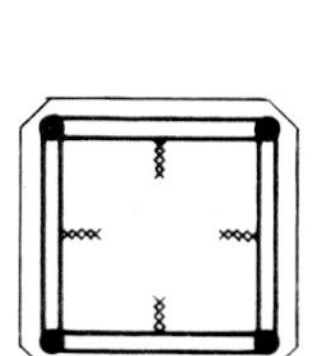

midwest became possible, when the railway and waterway systems were expanded. Chicago became the centre for the world's largest grain market. The timber, trade and food industries were established there and the manufacture of machinery and machine tools grew in this location. The earlier devastation of the city by fire, together with these commercial developments, led to an unparalleled burst of building activity from about 1880; with the consequent demand for land, its price escalated and, in order to maximise the use of land, multistorey buildings soon evolved into skyscrapers and this was possible only because of the development of structural steelwork.

Many of the architects who created the first modern steel-framed buildings in Chicago were trained in the office of William le Baron Jenney who founded the 'Chicago School' (1880-1910). By 1895, this construction method was firmly established in all major American cities, but, at that period, Chicago had more high-rise steel-framed structures than all the other cities put together, a state of affairs produced, on the one hand, by demand and, on the other hand, by the group that assembled around Jenney.

Their concern was not to produce a new architecture, but to erect tall, fire-resisting, stable buildings. The collective resolve that this group displayed to overcome the difficulties that arose characterises their work and links them together.

The emergence of the structural-steel frame, together with the introduction of successful passenger lifts, the need to minimise construction loads to make substructure designs sensible, and the growing demand for larger windows, profoundly influenced the work of engineers and inevitably resulted in the evolution of an architectural form that is still familiar. By the turn of the 19th century, skyscrapers were commonplace in America. The Park Row Building in New York, with its 36 storeys, was the tallest building in the world.

During this period, notable suspension bridges appeared in American cities, including Brooklyn, Williamsburg, and Manhattan, Williamsburg having a central span of 1600ft (492m). The Niagara and Clifton arched bridges were

*Continued on page 76*

*Figure 3*
*The Reliance Building, Chicago.*

The Reliance Building, Chicago, was built to the design of Burnham & Root (1895). It was said that 'its airiness and purity of proportion symbolised the spirit of the Chicago school', led by William le Baron Jenney from 1880-1910.

*Figure 4*
*Tower Bridge (1886-1894). An early photograph.*

*Figure 5*
*The Bridge under construction.*

completed in 1897 and their main arches each spanned 840ft (258m). Viaur Viaduct was of the same vintage but of more modest proportions. The art of bridge building was, like steel-framed buildings, developed in America on a much larger scale than in Europe.

The period commencing 1890 can claim, as its curtain-raiser in Britain, the opening of the Forth Bridge, designed by Sir John Fowler, which has been described in the previous chapter. This structure was a magnificent feat of engineering design and construction in steel and the forerunner of bridges all over the world, designed using the concept of balanced cantilevers.

Shortly after this, in 1894, another important structure was completed, this time in London. Like the Forth Bridge, Tower Bridge is immediately recognised throughout the world as the most famous bascule or lifting bridge. The bridge, which was designed by Sir Horace Jones, City Architect, in collaboration with Sir John Wolfe Barry, has always been a subject of controversy, but it cannot be

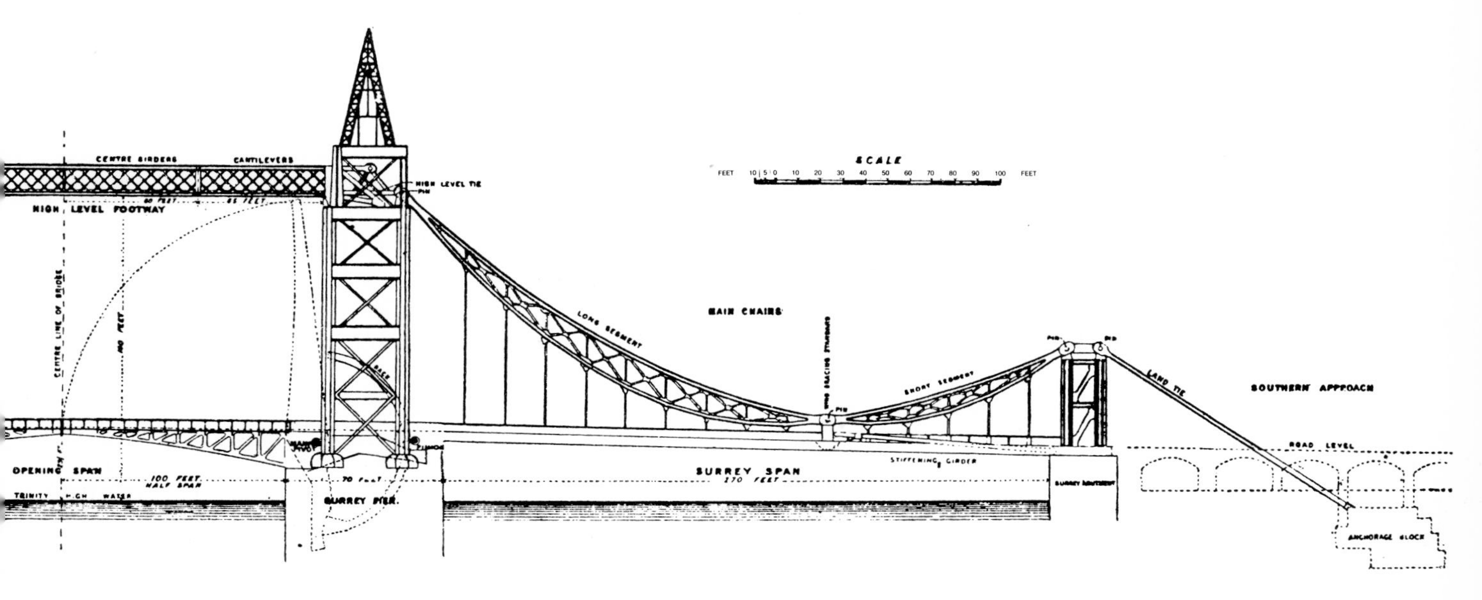

*Figure 6*
*Constructional details.*

denied that it is an important work, both of architecture and of engineering. Royal assent was given to an Act to empower the Corporation of London to build such a bridge over the Thames in 1885, and the construction started in 1886. The Government of the day required that the appearance of the bridge should accord with the appearance of its illustrious neighbour, the Tower of London.

The fixed parts of the structure of Tower Bridge consist of two shore spans each of 270ft (83m) and a central high-level span of 230ft (71m). The fixed spans are suspended from chains between the river towers and abutment piers. The river towers consist of four wrought steel stanchions, octagonal in section and made of built-up riveted plate construction connected by horizontal plate girders, the towers ultimately being clad with granite facings and Portland stone dressings.

Despite the progress in steel-framed construction that was already commonplace in America, this method was little used in Britain before 1900 and, on the continent, steel framing was restricted mainly to railway stations and factories. The first loadbearing steel-framed building of any significance to be built in this country was London's Ritz Hotel (1904), which was followed, two years later, by the east wing of Selfridges. The London Building Act of 1894 still required the external walls to be of full loadbearing thickness and prohibited the riveting of beam-to-stanchion connections. Neither of these requirements was enforced in these projects and other new features that were incorporated in the designs did much to increase pressure on the authorities to revise the London Building Act, which was inhibiting the development of steel frame construction.

*Continued on page 80*

*Figure 7*
*The Ritz Hotel.*

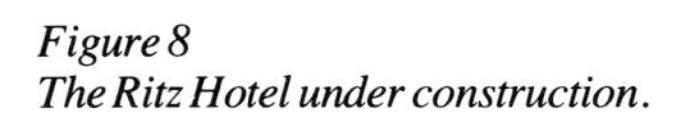

*Figure 8*
*The Ritz Hotel under construction.*

This building, completed in 1904, was the first fully loadbearing skeletal steel-framed structure to be constructed in Britain. The beam-to-stanchion connections were riveted. Neither of these procedures was permitted under the London Building Act at that time.

*Figure 9*
*The east wing of Selfridges.*

*Figure 10*
*Selfridges under construction.*

*Figure 11*
*The Glenfinnan Viaduct, 1897.*

The bridge known as Glenfinnan Viaduct links Fort William with Mallaig in the Western Highlands. It is 9750 ft ( 3000m ) in length and was constructed by Robert McAlpine using unreinforced mass concrete.

During this time, an alternative system of construction had already been developed in France, exploiting the use of concrete and steel as the composite material, reinforced concrete. The first official recognition of the merits of this material was the acceptance, in 1892, of Edmond Coignet's proposal to use reinforced concrete, instead of masonry, in the construction of a new main drainage system in Paris. In the same year, Coignet took out patents for precast beams and, in 1894, jointly with a collaborator, Coizeau, for piles and sheet piles. He had already patented, in 1890, the application of reinforced concrete to pipes, aqueducts and tunnels.

François Hennebique came to prominence in this field with a patent for reinforced concrete beams (1892) with round main reinforcing rods with fish-tailed ends and with flat hoop-iron stirrups, details that characterised his work for several decades. In 1897 he introduced the bent-up bar and in 1898 the V-stirrup, still formed in hoop-iron but clipped on to the main bars. He further adopted the T-beam although he was not the first to use it in reinforced concrete construction. However, the development of this system of construction was such that he could now combine all the structural elements into a completely monolithic structure.

Armand Considére began his contribution to this work in 1895, which led to

*Figure 12*
*The first watertower in Britain at Merrick Park, Bournemouth, built by Hennebique in 1900, had a capacity of 68 000 litres.*

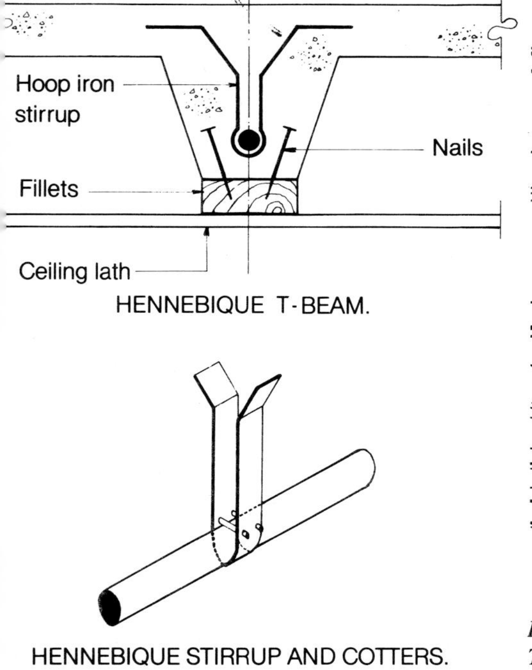


*Figure 13*
*Hennebique T-beam, stirrup and cotter.*

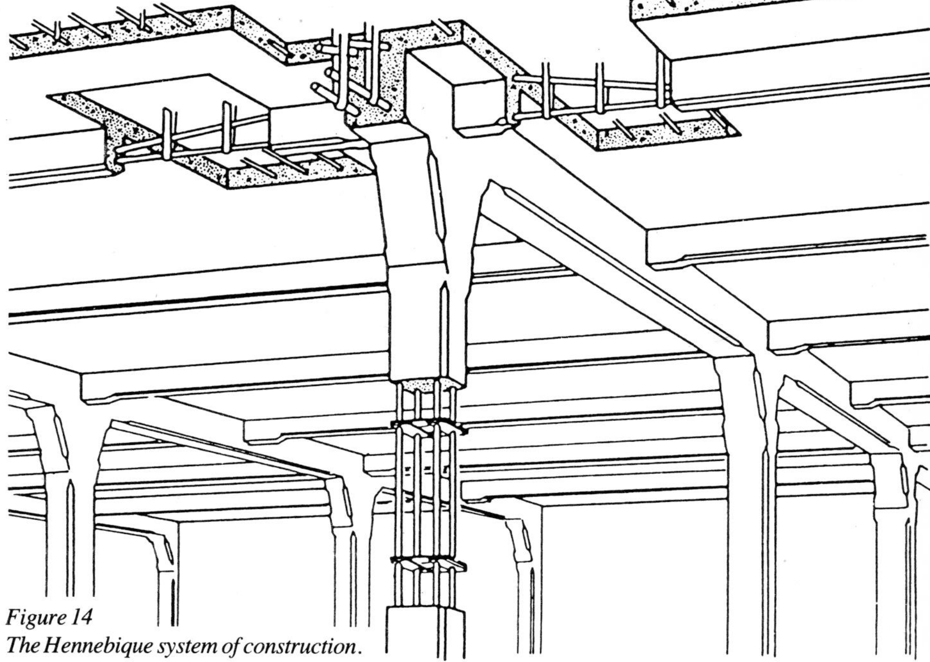

*Figure 14*
*The Hennebique system of construction.*

the use of helical secondary reinforcement in columns and provided the main reinforcing bars in beams with hooked ends to provide mechanical anchorage.

L. G. Mouchel entered the arena in 1897 when, acting as agent for Hennebique, the firm introduced the Hennebique system into Britain and enjoyed a monopoly in reinforced concrete construction until 1904 when Coignet opened a branch office here.

There were, of course, other notable figures working with reinforced concrete at the turn of the century, such as Joseph Monier; G. A. Wayss, and K. Keonen, in Germany; E. L. Ransome in America; Eugene Freyssinet; Robert Maillart; and, of course, William Wilkinson, regarded as the father of reinforced concrete, who lived until 1902 and witnessed the early development of modern reinforced concrete, a material that has changed little in its basic application to this day.

The first concrete-framed building to be constructed in the United Kingdom was the work of François Hennebique who, in 1897, was commissioned by the directors of Messrs Weaver & Co. to expand their business by constructing a

*Figure 15*

This house pioneered the use of precast concrete slab construction and was built as an entry in the 1904 Cheap Cottage Exhibition. The house is located in Letchworth's conservation area.

second flourmill in Swansea, using the system of ferro-concrete being applied in France by the firm of Hennebique and le Brun. This was the first collaborative effort by Mouchel and Hennebique, and the dominance of the Mouchel-Hennebique system became so great that, by 1910, over 40 000 structures of various types had been completed, including buildings, bridges, wharves, reservoirs, and boats. The Royal Liver Building, started in 1908, was to be Britain's first skyscraper, the 15 floors being constructed in a little over 12 months.

From 1905 Robert Maillart, who was a pupil of Hennebique, began to demonstrate in Europe, with a succession of bridges, that structural engineering was not simply the application of the use of steelwork or reinforced concrete, but that those entrusted with the task of building modern structures had a responsibility to care about the aesthetic quality of the structures they created and the manner with which they related to the natural environment. By 1910 Simon Boussiron had pushed the frontiers even further forward, when he constructed the first concrete shell roof over the Gare de Bercy in Paris.

*Continued on page 86*

*Figure 16*
*Weaver's Mill.*

Weaver's Mill is a listed building. It has not been possible to find an acceptable way of using the building and, as a result of a Public Inquiry in 1982, Listed Building Consent was given for its demolition.

*Figure 17*
*Royal Liver Building, Liverpool 1909.*

This Merseyside landmark is notable for being another Hennebique building and also the first framed reinforced concrete structure deserving the description 'skyscraper'.

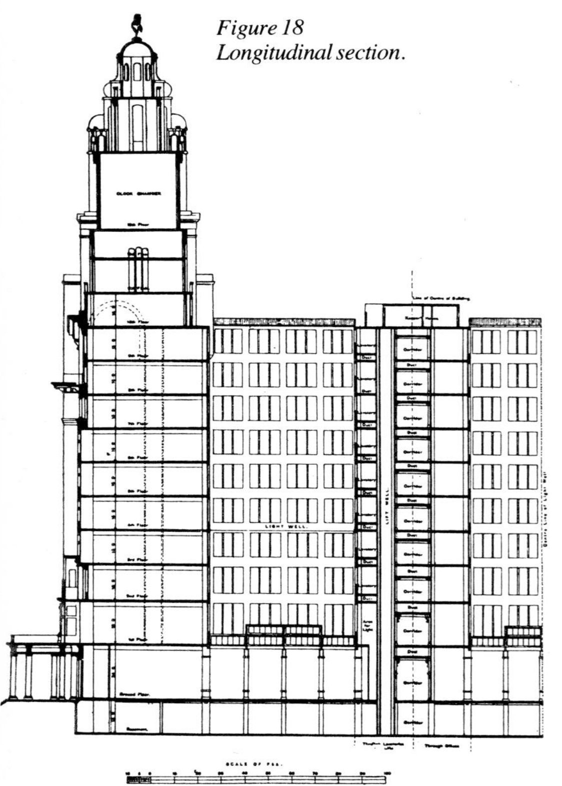


*Figure 18*
*Longitudinal section.*

*Figure 19*
*Under construction.*

*Figure 20*
*Section through Tavanasa Bridge.*

This section through Tavanasa Bridge illustrates the use of a box girder arch. Maillart, through his work, bridged the gap between art and science and revealed the possibilities for reinforced concrete to be used in the expression of a new structural architecture.

*Figure 21*
*Bridge at Tavanasa over the Rhine by Maillart, 1905.*

The period 1890-1910 is exemplified by what it made possible, rather than by what was actually achieved in Britain. All the essential ingredients for 20th century construction were available by 1910. Reinforced concrete and structural steelwork were established as the primary structural materials, and systems of design and analysis had been formulated. Time was to elapse before the contribution of the structural engineer to the design and construction process was recognised, but the possibilities opened up by the new approach to structure were acknowledged and the effects of this are described and illustrated in subsequent chapters.

It is hoped that the reader understands that it is not possible, in so short a space, to cover this period other than superficially. It is hoped that this 'broadbrush' picture of events at the turn of the 19th century has been sufficiently stimulating to encourage the reader to extend his knowledge by reference to more detailed works that are available, covering each essential element of the achievements of this period in terms of the development of the art and science of structural engineering.

# 1910-1939

Tom Harley-Haddow

T. Harley-Haddow OBE, CEng, FIStructE, FICE, FRIBA, FRIAS, FRSA, MConsE.

Tom Harley-Haddow began practice as a consulting structural engineer in 1950. From 1949 to 1959 he lectured in structures at the Edinburgh College of Art, School of Architecture and qualified as an architect in 1960.

Responsible for much innovative work in timber, brickwork, steel and concrete he has served as an advisor to the Building Research Establishment. He was a founder member of the Agrément Board, and since 1971 has been Chairman of the Building Standards (Scotland) Advisory Committee.

He was awarded the OBE in 1973

Although, by the end of the 19th century, framed methods of construction in steel and concrete had progressed beyond the pioneer stage to that of established practice for industrial buildings, such methods of construction for public buildings did not gain acceptance until the early 20th century. The first public building in England to utilise a framed structure was the Ritz Hotel of 1906, described in the previous chapter: the façade, however, did not indicate, or even suggest, the underlying structure. In other words, the frame was not yet recognised as a contributing component of building design but merely a convenient, though embryonic, method of bringing together other, more traditional and acceptable materials.

From about 1910, the structural frame began to exert an influence on the external appearance of public buildings as seen in a movement towards simplified ornament and increasing spaces between pilasters, as in Kodak House in London built in 1911 and later in buildings such as Heals in Tottenham Court Road. Structural engineering was emerging as a necessary adjunct to the construction of public and commercial buildings, although it was not yet recognised as a profession in its own right.

The upsurge of economic confidence in England following the end of World War I had produced an increasing demand for structural engineers. Compared with previous decades, large numbers of framed structures were constructed, often complex and heavy, mainly in steel, for civic, commercial, and entertainment buildings. The design, detailing, fabrication, and supervision of erection of such skeletal frameworks, thereby gained recognition as a highly specialised area of knowledge and skill which encompassed its own concepts of design philosophy, research and development, and which required integration into the planning, design, and execution, of all kinds of buildings.

In Europe, considerable political unrest, repressive movements and changes in national boundaries, had followed the cessation of hostilities, resulting in a movement of architects and engineers into countries with more political freedom, such as the United Kingdom. Among these architects were Eric Mendelsohn and Serge Chermayeff who were to influence the spread of the modern movement into England.

Symptomatic of the architecture of the '20s, however, was the British Empire Exhibition of 1924/25 at Wembley, where most of the buildings were, although temporary, neo-classical in style and mediocre in design. Structurally, the exhibition was important in that it introduced the public to the engineer Sir Owen Williams who, with architect Maxwell Ayrton, designed the only permanent building on the site, a great concrete stadium to seat 125 000 spectators, which

*Continued on page 89*

*Figure 1*
*Kodak House, Kingsway, London (1911)*
*Sir John Burnet, architect.*

The Industrial Revolution introduced new methods and materials to construction in the 19th century which, in turn, produced an upsurge of 'engineered' structures concerned principally with railway and maritime works, bridges, and factories. Towards the end of the century, engineered structures were beginning to emerge from this industrial background and to penetrate society in the design of the more socially orientated buildings. The Ritz Hotel in London (1906) was the first to envelope a steel framework.

The steel frame as an element in the design of urban buildings, however, received only tentative acceptance from about 1910. Early attempts to express the underlying structure are indicated by a move towards simplified ornament and increasing spaces between pilasters compared with the traditional classical Renaissance styles of earlier years.

Today, the significance of this movement is not easily appreciated. It is important to see it set against the establishment of the time; an establishment that consisted of such eminent architects as Sir Edwin Lutyens and Sir Reginald Bloomfield who conceived structure as only what was expedient and necessary to hold up their architectural canvasses which were concerned principally with the development of styles.

With the construction of Kodak House, Kingsway, London (1911) (*Figure 1*), (the first major attempt in England to express the underlying steel frame), a turning point had been reached: from here on the steel frame took its place beside brickwork, masonry, and timber, in the design vocabulary.

In Europe, rapid progress had been taking place in the development of reinforced concrete construction for buildings. An engineer of particular genius was Eugene Freyssinet who had demonstrated a remarkable exploitation of parabolic vaults in reinforced concrete in the airship hangars constructed at Orly between 1916 and 1924. Freyssinet and others influenced greatly ideas on construction methods in England, as can be seen in the Royal Horticultural Hall (1926) (*Figure 2*), one of the earliest applications in England of the parabolic arch in reinforced concrete as utilised in buildings. The interior demonstrates convincingly the potentialities of this most beautiful form of construction for large halls.

The arches are, in this example, of diaphragm slabs of approximately parabolic shape, being vertical for some distance from the springings, and are held together by a series of stepped slabs either side rising in diminishing steps towards the summit. The building is also important in that it is one of the earliest examples of ceiling panel heating on a large scale, having hot water pipes embedded in the underside of the horizontal slabs in order to provide the large area of low-temperature surface heat necessary for the horticultural exhibitions. With the construction of this building, the integration of services and modern structures was established.

*Figure 2*
*The Royal Horticultural Hall, London (1923-6)*
*Murray Easton & Howard Robertson, architects.*

increased the acceptance of engineering by the building, as distinct from the manufacturing and transport industries.

This period of early development of structural engineering coincided with the development of the new aircraft industry which, together with developments in ship design, was raising new problems in the design of structures. In ships, progress in metal hulls had highlighted problems in welding and in stress concentrations that were to lead to the theory of crack propagation propounded by Professor Inglis in 1913, which described the squeezing up of stress trajectories round openings to create areas of high concentrations of stress. In the design of airships the problem of solving the large numbers of simultaneous equations required to resolve the equally large number of unknowns or redundancies in segmental circular space lattice girders, led Sir Richard

Southwell to develop the method of tension coefficients, expressing the equations in cartesian coordinates and in matrix form, first published in 1920. In the same year A. A. Griffith, of the Royal Aircraft Establishment at Farnborough, at the age of 27 published a paper that described the mechanism of cracking in materials. He also formulated an expression for the work done in order to promote cracking and defined the nature of material best able to resist cracking, i.e. strong but of low resilience (high stiffness), a property particular to mild steel.

Later, in a more esoteric field, Griffith worked on the strength of fibres, publishing a definitive paper in 1928, and, in an equally esoteric field, Sir Geoffrey Taylor described, in 1934, the phenomenom of edge dislocations, whereby the spiral nature of molecular growth could result in high stress concentrations at the centre of the spiral, resulting in a breakup of the molecules. The work of Griffith and Taylor is now covered worldwide in good college textbooks on physics. Engineers working in the field of structures now ranged from empirical practitioners to scientists of considerable stature.

Such highly specialised aspects of the theory of construction fostered a growing appreciation of structural engineering as a science as well as an art. In 1922 the Concrete Institute (founded in 1908 almost simultaneously with the establishment, by the Institution of Civil Engineers, of a special committee to report on reinforced concrete as a result of expressed doubts as to its safety in construction) was renamed the Institution of Structural Engineers.

Two publications appeared in the 1920s, of such significance as to warrant special mention. In 1927 D'Arcy Thompson published his treatise *On growth and form*, the influence of which on structural form is still developing today, and Le Corbusier published the English version of *Vers une architecture* as *Towards a new architecture* which, praising engineers and denigrating architects, was so compelling in its arguments as to split the architectural profession into disparate factions of believers and disbelievers in technology – issues that are as vital now as in the '20s and '30s.

Another event of considerable significance was the invitation, by the Town Council of Dessau, to Walter Gropius in 1925 to design a new school of design, coupled with living accommodation, a labour exchange and a housing colony. This was the founding of the Bauhaus which, although Gropius left in 1928 and the school was closed by the Nazis in 1933, exerts a tremendous influence to this day on the relationship of form in design to the nature of materials.

The evolution of structural engineering as a separate discipline coincided with the polarisation of the architectural profession into the stylistic academics, on the one hand, and the pioneers of the modern movement, on the other, which division had, by the early 30s, become firmly established. In England the Royal Corinthian Yacht Club, at Burnham-on-Crouch in Essex, built by 1930, had rejected stylistic expression totally and relied on the facility of its steel framework and light cladding to define the purpose and form of the building, an early indication of the increasingly major contribution that structures were to make to modern building design and construction.

In the United States of America, steel structures had achieved a greater degree of importance because of the scarcity or cost of land in downtown New York and Chicago, coupled with the desire to achieve commercial stature by building high. The Woolworth Building of 1913, in New York, was built to withstand hurricanes and achieved a height of 241 m or 55 storeys. Technically excellent, the building, with a mock Gothic exterior, was controversial architecturally and much criticised by modernists. In 1930, 50 000 tons of steel were erected over a period of only 6 months in the construction of the Empire State Building, 85 storeys and 318 m high, later extended to 378 m when capped with its pylon. These constructions gave America a technical lead in the practical application of steel frameworks. Also, in 1930 Professor Hardy Cross published his paper on moment distribution in the *Proceedings of the American Society of Civil Engineers*, which provided a most significant practical tool for engineers in the design of continuous framed buildings.

On the continent of Europe the principle of prestressed concrete was taking root. The basic principles had been understood in the late 19th century but, for many years, the shrinkage of concrete equalled the value of prestress applied by iron bars and thus all prestress was lost. In 1921 Karl Wettstein, in Austria, patented the use of 0·3 mm piano wire in prestressed concrete planks, wherein concrete shrinkage equalled only a small loss in prestress and subsequent creep still left sufficient prestress for practical use. These planks introduced a phenomenon new to structural engineering, that of the recovery of original form following a large deformation. Eugene Freyssinet secured his first patent in 1928 and, by 1933, following the publication of his research, had put prestressed concrete on a scientific basis; by 1939 the material had become established in use in France and Germany.

The engineering search for lightness and economy had introduced welding to the steel building frame. Although based initially on a replacement of rivets in jointing methods, much as earlier steel frames had followed timber framing methods, it enabled progressive designers to demonstrate the resulting freedom from bulky supports permitted by an integrated welded structure of light steelwork, combined with reinforced concrete, in buildings. A very fine example in England was the De La Warr Pavilion of 1935 at Bexhill-on-Sea.

In the early years of the century, however, an entirely new principle of construction had been introduced in America by C. A. P. Turner and, in Europe, by the Swiss engineer, Robert Maillart, both experimenting around 1908. This was the concept of slab and column, as opposed to the column and beam system which had been traditional for centuries. Maillart developed the concept further, particularly in his bridges, to that of pure slab construction. Engineers in England later produced a number of impressive examples of these forms, among which were the Boots Drug Factory of 1931 by Sir Owen Williams, in slab and column, and the Penguin Pool at London Zoo of 1934 by Tecton and J. L. Kier & Co., in pure slab. The remarkable freedom of expression offered by these forms of construction, combined with their sophisticated specialised design methods, brought together new teams of architects and engineers.

Advances in constructional methods were, however, not without their problems and an awareness of the growing complexity of new methods and materials had resulted in the establishment of the Building Research Station in 1920. The aircraft industry, also, was developing research into more accurate factors of safety and structural engineers were searching once more for an ultimate strength theory. In 1928 the British Steel Structures Research Committee was formed and, by the early 1930s, large-scale testing of steel and concrete

*Figure 3*
*Royal Corinthian Yacht Club, Burnham-on-Crouch, Essex (1930), Joseph Emberton, architect. End elevation.*

*Figure 4*
*Royal Corinthian Yacht Club. Front elevation.*

While rapid progress had been made in reinforced concrete construction, the place of the steel frame in buildings had, in a short space of time, stepped forward into a new era. The 20 years between Kodak House of 1911 and the next example, the Royal Corinthian Yacht Club of 1930 (*Figures 3 & 4*), at Burnham-on-Crouch, Essex, is an insignificant timegap in the history of engineering or architecture, but the step forward is immense. This next phase of development is one of major significance to structural engineering and was fostered by events in Europe such as the establishment of the Bauhaus and the publication of Corbusier's *Towards a new architecture*. Fundamental to this phase was the total rejection of all stylistic expression. The Royal Corinthian Yacht Club was one of the earliest English buildings to develop this movement completely. The result was a steel framed structure clad with stucco faced brick cavity walls supported on a concrete platform resting on concrete piles founded in the river. The north and end walls facing the cold winds have only slit windows, while almost the whole of the south wall, facing the water, is of glass. Here the relevance of the steel frame to modern architecture is demonstrated in a quite convincing manner and in its day was, to quote Arnold Whittick's *European architecture of the 20th century* 'the finest example of its kind in England and not surpassed elsewhere in Europe'.

structures was underway. In 1936 the Final Report of the Steel Structures Research Committee was published, the chief technical officer for which had been J. F. (now Lord) Baker, and its recommendations were to hasten progress towards a more scientific age for structural engineering.

Dome construction, which had been popular for hundreds of years as a method of covering largish areas, found a new lease of life. In 1910 the Wesleyan Hall, Westminster, was covered over with a ribbed reinforced concrete dome 34·7 m diameter. This was much less in weight than the classical masonry domes but still considerably heavier than a membrane. Membrane theory was devised by Franz Dischinger in 1924 and used in the design of the first planetarium at Jena, 24·9 m diameter and only 60 mm thick and with no ribs. An approximate theory for bending in thick shells was published in Berlin by J. W. Geckeler in 1926.

In the 1930s many structures were built without theoretical solutions. Eduardo Torroja in Spain built an early thin shallow concrete dome for the Market Hall at Algeciras, 48 m span and 90 mm thick, which was increased to 450 mm thickness near the supports to cater for the bending and shear stresses set up by the discontinuity of the dome. The dome was supported at octagon points and hoop tension resisted by a prestressed beam with 16/300 mm diameter bars.

In Italy, Pier Luigi Nervi designed and constructed a latticed dome effect aircraft hangar at Orvieto based on testings of a celluloid model by Professor Guido Oberti of Milan Technical University. The strains in the model were measured by tensometers developed in the 1920s by a Swiss instrument maker, A. U. Huggenberger, and supplemented by deflection measurements using dial gauges. The electric resistance strain gauge based on a length of wire bonded to the structure was not invented until the late 1930s.

F. Aimand built several engine sheds in France in the late '30s, using the hyperbolic paraboloid form which had been discovered in the late 19th century during investigations to determine the shapes of a number of equations, among which was $z = kxy$. The simplicity of this equation enabled Aimond, early in the '30s, to derive the membrane theory for the hypar which he published in 1936.

Progress of a somewhat different kind was demonstrated in the building of the Empire Swimming Pool at Wembley, again by Sir Owen Williams, which was significant for the technical virtuosity of its construction. This vast concrete-covered space, measuring 104 m × 72 m, was started in October 1933 and completed by May 1934, such speed of construction resulting from the establishment of a modular grid of approximately 800 mm horizontally and 900 mm vertically and the use of standardised units of construction. While the form of this building, with its monumental three-hinged arches which taper heavily above the roof to resolve rather crudely into dominant vertical shafts, did not appeal to architects of the period (or, indeed, to later critics who found difficulty in perceiving in it any architectural merit), the sheer technical competence of the design and construction management could not be denied. A show of such technical expertise does much to persuade the public and professions of the value of structural engineering, and succeeding generations of engineers cannot but be grateful for the pioneering efforts of the period under review.

The general public might normally be unaware of revolutions in construction methods but, with examples such as Wembley, where the structure is paramount, such awareness is assured. In bridges the contribution of the structural engineer is more evident, as the structure is directly discernible and functionally understandable. The Royal Tweed Bridge at Berwick in 1928, by L. G. Mouchel & Partners, demonstrated to the public at large the development of the concrete arch with spans up to 110 m. Not far away the Tyne Bridge of 1930, by Mott, Hay & Anderson, illustrated the potential of the steel arch with a span of 162 m, a potential that was later impressively fulfilled by the British engineer, Sir Ralph Freeman, at Sydney Harbour in Australia, where an almost identical visual repeat, completed in 1932, produced a span of 509 m, just short, by 1 m, of being the longest steel arch span in the world.

The volume and quality of construction in the '30s in buildings and bridges do not appear to reflect the change from the optimism of the '20s to the economic depression years of the '30s. It is, indeed, remarkable that so many fine buildings were constructed during the depression, ranging from Battersea Power Station to Peter Jones Department Store, the Daily Express offices and countless others, less monumental in size. It is not surprising, therefore, that the period had its share of mistakes or errors of judgment, perhaps the most significant being the construction of the Quarry Hill Flats in Leeds. 938 flats were constructed from 1935 to 1940, utilising an imported system of light steel framing encased in concrete to give a new type of composite structure. The flats were built up to eight storeys, clad with precast concrete panels. Unfortunately, the development of mastics for sealing joints did not take place until the late '30s and the joints had been sealed with a cement–sand mortar. Progressive deterioration occurred and, by 1954, failure of the cladding through water penetration causing corrosion of corner steel angles and supporting brackets, which defeated attempts to repair, culminated in a decision in 1964 to demolish all the flats, a process that was completed by 1978.

British structural engineering, however, was firmly established as a profession in its own right by the granting of a Royal Charter to the Institution in 1934. Shortly afterwards, in 1935, one of the masterpieces of the modern movement, the flats at Highpoint 1 at Highgate in London by Tecton, architects, and Ove Arup, engineer, was completed – the culmination, perhaps, of reinforced concrete slab construction in the 1930s. In 1938 the Finsbury Health Centre was opened (Tecton, again, as architects, J.L. Kier & Co., engineers), looking a little dated today but, at the time, a progressive development of reinforced concrete design that integrated the building services into the structural concept, deep spandrel beams being hollowed to carry all horizontal runs of service pipework.

The period from 1910 to 1939, therefore, had seen the emergence of the structural engineer as an essential part of the building team – from the first faint beginnings of structure as a new factor in the design of urban buildings (as in Kodak House in 1911), through the emergence of the engineer/architect in the Boots Factory of 1931, to the establishment of the new teamworking of architects and structural engineers, such as Arup in the Highpoint Flats and Felix Samuely in the Bexhill Pavilion. The stage is now set for the full collaborative working of architects and engineers that followed the close of World War II.

*Figure 5 & Figure 6*
*Royal Tweed Bridge at Berwick (1928)*
*L. G. Mouchel & Partners.*

The story now diverges towards bridges, where similar advances in design and construction were taking place. A particularly fine example of the reinforced concrete arch as employed in bridge construction is illustrated by the Royal Tweed Bridge at Berwick, 1928 (*Figures 5 & 6*). The north east end of this bridge had, in its day, the longest concrete arch in the United Kingdom, at 110 m, while the remainder of the spans, diminishing in accordance with the fall of the roadway, show a rhythmic continuity of considerable aesthetic merit. Both the interior of the Royal Horticultural Hall and the elegance of the Tweed Bridge enlarged public awareness of structural engineering as a major contributing factor in the design of the built environment.

4-1-1930

4-6-1930

20-8-1930

1-11-1930

1-2-1931

OPENING 19-3-1932

*Figure 7 & Figure 8*
*Sydney Harbour Bridge, Australia (1923-32)*
*Sir Ralph Freeman, engineer, with Mott, Hay & Anderson.*

During the 1920s and 1930s, there was a growing demand for British engineering overseas. Few countries could provide the industrial background, combined with the technical expertise and contractural management ability, to handle large structural projects abroad. One such project was the latticed steel arched bridge at Sydney Harbour, Australia (*Figures 7 & 8*), built between 1923 and 1932. Residents in the United Kingdom may conceive some idea of the scale of this bridge by comparing it with the much smaller Tyne bridge of 1930 by Mott, Hay & Anderson, which, although of near identical form and the longest span steel arch in GB, at 162 m, is less than one-third of the span of the Sydney Harbour Bridge, at 509 m. Both bridges carry heavy industrial traffic which was the reason for the choice of the steel arch as opposed to the less rigid suspension or cantilevered types. In the case of Sydney Harbour, the width of the bridge is 48·8 m and the distributed design live load of 18t/m is 10 times the design load for the Forth and Severn suspension bridges. The technical problems involved were considerable, but British structural engineering was fully capable of meeting the challenge to follow the great traditions established by our bridge builders in the previous century.

Bridges of significant innovative design were, during this period, being developed in Switzerland by Robert Maillart who, abandoning the column and beam sections of traditional structures, designed elegant and graceful structures out of pure slabs in reinforced concrete, encompassing straight and curved arches, walls, piers, and roadways. Maillart also used the slab as the principal element in the construction of factories and warehouses, where slab floors were supported on columns with inverted mushroom-shaped heads again eliminating the use of beams. Work similar to this was being carried out in the United States by C. A. P. Turner but, at home in the UK, an engineer of equal genius was to demonstrate the essential unity of engineering and building.

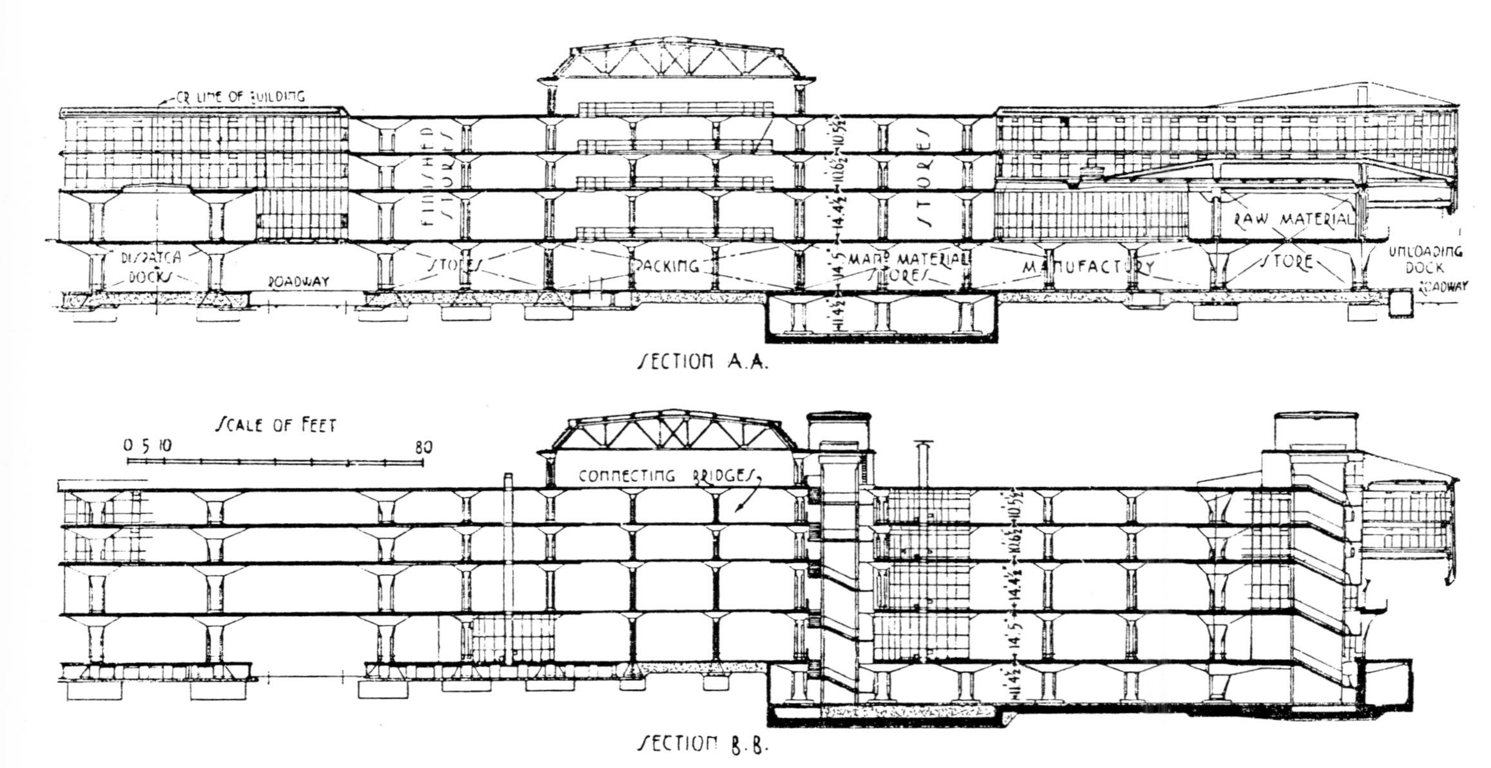


Cross sections through the lines A-A and B-B on plan

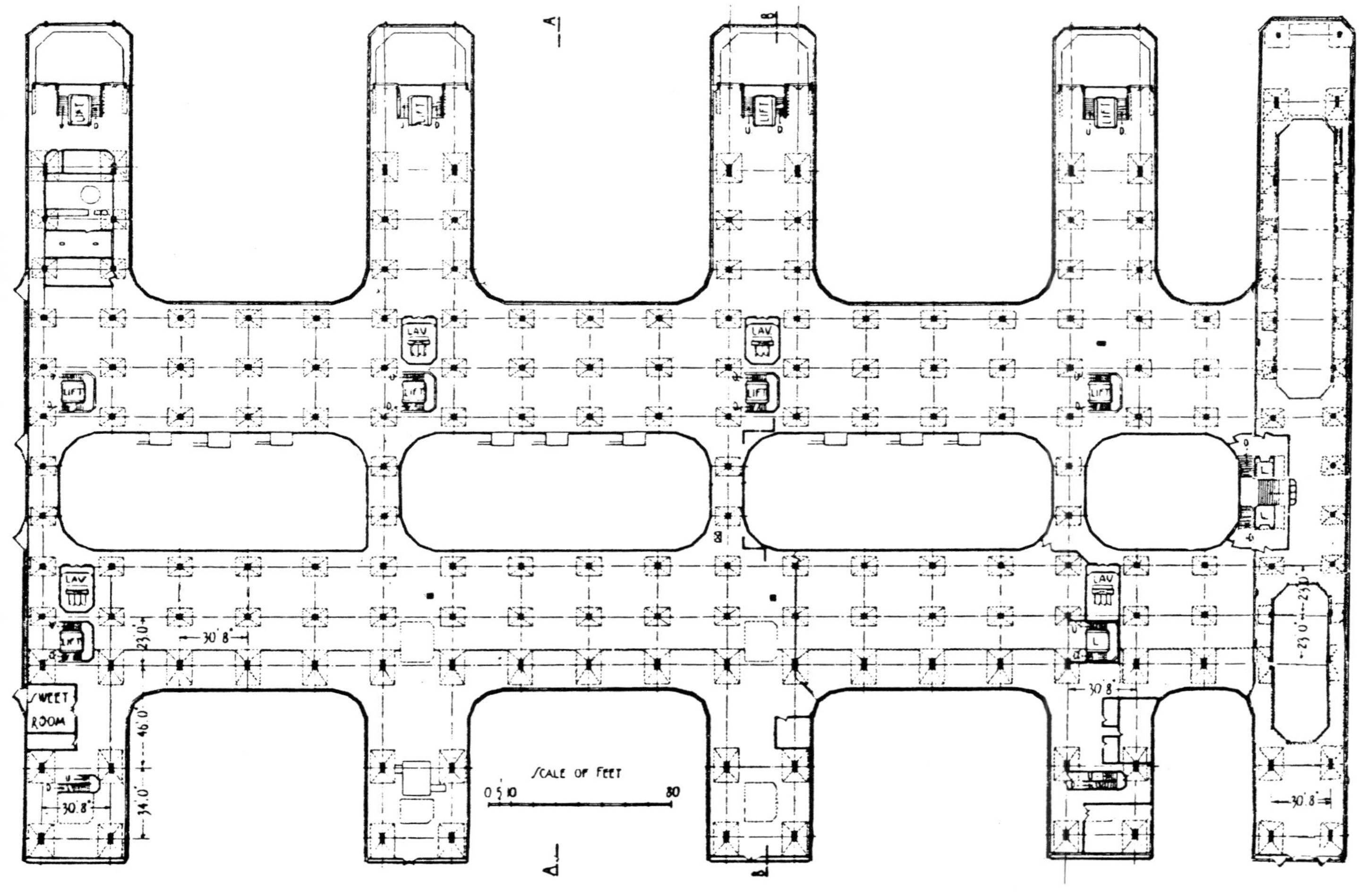


**The third-floor plan**

*Figure 9*
*Plans & sections.*

*Figure 10 & Figure 11*
*Exterior photographs.*

## Boots Factory at Beeston, Nottinghamshire (1931)

*Sir Owen Williams, engineer.*

Sir Owen William's Drug Factory for Boots at Beeston in Nottinghamshire in 1931 (*Figures 9, 10 & 11*) summed up 2 decades of development of the new principle of slab and column construction. In the early years of the century, Turner had developed a system of slabs supported on capitals with thickened slab areas reinforced with bars top and bottom at right-angles, while the main slab area was diagonally reinforced between columns. Turner's method was codified by the American Concrete Institute in 1917. In Europe, Robert Maillart had developed, almost simultaneously, a system of slabs supported on column heads tapered into the slab soffits, the slabs being reinforced in two directions only, a system later adopted universally in Europe and America. Other systems were developed, principally in the USA, but, by the mid 20s, a method of calculation based on Westergaard & Slater's theoretical and experimental investigations, together with the Maillart layout of reinforcement, had been adopted in the American Code and subsequently in most other national Codes. In 1933 an equivalent frame method of calculation was introduced into the Californian Code, the complexity of whose analysis was brought within feasible limits by Hardy Cross's development of the method of moment distribution.

Boots was a consolidation of the methods of construction (*Figure 16*) and calculation. However, the importance of Boots lies not only in the selection of the system of construction (although this in itself has considerable merit and proved the value of the engineering approach to the choice of structural form) or in the use of the Maillart or European method of reinforcement as distinct from the Turner or American method, but in the total handling of the project. The engineer's contribution to what the architect conceives of as building design is firmly established. No longer can the engineer be regarded as a mere technician, quite capable of handling the odd bridge or railway station with perhaps a little help and guidance on aesthetics; it is almost as though the engineer has said 'who needs architects anyway. Here is the

*Figure 12*
*Hoisting one of the girders of main hall.*

*Figure 13*
*Reinforcement and shuttering to cantilevers.*

modern movement – pure technology'. From this date the engineer had to be integrated into the building team or the architect would lose all credibility.

In this building the roofs over the high wings are of glass bricks set in concrete (*Figures 12-15 & 17*), whereas the walls are entirely of glass uninterrupted except for the edges of the concrete slabs. York & Penn in *A key to modern architecture* (1939) state 'The building demonstrates admirably the interdependence of engineering and architecture. It is probably the finest factory building in the world'. In the UK, reinforced concrete had now been brought to the same level of acceptance for industrial buildings as had steelwork.

*Figure 14*
*'Centring' bull's-eye lights.*

*Figure 15*
*Interior of main hall showing steel roof trusses supporting reinforced concrete roof containing bull's-eye lights.*

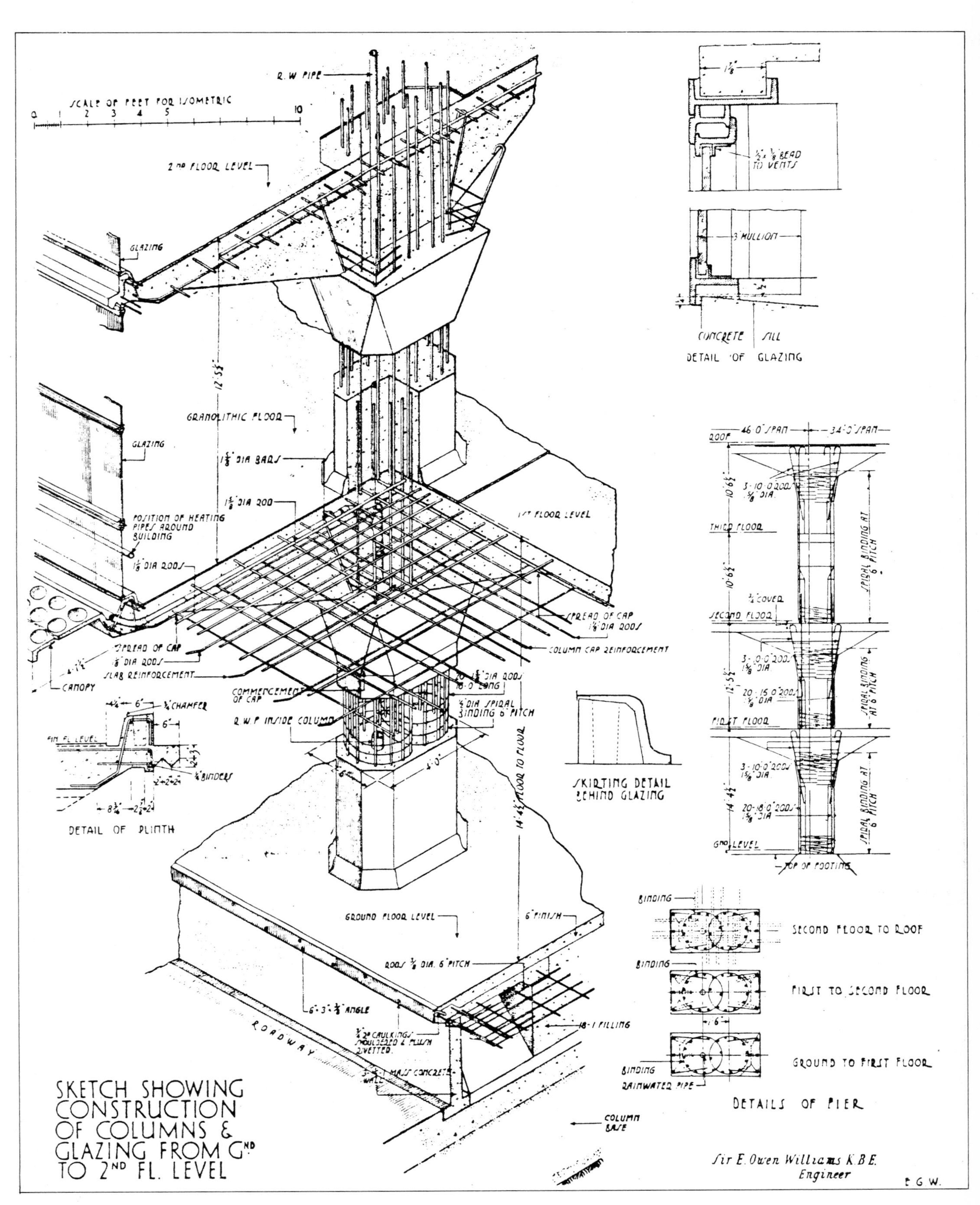


Figure 16
*Isometric details of typical floor, column, and wall construction.*

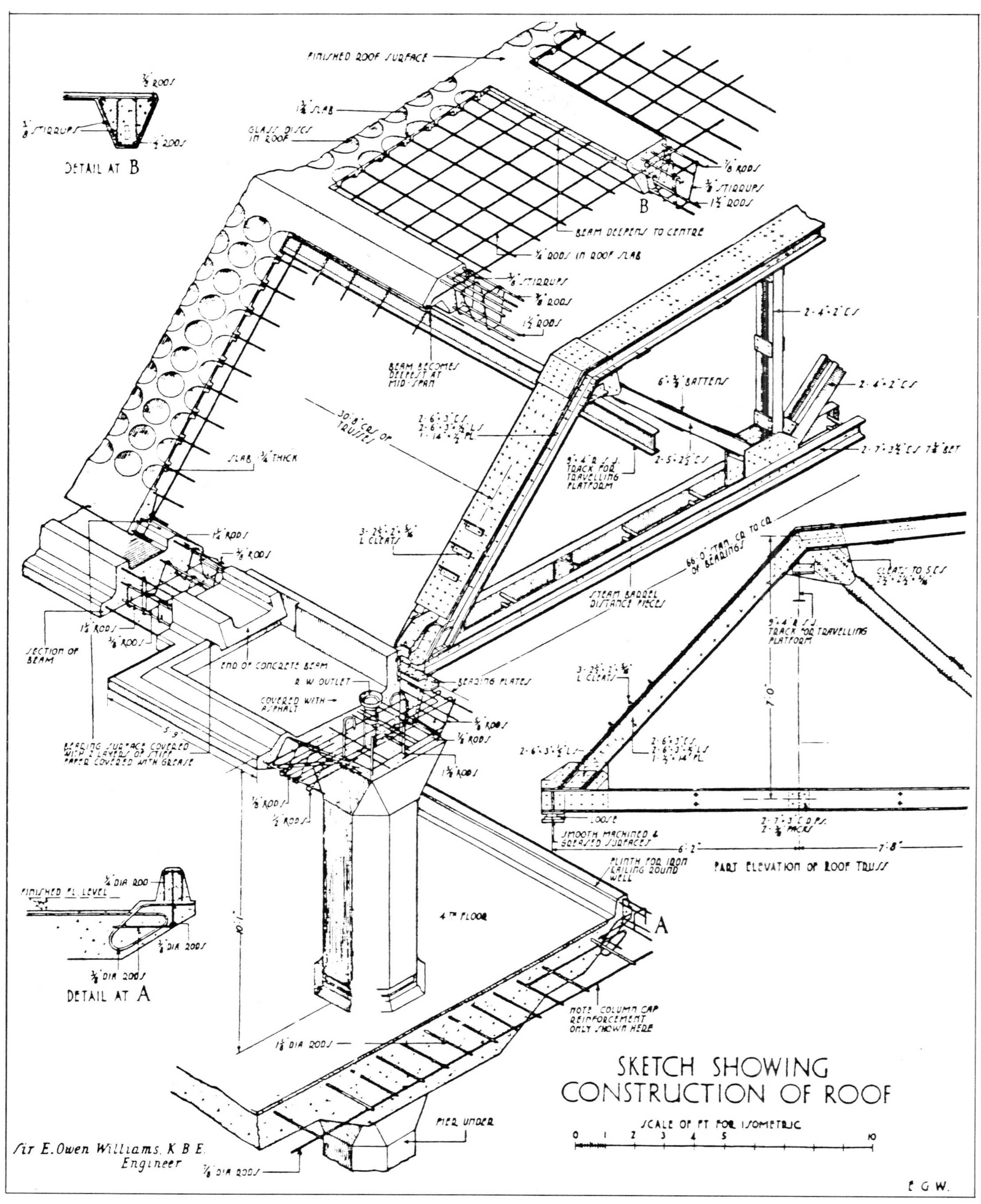


*Figure 17*

*Boots factory. Isometric details of construction of the roof to the main hall.*

# De La Warr Pavilion, Bexhill (1935).

Architects Mendelsohn & Chermayeff.
Engineers Helsby, Hamann & Samuely.

The growing importance of structural engineering to building is well illustrated by the De La Warr Pavilion at Bexhill (1935) (*Figures 18, 19 & 22*), the winning scheme of a competition run by an enlightened public authority which provided a rare instance of an award to a modern architectural design and an opportunity for an early exercise in teamworking between architects and structural engineers. The structural framework in steel is remarkable of its period for its lightness and grace and also for the early use of welding in building structures. Reinforced concrete floors provide stiffness to slender columns in the restaurant wing. The integration of the structure within the total building concept has enabled the architects to exploit new concepts of space free from heavy supports within the building and, where required, clear spans, the use of cantilevers, and all-glass façades.

*Figure 18*
*De La Warr Pavilion, south staircase and terrace to restaurant.*

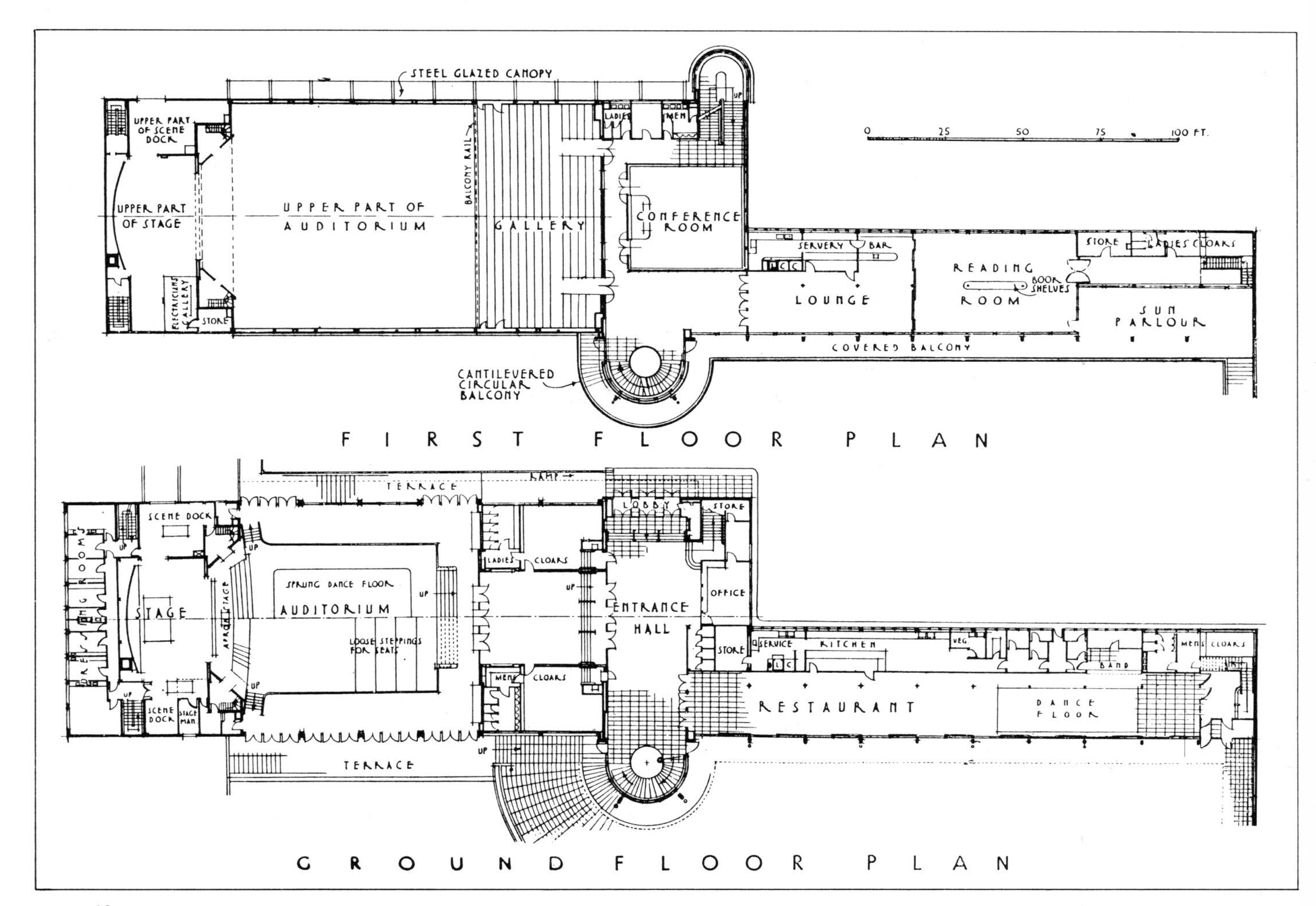


*Figure 19*
*Plans of De La Warr Pavilion, Bexhill (1935).*

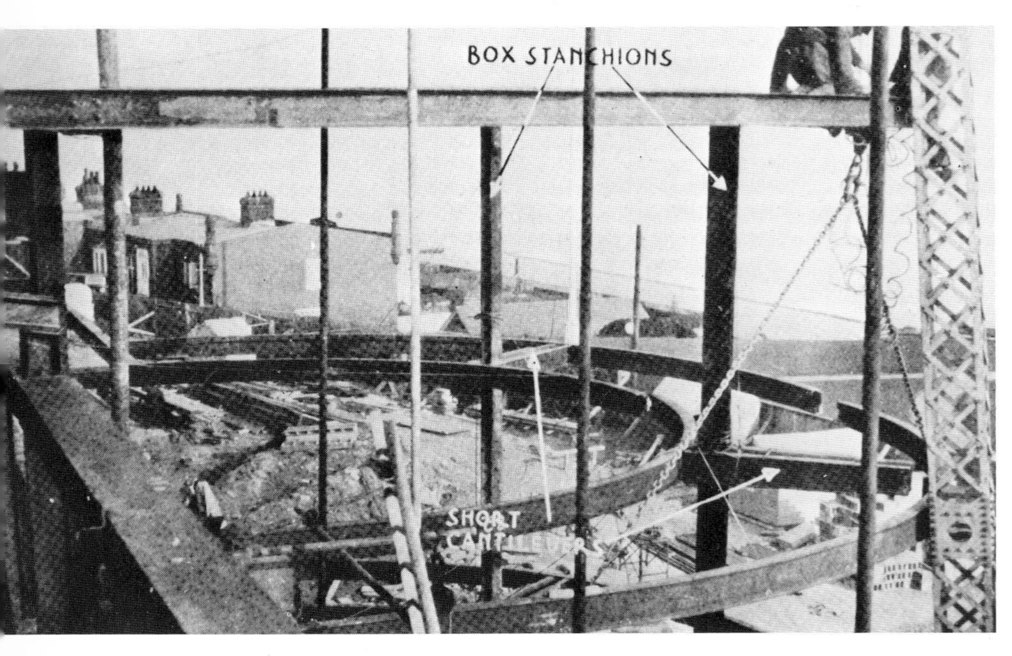


*Figure 20 (left)*
*South staircase under construction.*

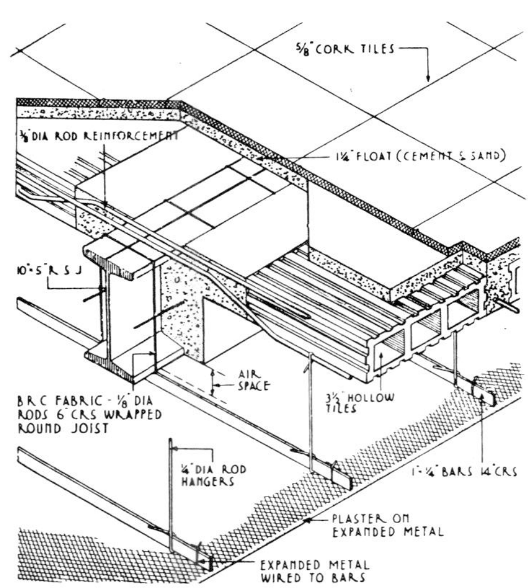


*Figure 21*
*Typical method of floor construction.*

*Figure 22*
*De La Warr Pavilion, the Library.*

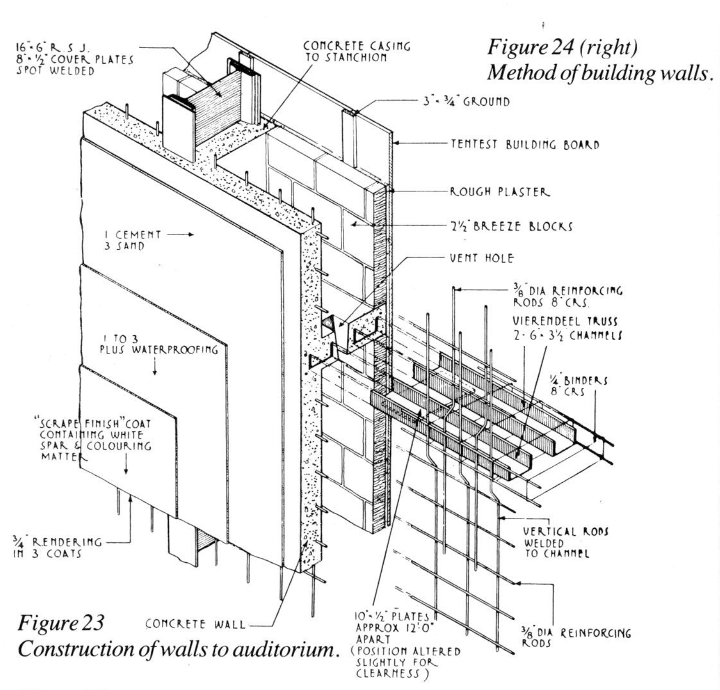


*Figure 23*
*Construction of walls to auditorium.*

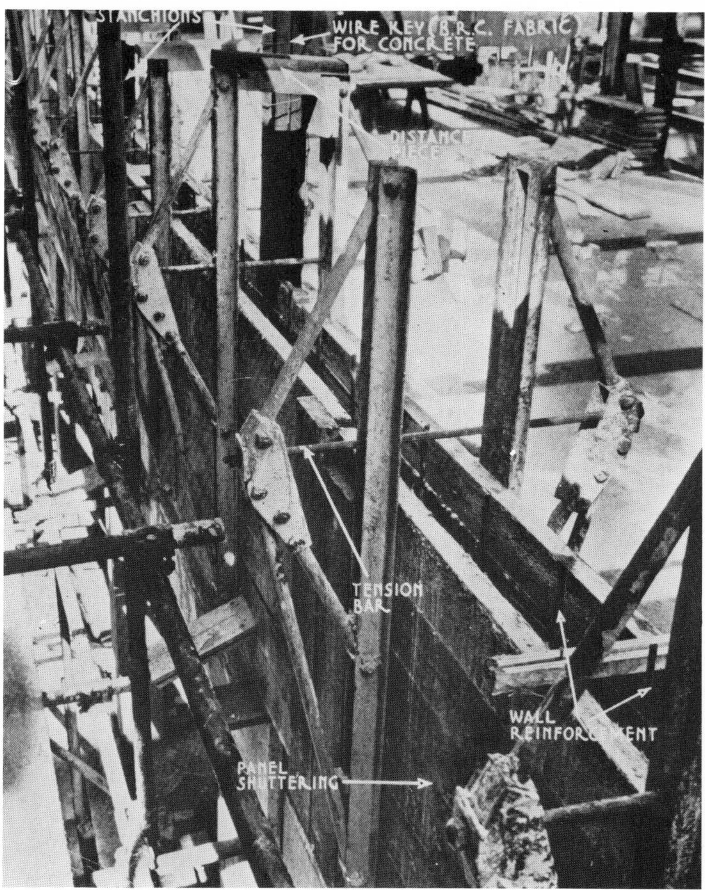


*Figure 24 (right)*
*Method of building walls.*

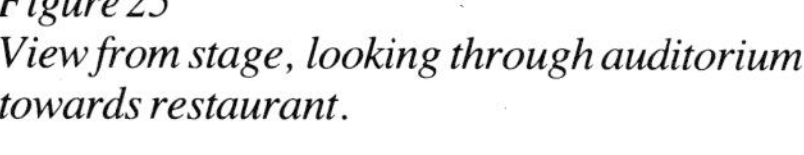

*Figure 25*
*View from stage, looking through auditorium towards restaurant.*

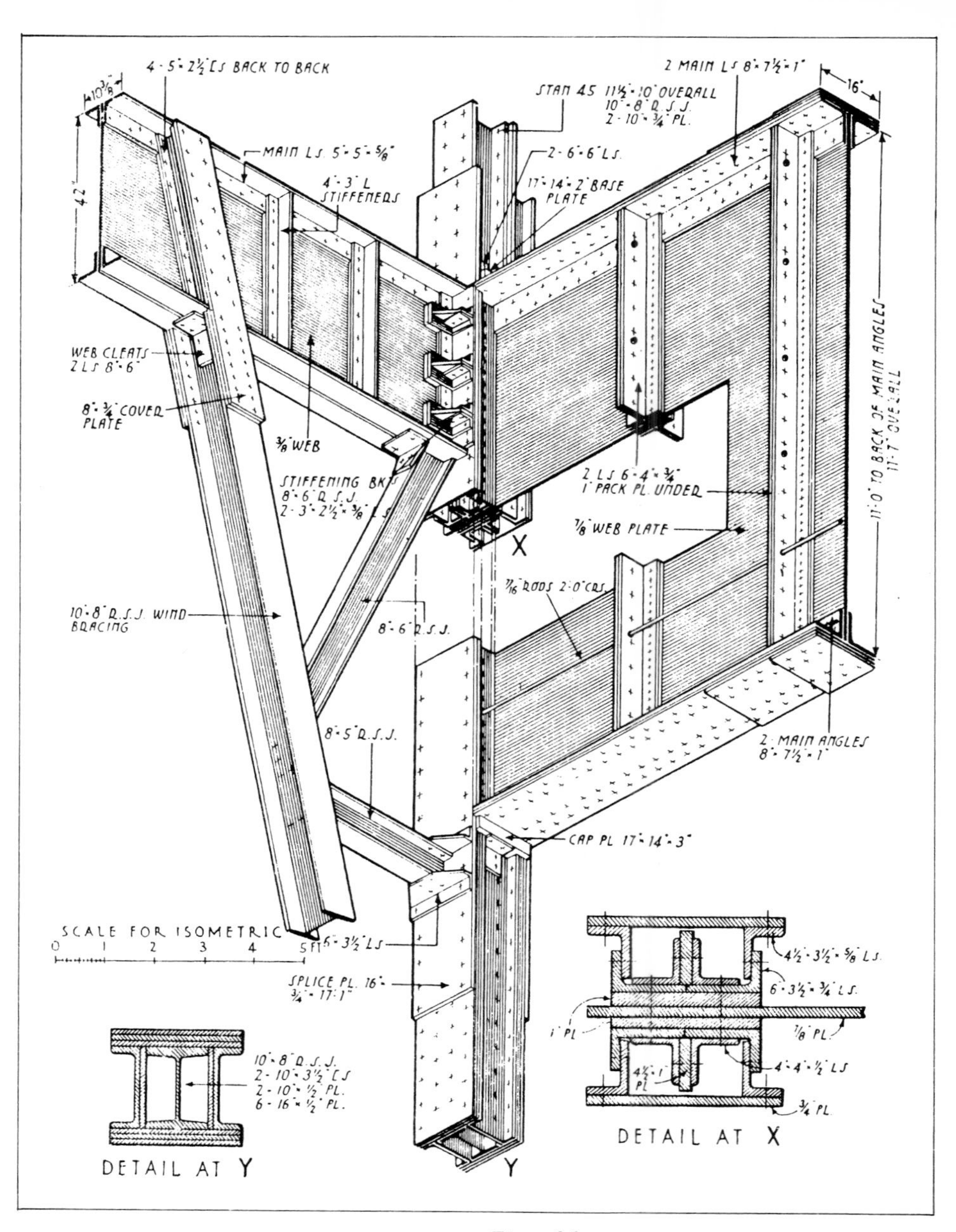

Figure 26
RIBA headquarters, detail of main beams. Architect Grey Wornum, engineer R. T. James & Partners.

It is interesting to compare the details of the Bexhill Pavilion with those of a contemporary competition-winning scheme, that for the RIBA headquarters. Both competitions were held in the spring of 1932 but while one, the RIBA, shows the prevailing heavy riveted steel construction produced by the average technicians of the period (*Figures 26-28*), the other, the Bexhill Pavilion, by the imaginative use of light welded steelwork of considerable grace (*Figure 20*) and the latest techniques of hollow tile concrete floors, (*Figure 21*) and panel shuttered concrete walls, (*Figures 23 & 24*), pointed the way to new technologies and a clear future for the structural engineer integrated within the design team.

What is not traditional in the more traditionally appearing RIBA headquarters building is the plan unrelated to the structures, a feature unheard of in loadbearing masonry construction. In this building, clear spaces pass under loadbearing walls which are then carried by heavy riveted pláte and Vierendeel girders. This demonstrates a new freedom in planning which architects found in the technology of structural engineering, and most engineers were willing enough to demonstrate their skills in devising solutions. To the more enlightened, however, the discipline of integrating structural

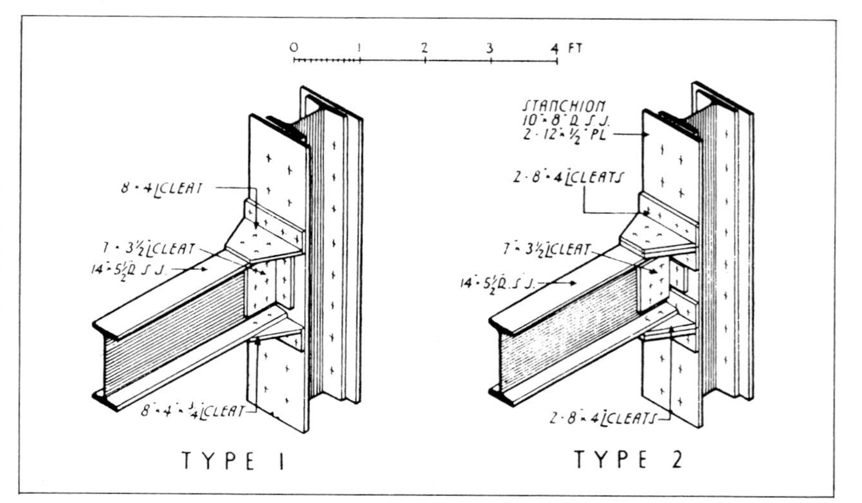


Figure 27
RIBA wind connection details.

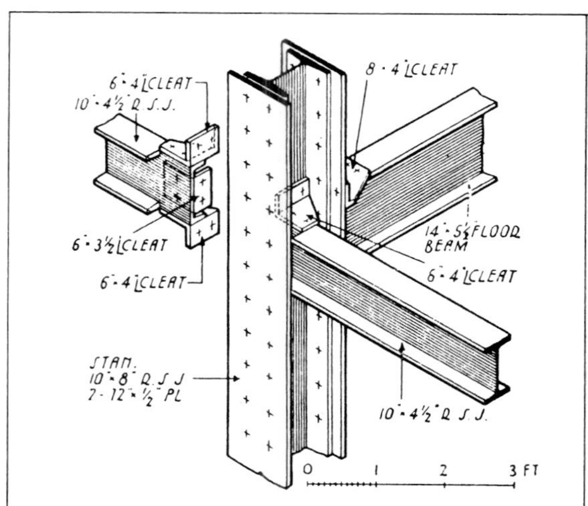

Figure 28
RIBA beam connections.

*Figure 29*
*De La Warr Pavilion, junction of cantilever and transverse girder.*

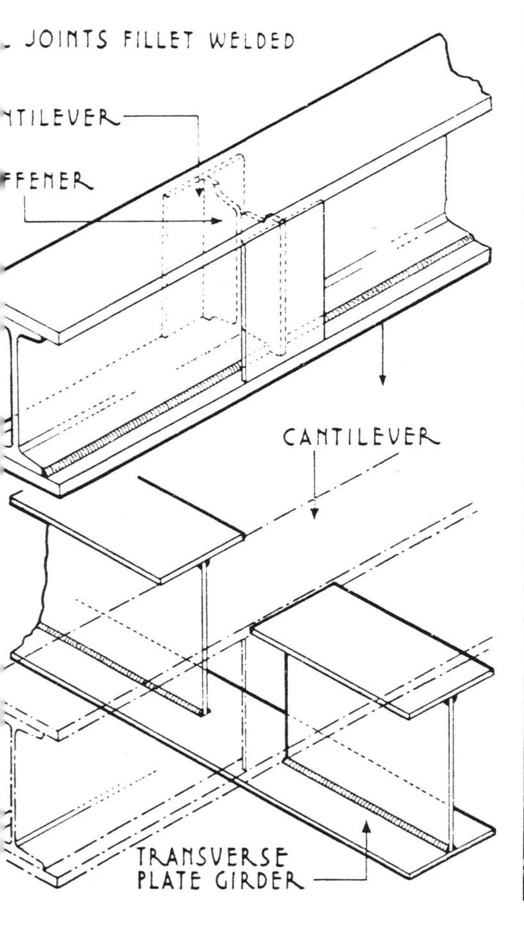

*Figure 30*
*De La Warr Pavilion, north staircase showing cantilever beams and suspended construction.*

form and plan was emerging not as a necessity, as in masonry construction, but as an elegance of choice. Such a mental attitude leads to the exploration of the potentialities of the new materials and methods of construction.

The Bexhill Pavilion is a supreme example of this progressive attitude where the architect's carefully studied relationship of plan and structure and finish is supported by imaginative engineering, epitomised in every detail of the structure:

(Figures 20 & 30) the facility of welding to give cantilevered and hanging construction is exploited in the stairs and balconies including box section columns;

(*Figure 25*) in the hangars from wall trusses supporting beams over large areas of clear glass at groundfloor level;

(*Figure 23*) reinforcement to poured *in situ* concrete curtain walls spot welded to steel columns;

(*Figure 24*) reinforced concrete curtain walls cast in lifts in panel shutters 10 ft long x 3 ft 3 in high supported by patent spacer clips at the bottoms and wooden distance pieces at the top; the inside of the outer shutters with retarders to allow brushing off the cement face to provide a key for rendering.

The building abounds with forecasts of the future of construction.

*Figure 31*
*Penguin Pool, London Zoo, under construction. Tecton, with J. L. Kier & Co., engineers.*

*Figure 32 (bottom)*
*Penguin Pool, completed (1933).*

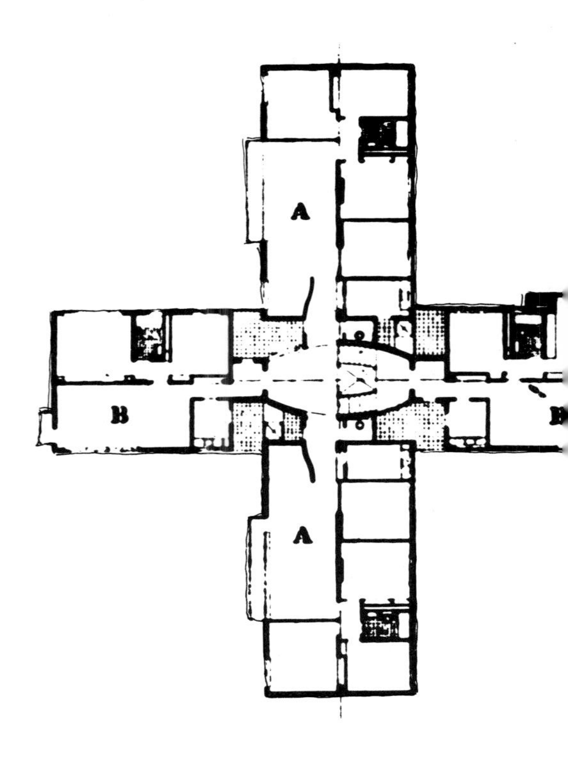


*Figure 33*
*Highpoint 1 flats at Highgate, London. Plans.*

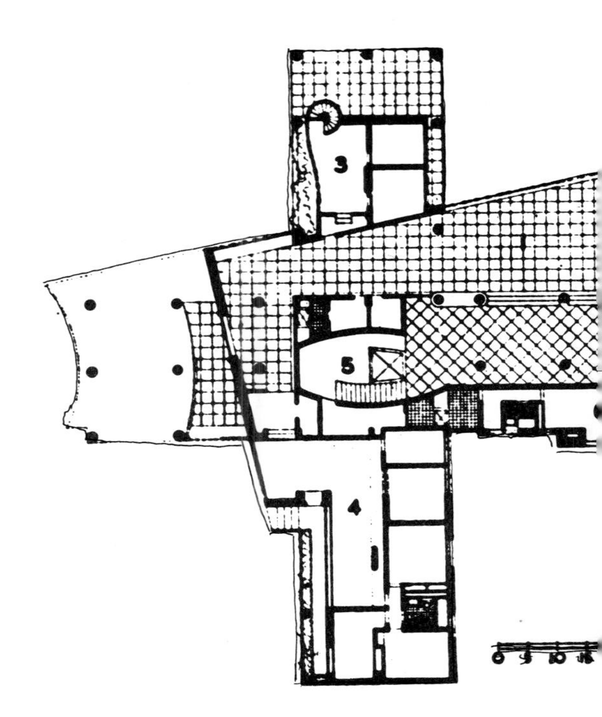

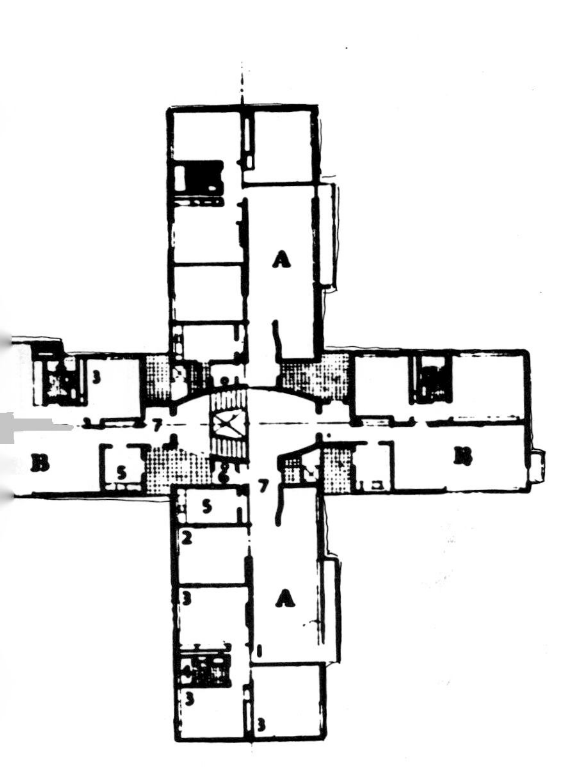

UPPPER FLOOR

1. LIVING ROOM
2. DINING RECESS
3. BEDROOMS
4. BATHROOM
5. KITCHEN
6. W.C.
7. ENTRANCE HALL

GROUND FLOOR

1. HALL AND WINTER GARDEN
2. HALL
3. PORTER'S FLAT
4. LARGE FLAT
5. LIFTS AND STAIRCASES
6. ONE-ROOM FLATS
7. TEA-ROOM
8. MAIDS' BEDROOMS

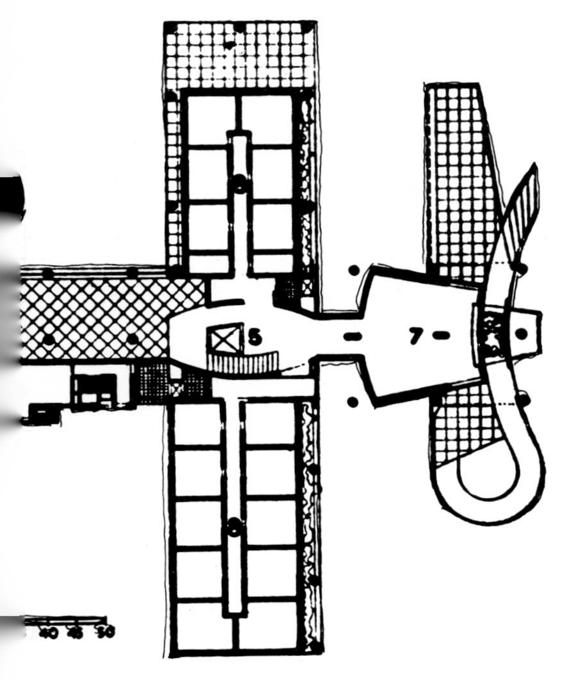

*Figure 34*
*Highpoint 1 under construction.*

## Tecton

In each period of architecture, certain buildings catch the imagination and, in a sense, define that period. In the '30s the firm of Tecton produced a number of designs which, for professionals and public alike, caught what was progressive in the spirit of the age. These buildings were the Finsbury Health Centre, the Highpoint Flats at Highgate in London, and the works for the Royal Zoological Society in London and Whipsnade. The Penguin Pool at the London Zoo, 1933 (Figures 31 & 32), in particular, with its interlacing spiral ramps and cantilevered slabs, showed to a large section of the public something of the imaginative sculptural forms possible utilising the skills and technologies of the structural engineer allied to the inspiration of architectural genius. The pure slab construction, first demonstrated by Robert Maillart, is here utilised with boundless verve and delight, although in the more mundane area of functional building reinforced concrete slab construction in the '30s reached perhaps its pinnacle of achievement in the construction of the flats at Highpoint, 1935 (Figures 33, 34 & 35). The entire structure over the first-floor level

*Figure 35*
*Highpoint 1 completed (1935).*

is of continuous and homogeneous slab construction with walls of reinforced concrete panel construction 100 mm or 150 mm thick, pierced as necessary for windows and room openings and insulated on the inside of the external walls with slabs of cork. The groundfloor entrance hall is a quite independent structure with columns supporting the slab construction over. As with the contemporary Bexhill Pavilion, this building convincingly demonstrates the value of teamworking between architects and structural engineers, thus setting the pattern for postwar collaborative working and the indispensability of the modern structural engineer.

# 1939-1955

## Frank Newby

F. Newby MA(Cantab), CEng, FIStructE, MConsE, HonFRIBA.

Frank Newby joined F. J. Samuely as a junior engineer in 1949. He later became a research assistant and spent time on the development of composite construction. He was awarded a U.S. Government Scholarship in 1952 to study building methods in the U.S.A. He returned to F. J. Samuely in 1953, became a partner in 1956 and senior partner on the death of F. J. Samuely in 1959.

He has been responsible for the structure of many notable buildings such as the U.S. Embassy in London, the British Buildings at the Brussels Exhibition, the Snowdon Aviary, the Clifton Cathedral, Milton Keynes Shopping Centre, the Wills Tobacco Factory in Bristol, and the SAMA Banks in Saudi Arabia.

He is keenly interested in the education of both engineers and architects. Has been on the RIBA Board of Architectural Education, has been an external examiner at various schools of architecture and is at present a technical tutor at the Architectural Association.

He is an honorary fellow of the Royal Institute of British Architects.

He has an extensive collection of books on engineering history, feels strongly that history should be taught at universities and has written and lectured on the subject.

The outbreak of war in 1939 created many new problems for structural engineers. Studies on civil protection were intensified with further research undertaken on the effects of explosions on buildings. The Institution published a report on Air Raid Precautions in 1939 and a number of scientific papers and books appeared very soon afterwards.

It can be shown that war has often been instrumental in initiating scientific research and engineering progress. Some of the first welded steelwork was used in the 1914-18 war for the construction of ammunition barges, while earlier, in the 1840s, concrete technology was developed at the Royal Engineers Establishment at Chatham for the construction of forts along the Thames Estuary. In the 1939-45 war the most significant progress was made in the welding of high-tensile steel for lightweight temporary bridges and in the design and construction of aircraft. Not only did the aircraft, developed for the Schneider Trophy air-races, have to have their speed increased by a reduction in weight, but from research their design had to cope with the higher loads from faster flight and with flutter, a dynamic problem encountered now in the vibration of tall buildings and tensile structures. Aircraft weight was reduced by the use of high-strength steel and aluminium alloys in cast and rolled forms in lieu of timber. Riveted and bolted connections were gradually replaced by welding for maximum economy. The structural design was based on 'ultimate load' or the load at which airworthiness was impaired. Unlike the design of building structures under load, materials were allowed to be stressed well above the level where the material ceases to have elastic properties. Today, both steelwork and reinforced concrete structures are designed on an ultimate load basis or the load at which the structure is unusable.

The engineer on active service or attached to the armed services had to solve structural problems not encountered in peacetime. Expediency was paramount, be it in the development of quicker bridging techniques, of temporary aircraft runways and of the Mulberry harbours, which also taxed the resources of the construction industry.

The shortage of materials at home led to great efforts to reduce the weight of structures by creative design. Interest turned to concrete shells, first developed after the 1914-18 war in Europe, with the concert hall at Frankfurt in 1927 being the premier example. The system was pioneered by Blumfield and others in the UK, and in 1942 a bus station at Wythenshawe was one of the first.

In 1936 Freyssinet introduced to the UK the concept of prestressed concrete which he had patented in France some 8 years earlier. In describing prestressed concrete, he writes 'By prestressed construction I understand a structure that is subjected to a system of artificially produced permanent forces before the

*Continued on page 114*

## The Mulberry Invasion Harbour 1942-44

Designed by Port Construction and Repair branch Quartermaster General's Dept. of the British Army

In 1942 it was proposed that, for the invasion of Europe, floating piers a mile long, strong enough to carry the heaviest tanks, guns and lorries, flexible enough to ride out summer storms, be so designed as to be capable of being installed in a day or two. The solution called for a series of bridge units supported on floats. The problem of temporary bridging was tackled afresh from the start, and a new type was designed that had flexibility in all directions to a degree never before thought possible. Each bridge unit consisted of two 80 ft (24.4 m) girders and a 10 ft (3 m)-wide roadway designed so that, under working load, it could twist until one end was at an angle of 40° to the other. The majority of floats were of reinforced concrete using precast panels of 1¼ in (3.1 cm) thickness, with *in situ* concrete ribs connecting them. The design was tested successfully in 1943.

To protect the pierhead for 90 days from gales, it was decided that a breakwater was necessary to produce a sheltered harbour, code-named Mulberry. The solution was to use reinforced

*Figure 1*
*View along the breakwater.*

*Figure 2*
*Oblique aerial view of Harbour looking SW.*

concrete pontoons 200 ft (61 m) × 60 ft (18 m) × 60 ft (18 m) deep of wall thickness 15 in (38 cm) open at the top but with diagonal bars to give torsional stiffness. The pontoons were towed across the channel and then sunk in their final position. Over 220 were made within a year in time for the invasion.

*Figure 3*
*Sherman tank commencing journey to shore along floating bridge.*

*Figure 4*
*Floating bridge under stress during gale (note twisting effect).*

## Factory for Brynmawr Rubber Ltd., Wales. 1947-1950

| | |
|---|---|
| Architects: | Architects Co-operative Partnership |
| Consulting Engineers: | Ove Arup & Partners |

Each of the nine reinforced concrete domes over the production floor covers an area of 82 ft (25 m) × 63 ft (19 m) with a rise of 8 ft (2.4 m), varies in thickness from 3 in to 3½ in (7.6 cm to 8.9 cm), and is supported along its edge by a reinforced concrete bowstring-type truss, the open spandrels being glazed to provide natural light. This clerestory lighting is supplemented by a 6 ft (1.8 m) circular glazed opening in the shell.
Cylindrical reinforced concrete shells of 3½ in (8.9 cm) thickness spanning 45 ft (13.7 m) and 64 ft (19.5 m) roof the adjacent drug and mill rooms.
The weights of materials were minimal, and visually it is an excellent example of architect-engineer collaboration.

*Figure 5*
*General view of the factory.*

application of the imposed loads or, in the case of permanent loads, at the same time.' As concrete is weak in tension, the invention was to provide initial compression in the structure so that, under the worst loading conditions, the concrete was subjected only to compression stresses which could be carried indefinitely and with complete safety.

Freyssinet provided the initial compression with the aid of tensioned steel tendons anchored to the concrete. He spent many years developing high-strength concrete and he acknowledged the research work carried out at the Building Research Station by Glanville in the 1920s on the properties of concrete, particularly creep and shrinkage, that had led him to conclude that high-strength concrete and high-tensile steel were essential for prestressed concrete. Arup has since described prestressed concrete as a new material and Freyssinet himself refers to it as a state of mind. The possible large reduction in weight of steel using prestressed concrete, as compared to the equivalent reinforced concrete construction, stimulated interest at the beginning of the war. The results of research into the design of concrete mixes for high-strength concrete were

*Figure 6*
*The main production area before the installation of plant, showing part of the 77 000 superficial ft$^2$ (7157m$^2$) of floorspace and one of the nine domes of shell concrete.*

## Rosebery Avenue flats, Finsbury, London. 1949

| | |
|---|---|
| Architects: | Tecton |
| Consulting Engineers: | Ove Arup & Partners |

*Figure 8*
*View during construction, showing the use of a new system of hydraulically-jacked shuttering.*

The increase in mechanisation of site operations kept pace with the development of prefabricated systems of construction.

*Figure 7*
*General view of the structure.*

The eight-storey block contained 48 flats. It was constructed on the box-frame principle with continuous *in situ* concrete walls and floors without projecting columns and beams. Ove Arup's structure was stiff, economic, and very buildable, and became one of the main systems of multistorey flat construction.

published in 1939. Details of European tests on prestressed concrete beams were presented to the Institution in 1940. Two practical solutions to the anchoring of the tensioned tendons to the concrete had emerged. In the first the tension in the steel is transferred to the concrete by bond, which means that the tendons are tensioned before the concrete is cast, i.e. the pre-tensioned system. In the second, the tendons are held in anchorages and tensioned against the hardened concrete, i.e. the post-tensioned system. By 1940 the Ministry of Transport had decided to build, at the Road Research Laboratory, the first factory in the UK to produce standard pre-tensioned prestressed concrete bridge beams for repairing bomb-damaged bridges. In 1943 a factory producing prestressed concrete railway sleepers at Tallington was also in production. Much of the experience in pre-tensioning gained from these operations was of use later for the manufacture of precast concrete floor units for postwar reconstruction.

Although the earliest welded-steel frame was erected outside London in 1921 and in London for Simpsons, Piccadilly, in 1936, the economy of material achieved by welding was not investigated seriously until during the war. Not only was there a saving in the weight of bolted and riveted connections by their being replaced by welded joints but, with welding, it was possible to connect steel sections such as tubes, rods and built-up shapes which had better strength-to-weight ratios than normal rolled steel sections. At Cambridge, Professor Baker carried on his research on the ultimate-load or plastic design of steel frameworks which assumed welded joints. Theory and practice came to fruition in the postwar period.

Similarly, the search for truth, characteristic of engineers at all times, continued at other universities. At Imperial College, Professor Skempton's contribution to the new science of soil mechanics was fully appreciated when the results of his research work were used by structural engineers in the design of tall buildings in London after the war. From tests on the clay subsoil, it was possible to estimate the strength of the ground and its settlement under different loading conditions. With this information a safe design of foundations became possible.

Before the end of the war the problems of planning and reconstruction were being widely analysed. Future collaboration of the architect and engineer, as well as Government, was considered essential. As professional barriers had been dented, if not destroyed, during the war, close working relationships evolved in the early energetic and exciting years of peace. Young architects returned to complete their studies with the highest ideals. Collaboration of architect and engineer was encouraged by engineers Samuely and Arup who came to prominence before the war with their work with the leading architects of the Modern Movement in Britain. Samuely taught structures at the Architectural Association during the war and continued in this role in the early postwar period, as both he and Arup established their consulting practices. They both continued to be closely associated with architects who strove for minimum structures and maximum economy in their designs. Architects were receptive to the new exciting structural possibilities proposed by engineers. However, the serious lack of structural materials, particularly steel, and of skilled building operatives, retarded the growth of construction.

The Cement & Concrete Association did much to promote prestressed concrete by its research, publications, and visits abroad. In 1948 the Prestressed Concrete

*Figure 9*
*General view during construction showing precast concrete frames and prestressed concrete ties.*

Company was in operation with A.J. Harris, who had worked with Freyssinet for 3 years, as Chief Engineer and later Director. Abeles, a consulting engineer, and Walley of the then Ministry of Works, were very active in this field and each published a book on prestressed concrete. In September 1951 the Institution published the *First report on prestressed concrete* which gave recommendations based on practical experience to its members. It wisely pointed out that the report was not to be used as an instrument to limit the proper development of prestressed concrete. Factory production of precast, prestressed concrete units increased enormously, using the imported Hoyer system of pre-tensioning. Post-tensioning systems, such as Magnet-Blaton and Lee McCall, competed with Freyssinet. The shortage of high-tensile wires was so serious that even balloon cables, used during the war, were successfully employed for prestressed concrete. The ideal that the maximum amount of building work should be carried out in controlled factory conditions led to the extensive use of precast concrete for structural frames and floors.

To minimise the relatively expensive factory-produced precast concrete, a combination of precast and *in situ* concrete, i.e. composite construction, which acted in a manner similar to *in situ* concrete, evolved. Samuely presented a paper on this subject at the Institution of Civil Engineers in 1954. At the same time, Arup was perfecting his *in situ* concrete box-frame system of construction for multistorey dwellings. All walls and floors that were required to provide sound

## Factory at Malago, Bristol, for Messrs Colodense. 1949-1951

Architects: J.E. Collins and E.F. Peat

Consulting Engineer: Felix J. Samuely

With the wider availability of high-tensile wires by 1949, prestressed concrete became a viable structural material. A shortage of timber for shuttering, and of skilled craftsmen, led Samuely to design his most inventive structure of precast and prestressed concrete. The heavily loaded floors were supported on three-hinged precast concrete frames with prestressed concrete ties on a structural grid of 33 ft 4 in (10.1 m) by 30 ft (9.1 m) and of overall depth 8 ft 3 in (2.5 m) within which was the service floor. The precast concrete units were jointed with mechanical connections capable of carrying construction loads and taking up manufacturing and erection tolerances. The floors themselves were of composite construction, of thin coffered precast concrete units with a structural topping of poured concrete, which also tied together all the precast concrete units, giving overall stability to the building.

For long-span floors, factory-made prestressed concrete planks were used in a similar way to steel reinforcement, placing them at the bottom of the slab at midspan and at the top over the internal supports.
The continuous foundation beam, which transmitted the load from the columns onto piles, was also of prestressed concrete, using the post-tensioned Freyssinet system. The beam was curved on elevation enabling the prestressing cables to remain straight.

*Figure 11*
*Continuous concrete floor using precast prestressed concrete units in a similar manner to reinforcement.*

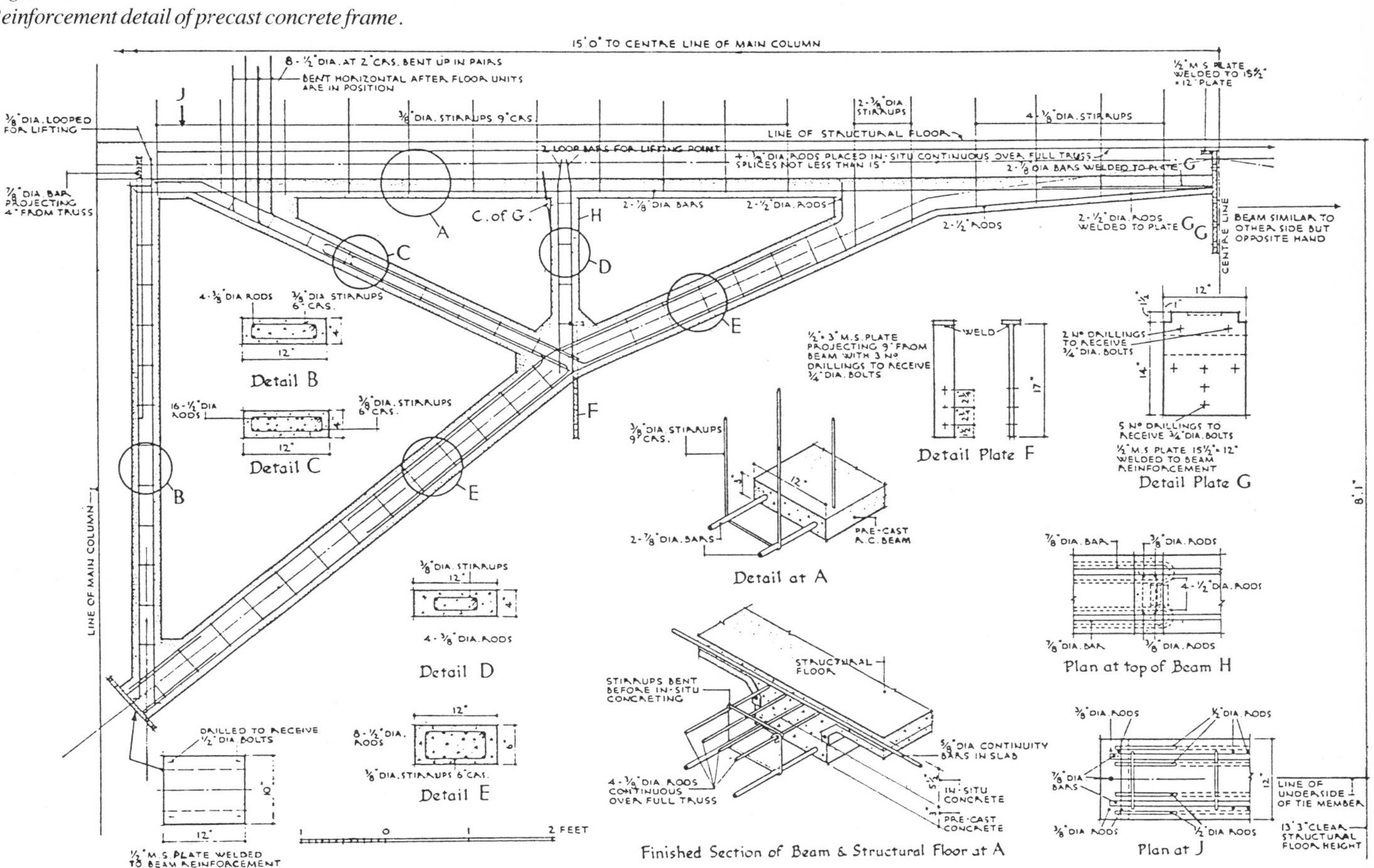


*Figure 10*
*Reinforcement detail of precast concrete frame.*

## Hangar at London Airport. 1951

Consulting Engineers
for the Air Ministry: Messrs Scott and Wilson

Structural design was by the Prestressed Concrete Co. Ltd. in collaboration with Messrs Holland, Hannen and Cubitts.

The winning design of spring 1950 for the hangars was in prestressed concrete, as opposed to steelwork or reinforced concrete. Post-tensioned *in situ* concrete primary box beams 14 ft (4.26 m) high and 5 ft 3 in (1.6 m) wide span 150 ft (45.7 m) and support 110 ft (33.5 m) span secondary beams. The latter were made up from 7 ft 2 in (2.2 m) long precast concrete units post-tensioned together. The scale and possibilities of prestressed concrete were clearly illustrated. A.J. Harris, of the Prestressed Concrete Company, later founded the consulting engineering firm of Harris & Sutherland who furthered the development of prestressed concrete.

*Figure 12*
*110 ft (33.5 m) span secondary beams being erected onto the 150 ft (45.7 m) span main beams.*

insulation were made structural and were of *in situ* concrete, the continuity of concrete providing a more efficient design than jointed precast concrete. His flats at Rosebery Avenue are a good example. Site labour was kept to a minimum by prefabrication of shuttering and the use of tower cranes.

Timber also played a leading part in the reconstruction of houses. The results of wartime research, particularly in the USA, where bridges, hangars and floating docks of timber were developed, helped to provide new design rules. The quality of timber was reassessed and, with a system of grading, it was possible to allow high stresses in good timbers. It also meant that, in laminated timber, where structural members are made up from a number of timber planks glued together, the best timber needed to be used only in the areas of high stress. Thermo-setting resin-glues were developed to withstand all weather conditions and they superseded the traditional casein glues for structural members. Laminated timber appealed to the architect, for it meant that many new shapes of members were possible, depending on the flexibility of the laminations prior to gluing. In particular, corners could be made continuous and members could be much larger than any natural section available. A whole new aesthetic and use of timber in building appeared.

The development of shell roofs was stimulated by the publication, in 1947, by Jenkins, who became a partner of Arup, of his definitive *Theory and design of cylindrical shell roofs*. They were responsible for many major curved shell roofs such as for those of the Brynmawr factory in 1947 and the Bank of England printing works at Debden in 1953.

On the other hand, Samuely considered that better economy came from shells where the curved sides were replaced by a series of planes. As early as 1937 he

*Continued on page 126*

## FESTIVAL OF BRITAIN, 1951.
## **The Skylon**

Architects: Powell and Moya
Consulting Engineer: Felix J. Samuely

*The Skylon*, the winning competition scheme for a vertical feature 250 ft (76.2 m) high, was a latticed steel cigar-shaped tube suspended in mid-air with wire cables which, in turn, were supported on welded steel pylons with ties to the ground. To provide an adequate stiffness to the structure, to limit deflection, and to prevent flutter in wind conditions, the wire cables were pre-tensioned so that they could effectively carry compression from the applied loading.

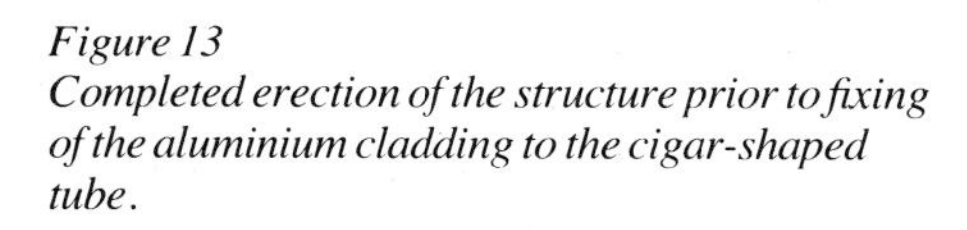

*Figure 13*
*Completed erection of the structure prior to fixing of the aluminium cladding to the cigar-shaped tube.*

*Figure 14*
*Base of supporting pylon showing the jacking device which raised the pylon and hence pre-tensioned all the cables.*

## FESTIVAL OF BRITAIN, 1951
## The Dome of Discovery.

| | |
|---|---|
| Architect: | Ralph Tubbs |
| Consulting Engineers: | Freeman and Fox |

A 365 ft (111.25 m) diameter latticed aluminium dome with a steel ring beam, was the centrepiece of the Festival. The rise of the dome was approximately 45 ft (13.7 m) and the main ribs were triangular section lattices of overall depth 2 ft 10 in (88 cm). The ring beam at a height of 45 ft (13.7 m) from the ground was

*Figure 15*
*General view of the dome prior to the fixing of the roof sheeting.*

supported on inclined latticed columns. The structural design of Freeman and Fox was the hallmark of minimum weight structure – a mere 4.41 lb/ft$^2$ (21.53 kg/m$^2$). The use of aluminium in structures had been encouraged by the publication by the Institution in 1950 of a report *The structural use of aluminium alloys in building*.

## FESTIVAL OF BRITAIN, 1951.
## **The Fairway Cafe.**

| | |
|---|---|
| Architects: | Architects Co-operative Partnership |
| Consulting Engineer: | Ove Arup & Partners |

*Figure 16*
*Aerial view of the roof after post-tensioning of the cables and before the erection of the metal box roof.*

The 60 ft (18.28 m) × 50 ft (15.2 m) building was roofed with a diagonal grid of prestressed concrete beams supported along the perimeter. Precast concrete units 6 ft 8⅛ in (2 m) long × 1 ft 3 in (38 cm) deep × 3½ in (8.9 cm) wide were assembled on temporary supports and Freyssinet prestressing cables threaded through cable ducts so formed that the cables had the correct curvature. The cables were tensioned in stages to produce a homogeneous two-way span structure.

FESTIVAL OF BRITAIN, 1951.
## Transport and Communications Pavilion.

Architects: Arcon
Consulting Engineer: Felix J. Samuely

The main building was a very high single-storey hall 100 ft (30.5 m) long and 108 ft (32.9 m) deep with three levels of galleries at the rear. The roof was of welded steel in a series of inclined lattice girders forming a folded plate construction. It spanned 49 ft (14.9 m) with a cantilever of 28 ft (8.5 m) at the front and a further 21 ft (6.4 m) at the rear.

*Figure 17*
*Internal view of the pavilion showing aircraft hung from the latticed steel folded-plate roof. The front wall had sliding glazed panels.*

FESTIVAL OF BRITAIN, 1951.
## The Station Gate and Escalator Hall Building.

Architects: Sir John Burnet Tait & Partners
Structural Design: Timber Development Association

Five parabolic glued laminated timber arches fabricated by the Airscrew Company and Jicwood Ltd. spanned 110 ft (33.5 m) and rose to a height of 62 ft (18.9 m). They were the largest of their kind in the UK and heralded the extensive use of laminated timber in the postwar construction of schools, community halls, and churches.

*Figure 18*
*The arches were 13" wide and varied in depth from 20" at the springing to 14" at the crown and are shown here during construction.*

had proposed such a system in latticed steel but it had to wait until 1948 before he built his first folded-plate roof (as they came to be known) of *in situ* concrete for a bakery at Saltash.

The Festival of Britain in 1951 was the showpiece of the state-of-the-art of structural engineering. As often occurs in exhibitions, the architects wanted to use the very latest structural ideas in their buildings. The aluminium Dome of Discovery, the Skylon, the welded lattice trusses and folded-plate roofs of the Transport and Engineering Pavilions, the prestressed concrete roof to the Fairway Cafe, and the laminated timber arches of the Station Gate, were at the forefront of technology.

Addressing the RIBA in 1952 Samuely spoke of space structures: 'I think that at the moment we are on the eve of a great revolution and that hundreds of years hence people will look back on this time as being the one when construction changed over from ''plane'' to ''space'' and saw the birth of a new architecture' Many engineers in different specialised fields expressed similar sentiments. In 1955 the stage was set for a construction revolution in which the structural engineer was to play a major part.

# 1955-1970

Peter Dunican

P.T.Dunican CBE, FEng, FIStructE, FICE, FIEI.

Born in Surbiton in 1918, Peter Dunican was educated at Central School and Clapham and Battersea Polytechnic. His professional career began as assistant to S.H. White & Son, Civil Engineers 1936-43. In 1943 he joined Ove Arup & Partners Consulting Engineers as a structural engineer and became a senior partner in 1956 and since 1978 has been Chairman of the Partnership. He has been a part-time Director of the National Building Agency since 1964, and was its Chairman from 1978 to 1982. Has been a Member of the Council of the Institution of Structural Engineers since 1964 and was President of the Institution 1977-78. He was made a Member of the Council of the Fellowship of Engineers in 1983.

In 1957 he served as a Member of the LCC Advisory Committee on the London Building Act and Byelaws, and in 1960 he served as a Member of the Ministry of Housing Working Party to revise the Model Building Byelaws, and from 1962 to 1965 was a member of the Building Regulations Advisory Committee.

He was a Member of the Council of the Architectural Association in 1968, and from 1968 to 1971 was a Member of the Aeronautical and Civil Engineering Committee of the University of Science and Technology Board of the Science Research Council, was a member of National Joint Consultative Committee 1974-1977; Chairman Joint Building Group, 1973-1976; Chairman Ground and Structures Research Committee, BRE, 1979 to date; Chairman BSI/CSB/26 Committee 1979-1982; Chairman Structural Codes Advisory Committee 1979-1982.

To review structural engineering achievements during this period demands some brief reference to what happened in the previous 5 years and particularly to the Festival of Britain which King George VI opened on 3 May 1951 exactly 100 years and 2 days after the opening of the 1851 Exhibition in the presence of Queen Victoria and Prince Albert.

Philosophically, what happened of consequence during this period was dominated, and perhaps determined, by the thinking of two men, Ove Arup and Felix Samuely. These two men were dreamers, inventors, and inspirers beyond belief, although apparently quite opposite in their approach. To realise their potential, they needed, and were given, the committed service of devoted supporters and subordinates. With this support, their influence and force were almost irresistible.

Through these dedicated structural engineers, the essence of the modern architectural movement – form, function, and structure – became a reality. It was an article of faith that, if the structure was right and the functional concept was correct, then an acceptable form was inevitable; although aesthetic considerations, more often than not, were the ultimate determinant.

However, through the predominance of such outstanding personalities, a significant change came about in the appreciation, by architects, of the role of the structural engineer and his contribution to the design of buildings. In fact, it was the younger architects and engineers inspired and motivated by Arup and Samuely, and some others, who overcame the resistance to such simple, logical ideas as multidisciplinary practice and professional togetherness in the service of the deserving community. In essence, structural engineering as an art and a science is dominated by people, technology, materials and ideas, but ultimately it is the people who matter most.

At this time, there was only one physical structural idea of any real significance that influenced design and construction deeply. It was not a new idea, but its physical embodiment needed particular material developments to bring about its general realisation. It was Freyssinet's invention of prestressing, which had two main consequences. First, it helped engineers to overcome the hitherto overriding external effects of gravity on structural systems by the application of internal forces and so resist the external forces and thus enable designers to influence, if not determine, how their structures would behave in reality. And, secondly, it enabled structural engineers to conceive precast concrete structural systems where the concrete elements, simple or complex as they may be, could be produced in a factory, either on or off the site, and then joined together and made into structural unities through prestressing.

Also, there was the growing recognition of the philosophical notion, which manifested itself very strongly on the South Bank, that structures must be considered as 3-dimensional systems, even if some, at the time, could be analysed only 2-dimensionally. This led naturally to an increasing awareness of the importance of the geometry of the system and its relevance to the conception, analysis and construction of the structure; a circuitous, interdependent circumstance that only the structural engineer could cut through.

All these ideas were deployed at the Festival of Britain where Arup and Samuely, each in his own way, made such a significant contribution.

The structural engineering achievements from 1955 to 1970 can be reviewed under five broad headings. First, the final transition from war to peace hallmarked by the consequences of the Festival of Britain; secondly, the intensive and extensive programme of social building (housing, schools, colleges, universities, hospitals, and the like); thirdly, the industrialisation of the building process which was punctuated by Ronan Point, leaving building systems in some disrepute, if not in disarray; fourthly, the redevelopment, if not rape, of our towns

*Continued on page 132*

*Figure 1*
*Christ's College, Cambridge University.*

Systematic accommodation for students, using a specially conceived precast concrete structure.

*Figure 2*
*The Cathedral Church of St. Michael, Coventry.*

The columns supporting the canopy and the canopy structure were made with precast concrete elements prestressed together.

*Figure 3*
*Abbotsinch Airport Terminal Building, Glasgow.*

A composite steel and concrete, large span structure.

*Figure 4*
*The Metropolitan Cathedral of Christ the King, Liverpool.*

The second of the Institution's Special Awards, made in 1968; a consummate example of architectural engineering.

*Figure 5*
*Queen Elizabeth Hall and Hayward Gallery, South Bank development.*

An exposed, introverted, articulated architectural concrete sculptured structure.

*Figure 6*
*Thamesmead Housing.*

A new town created by the Greater London Council at Woolwich using industrialised system building in precast concrete.

and cities in the hoped-for interest of community gain and the reality of corporate and individual profit; and lastly, civic and industrial constructions of special significance, reflective of the nature and concern of our society for itself, its monuments, and its reality.

Up to the time of the war, structural engineering in Britain had been dominated by steelwork. But by 1950 structural concrete had emerged as the major material for building structures, not only because steel was in short supply but also because structural concrete was cheaper.

There was also, at this time, a significant difference in the intellectual approach of the two particular sorts of designer. Structural concrete designers did have a finer understanding of structural behaviour, which resulted in more economic solutions to the structural problems of buildings; bridges, on the other hand, were quite another matter.

However, this change from the linear inflexibility of steelwork to the free-form plasticity of structural concrete, the ability to mould it easily into the desired or necessary structural shape, made a significant impact on the thinking of forward-looking architects and structural engineers and also on the design of buildings, particularly when it was eventually realised that structural concrete should not be used as a direct replacement of the forms of structural steelwork but that it was an entirely new constructional material in its own right and with its own values. A simple example here is the use of cross-wall construction in high flats in place of beam and column structures.

From this point in time, it might be said that the design of buildings cantilevered out into the future. Engineers were in a position to design and construct buildings and structures that, until then, had been mostly figments of the imagination.

We also began to take a wider view of our social responsibilities, but most engineers designing structures for buildings were still more concerned with the structure than with the building it supported. Nevertheless, a small number of architects and engineers began to explore their new-found freedom with considerable help from a benevolent state, devoted and committed as it was then to an unprecedented social building programme of housing, schools, colleges, universities, hospitals, and so on.

During this period, however, contradictions began to emerge. While the inherent plastic qualities of structural concrete enabled the engineer to provide a structure that embodied the form and function of the building, as conceived and interpreted by the architect, such a structure could not always be realised economically. Before these potentially exciting shapes could be constructed, their external forms had first to be created using temporary formwork. This could be expensive, particularly with the limited means available. Furthermore, it often meant that these structures took longer to build. Cost was increasing and productivity was reduced at a time when more building was required than ever before.

One response to the demand for increased production was the idea of industrialising the building process – so-called 'system building'. This implied simplicity of design, repetition of elements and units, and a continuing building programme that could be directed and managed efficiently. It also meant that architects and engineers had to work together even more closely and create

*Figure 7*
*The University of Essex.*

One of the new universities created in the '60s with an effective environmental use of water.

designs that could be mass-produced and managed without losing their aesthetic value and social consequence.

Here we had some success; buildings were constructed that essentially met the requirements, or at least provided what was thought to be needed. But building systems have their own inherent disciplines which must be followed if they are to be effective in use. These disciplines, which some began to find irksome, led to considerable efforts to deviate from the rules, much to the detriment of the effective use of the systems.

Systems were also used in circumstances beyond the limits envisaged by their originators. By 1968, at least so far as it involved the use of precast concrete, system building was falling into disrepute, but it was finally toppled by Ronan Point, or, to be more precise, by the Report of the Public Inquiry, the Griffiths Report, and its political interpretation of the technical facts, which were very much to the disadvantage of the community and the realisation of its building needs within acceptable limits of efficiency and economy.

But system building did not equate only with precast concrete, as many thought. Probably the most significant building system conceived in Britain during this time was CLASP. It was originally intended to be a system for building schools in areas subjected to mining subsidence. Essentially, it was a

*Continued on page 137*

*Figure 8*
*A view to the north over the City of London from the top of the Monument.*

The seven major buildings and their completion dates are, from left to right: 40 Basinghall Street (1964), Cromwell Tower, Barbican (1972), Moor House (1960-61), BP House (1967), Angel Court (1978), Drapers Gardens (1965), and the Stock Exchange (1972). All of these buildings embody one or another of the ideas and developments mentioned in the text.

*Figure 9*
*The Severn Bridge.*

One of the first two projects to receive the Institution's Special Award in 1968 which was introduced by the Council the year before to recognise physical achievements in structural engineering in its widest sense.

*Figure 10*
*Dunelm House and Kingsgate Bridge, University of Durham.*

Students' Council Building and Staff House and footbridge over River Wear, all demonstrating architectural inspiration, structural originality, and constructional ingenuity.

steel structure designed to flex with the movement of the ground and return to normal when the subsidence had finished. But it was so finely developed and industrially organised that it was competitive with schools built in traditional methods on normal sites.

During the '60s there also came about the redevelopment of our towns and cities, particularly their central areas. These programmes of intended betterment were often originated by construction interests and it is interesting to observe that not many of them used industrialised building systems, the developers preferring to use tried and tested conventional forms of construction, capable of being quantified and costed precisely; private enterprise in theory being very unenterprising in practice! Fortunately, in the event, there were some manifestations of private enterprise that not only added to but also advanced our built environment.

So far we have been discussing buildings, but some reference must be made to bridges; a concern that we have in common with others who do not so deeply

*Continued on page 141*

*Figure 11*
*Commonwealth Institute.*

The main element of the Institute has a parabolic hyperbolic shell concrete roof.

*Figure 12*
*Post Office Tower.*

At the time the highest *in situ* concrete structure in London and an outstanding landmark attracting many visitors.

*Figure 13*
*Crystal Palace Sports Centre.*

An architectural essay in structural geometry using steel and concrete to provide Olympic sports facilities for the Central Council for Physical Recreation.

*Figure 14*
*Grandstand at Doncaster Racecourse.*

An Institution Special Award was made in 1970 for the design of this structure with its fluted canopy in lightweight prestressed concrete and 15·2 m cantilever. The Judges and Commentators Box on the outside edge of the canopy is made of light fibreglass.

*Figure 15 (left)*
*The new Stock Exchange Building framed by the P & O and Commercial Union Buildings.*

These all embody advanced contemporary ideas on the design and construction of high-rise office blocks and inner-city centres, i.e. the use of deep basements, sliding construction, precasting, prestressing, and the application of computers to structural analysis.

*Figure 16*
*The Aviary, London Zoological Gardens.*

A 3-dimensional lattice structure in steel tubes and cables.

*Figure 17 (above right)*
*Elephant and Rhinoceros Pavilion, London Zoological Gardens.*

Robustly-tooled concrete surfaces for housing some fairly robust pachyderms.

share our concern for building structures. Here we should concentrate on what might be called the 'numbered' bridges, the Forth and the Severn, or should it be the Severn and the Forth. These two long-span bridges hallmark the most significant development in the design of bridges in this country. The Forth Bridge was designed in a more or less conventional manner but, for the Severn Bridge, of equal span, an entirely new approach was used, based on a fundamental reappraisal of the aerodynamics of the bridge deck and of the 3-dimensional characteristics of the suspension system and the deck. This led to a considerable saving in construction costs; the cost of the Severn Bridge was about two-thirds that of the Forth Bridge: an unprecedented saving. Small, but not necessarily less important, bridges, especially for the motorway programme, also skilfully exploited new ideas – the potential of precasting and prestressing together large and often complicated elements into aesthetically and technically acceptable solutions.

Other communications projects were concerned very much with the rapidly developing television and VHF radio networks, which required towers and masts, sometimes much higher than the highest buildings then made in Britain. Although buildings are increasing in height in response to demand, the resulting cost penalty is being reduced by significant developments in geotechnical engineering and constructional techniques.

The '60s were also dominated by a resurgence in civic building, usually concerned with some community purpose, mainly for people-dominated

*Continued on page 144*

*Figure 18*
*Boeing 747 Hanger at Heathrow.*

An Institution Special Award was made in 1970 for the design of the roof structure of this hanger which was then the largest diagonal steel grid in the world.

*Figure 19*
*Sydney Opera House.*

According to the Queen's Award citation, this is a technological innovation in prestressed concrete roofing. But it is not only roofing; it is a technological triumph in the service of art.

activities such as music and loud-noise making, but sometimes for animals, large and small, and even birds.

During this period the design of buildings was also influenced advantageously by developments in the use of coffered slabs and concrete shells and domes which led to further developments in the form of 3-dimensional lattice structures in linear materials. These developments also influenced the processes of construction which are of such significance to the structural engineer. The most important influence here was the tower crane which, during the '60s, dominated the urban skyline and represented the extreme extent to which the building process had been industrialised by foreign importations.

Structural design during this time was also influenced by many new theoretical ideas such as influence coefficients, limit state design, yieldline theory and finite element analysis, which, with the rapid increase in the application and use of computers, has enabled the analysis of complex structures to be carried out quickly and also allowed the more rapid analysis of alternative structural systems, which should lead to better structures. So far it has not, but one day it will. Until then we must continue to rely on the professional judgment of the individual chartered structural engineer to determine the most appropriate structure for the particular purpose.

The last observation leads directly to the one structure, above all others, that dominated this period, the Sydney Opera House. Its structure was on the edge of, if not beyond, contemporary technology and embodied all of the most advanced structural thinking since 1945. Its analysis was computer dominated but, in its conception, it was a triumph of technology in the service of art. Possibly, it is the structure of the century.

# 1970-1983

Stephen Bate

S.C.C. Bate CBE, BSc(Eng), PhD, CEng, FIStructE, FICE.

After graduating in 1938 from Battersea Polytechnic (now the University of Surrey), Dr Bate joined the materials consultancy of Mr R.H. Harry Stanger gaining experience of testing in the laboratory and on site. This was interrupted by service in the Royal Engineers. In 1948 he went to the Building Research Establishment where he was responsible for research, firstly on structural concrete, but later taking in geotechnics, materials and structures by the time he retired as an Assistant Director in 1979. He then became a consultant to Harry Stanger Ltd.

Dr Bate has served on many of the committees of the Institution, was a Member of Council for 14 years, and became Vice President in 1979/80. He has also served on many other committees including BS Codes of Practice and Standards Committees and has contributed a number of papers to professional and technical publications. He was made a CBE in 1979 and was awarded the Lewis Kent Award by the Institution in the same year.

The structural engineering industry, at the beginning of the 1970s, was fully engaged in new design and construction to meet the needs for the expansion of industry and its power supplies, of transportation systems on land and water and of housing and leisure facilities. By the end of the decade, the industry was experiencing a lack of work and severe unemployment brought about by the substantial rise in the cost of energy and worldwide recession, which led to major cuts in public and private investment in almost all areas of structural engineering activity. This was offset only partly in its effect by spending on new construction in the oil-rich countries and by the resulting greater urgency for the recovery of gas and oil from the North Sea.

Despite what should have been an optimistic start to the period, structural engineering was still overshadowed by the implications for design of the partial collapse of the Ronan Point multistorey blocks of local authority flats at Newham in East London, which had occurred as the result of a town-gas explosion in May 1968. Its immediate effect had been to bring to an end the construction of tall point blocks for housing of local authority tenants, which was a form of construction already being seriously questioned for this purpose on social, environmental, and economic grounds. In a wider context, however, the failure had caused some disquiet in the minds of the public on the safety of buildings comprising precast concrete panels and also in the minds of engineers in relation to the general principles that should govern design for structural adequacy.

The problems in design and construction for making proper provision for structural safety were further emphasised by a number of failures during construction of box girder bridges in this country and abroad during 1969 to 1971, which included bridges over the Danube, at Milford Haven, in Australia, and at Koblenz. These bridge failures were followed, in 1973 to 1975 in the UK, by the failures of the roofs of a number of educational buildings built with different materials, including precast concrete, steel, timber, and masonry; these failures were partly the results of poor detailing in design and of defects in prefabricating techniques. In each case, the immediate consequences were changes in Government regulations and amendments to design Codes of Practice. In the longer term, however, they had some influence on the developing approach to design for structural safety.

Following the war, there was a very considerable expenditure of effort on an international scale on structural engineering research. It was concerned mostly with the performance of different structural materials and with the analysis and behaviour of various forms of construction and substantial links were reestablished for the international exchange of ideas and information. One of the

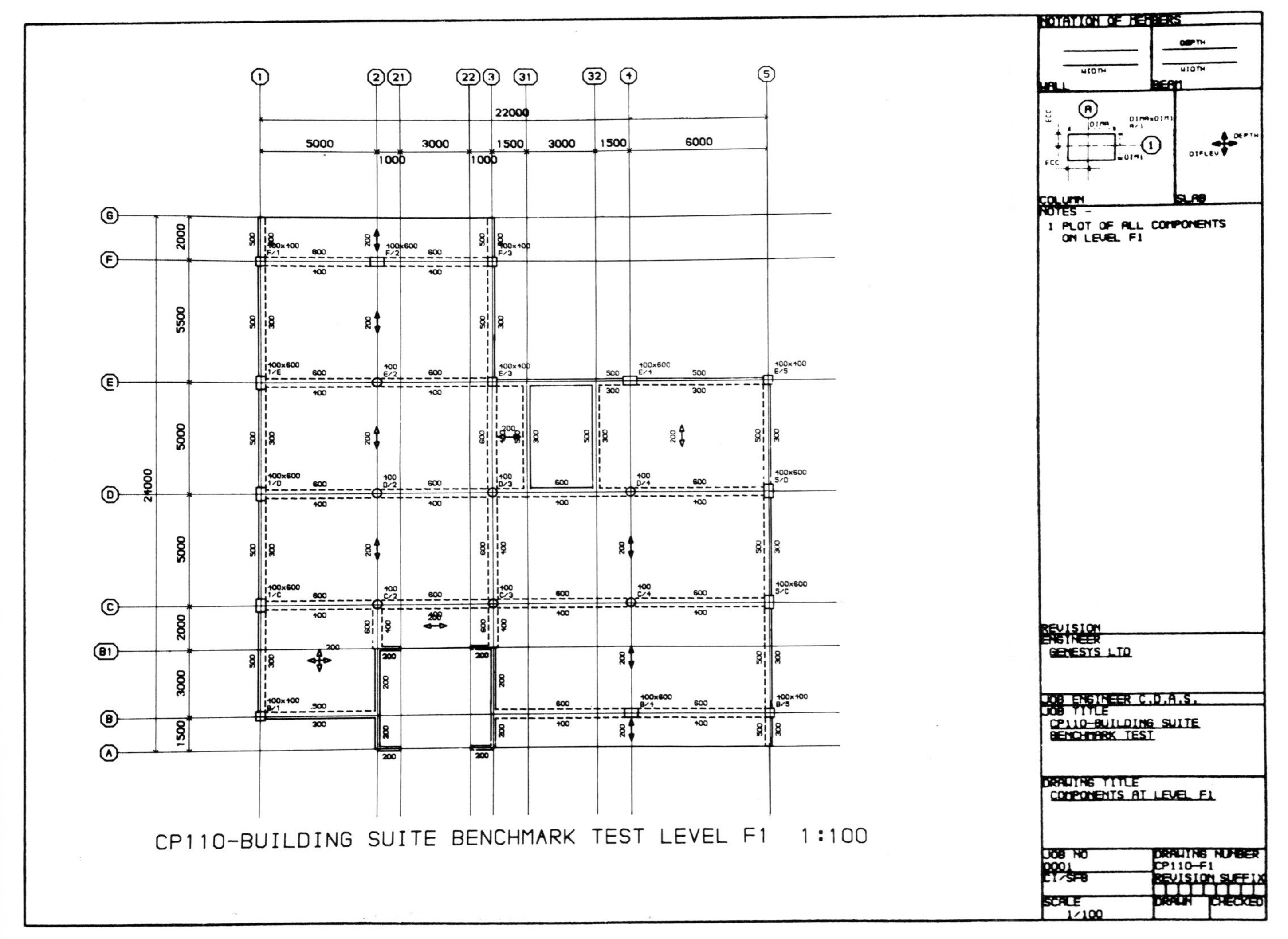


*Figure 1*
*General arrangement drawing prepared by computer.*

Apart from the facilities provided by computers for complex analysis and the design of structures, computers can now be used for the routine activities of design offices, such as the generation of drawings from data obtained in design calculations.

areas, in which the response between different countries was particularly effective, was that of rationalisation of the codification of structural design. By the beginning of the 1970s, international agreement on principles had been reached and a start had been made on introducing the proposals into British Standard Codes of Practice. Described as limit state design, the design procedure required that all situations that the structure might reasonably be expected to experience, should be provided for, and that the risk of failure to withstand them should be acceptably remote. In the revisions of the Codes that then took place, the experience of the structural failures that had occurred encouraged the avoidance of undue complication in the provisions made for dealing with structural safety.

There is always a tendency to highlight the structural mishaps, defects, and collapses, as they occur and largely to ignore the successes and their significance. Thus the relatively minor difficulties encountered in the hoisting into position of one of the many box sections of the Humber Bridge received nearly as much publicity as the completion of the bridge itself. It is not widely realised that

*Figure 2*
*Kingston Bridge, Glasgow – an aerial view of the complete project.*

During the 1960s and 1970s, many steel and concrete bridges were built in the general improvement of the transport system of the country. Kingston Bridge, opened in 1970, forms part of the inner ring road for the city. It consists of two separate box girders of prestressed concrete and was cast *in situ* by cantilevering out from each pier. The girders are continuous over three spans, having a central span of 143·5 m and side spans of 62·5 m.

*Figure 3*
*Kingston Bridge – cantilevering during construction.*

the risk to life for the general public resulting from structural failures is very much less than that in fires and less than 0·1% of the death-rate on the roads. It may have appeared that much of the decade was taken up with the investigation of failure and the reappraisal of design procedures as a preliminary to the reduction in constructional work, but the period, in reality, was also one of substantial consolidation of earlier innovation and development. With the experience gained, many of the new techniques in design and construction were further developed and widely applied, but with greater circumspection than before.

Twenty-five years ago, the computer was already recognised as a new tool for the structural engineer, which could free him from much tedious analytical work and allow him to use analytical procedures for complex structures that were previously prohibitive. Then, the computer installations were large and their cost was beyond the resources of all but the largest engineering firms, and it was foreseen that, if their use was to become widespread, it would be necessary for smaller organisations to operate in groups with cooperation between designers in the preparation of programmes. Since then, developments in the use of computers have proceeded much further and, while there are both large and small computer bureaux to meet analytical and design requirements, equipment has become available, at relatively modest cost, that can satisfy many of the specific in-house needs of even the smallest design office. Although computers are not yet as widely used in the construction industry as they might be, they have revolutionised procedures in the more progressive firms, not only in the solution of design problems, but also the preparation of detailed drawings and bar bending schedules, the control of contracts, and the storage and retrieval of technical and accounting data.

By the beginning of the 1970s, the improvement of the outdated transport systems was already far advanced and planning for their further future development was in hand. This applied, in particular, to the construction of new motorways and the realignment of trunk roads; in consequence, a large number of bridges and viaducts either had been completed or were under construction. By this time, the use of prestressed concrete had become fully established and was being adopted widely as a normal form of construction wherever its advantages of greater flexibility in choice of structural form and of constructional procedure could be realised with economy. It was natural, therefore, that prestressed concrete construction should contribute very extensively to the bridge-building programme, most of which was completed by the end of the decade. Prestressed concrete was used in a wide variety of ways; precasting of components was employed for the beams of bridges of shorter span and for the elements of segmental viaducts where repetition in manufacture was practicable; for some of the longer span bridges, the concrete was cast *in situ* for the construction of arches, box girders, and suspended spans. Although concrete was used for the majority of the bridges, steel contributed to an important part of the bridge programme with the evolution of box girder construction which, once the design problems were overcome, offered an economical solution. The most notable achievements in structural steelwork were, however, the series of suspension bridges spanning the Forth, the Severn, and the Humber.

Until 1964, when the Forth road bridge was opened, all the major suspension bridges had been built in the USA. Two years later, in 1966, the Severn Bridge

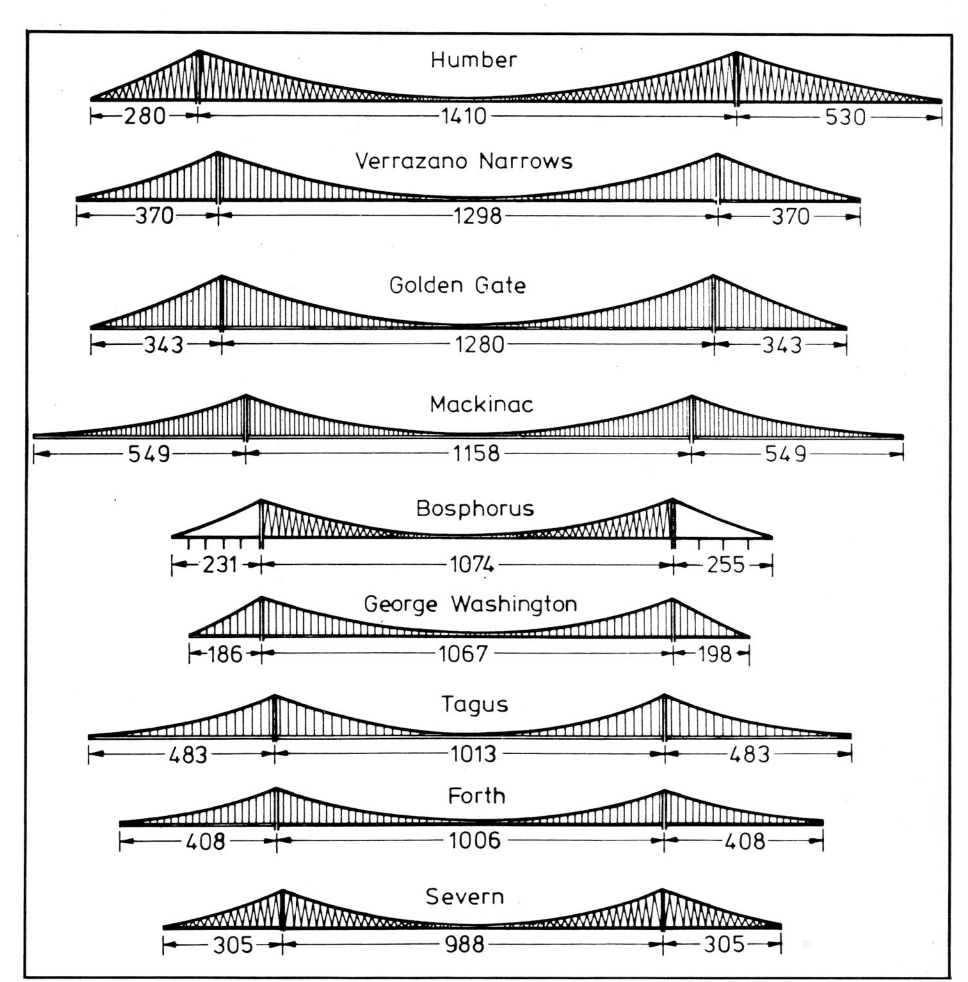


*Figure 4*
*Comparison between the Humber Suspension Bridge and other major suspension bridges.*

The Humber Bridge, opened in 1981, has the longest clear span of those yet built. Bridges of greater span are proposed for construction during the 1980s in Hong Kong and in Japan.

was completed and was the precursor, in having a trapezoidal box deck for improved aerodynamical stability, to those opened later over the Bosphorus (1973) and over the Humber (1981), which, at that time, had the longest clear span in the world of 1410m. Proposals for the crossing of the Humber were first considered in the mid-19th century and carried further in the 1920s but then rejected on the grounds of cost in the financial climate of 1930. The present bridge received Government authorisation in 1969 and construction started in 1972. During an early stage of construction, difficulties were encountered with the foundations of the tower at the southern end of the bridge, but the choice of slipformed concrete for the construction of the towers, instead of structural steel as in the previous bridges, proved to be a valuable innovation. Following earlier practice, the main cables of parallel wires of 5 mm diameter were 'spun' in position between the anchorages but, because of the delays that occurred as a result of bad weather and low productivity, it has been questioned whether the use of 'preformed cables' might not have been more satisfactory. The box sections for the bridge deck were fabricated downstream of the site and floated upstream on pontoons for hoisting and welding into position. As a consequence of the delays during construction, the bridge took 9 years to complete, but neither the

*Continued on page 155*

*Figure 5*
*The completed Humber Bridge.*

The clear central span is 1410 m with north and south suspended spans of 280 m and 530 m, respectively, providing a clearance at high water of 30 m. The total weight of steel in the deck is 16 500 tons and in the main cables is 11 000 tons.

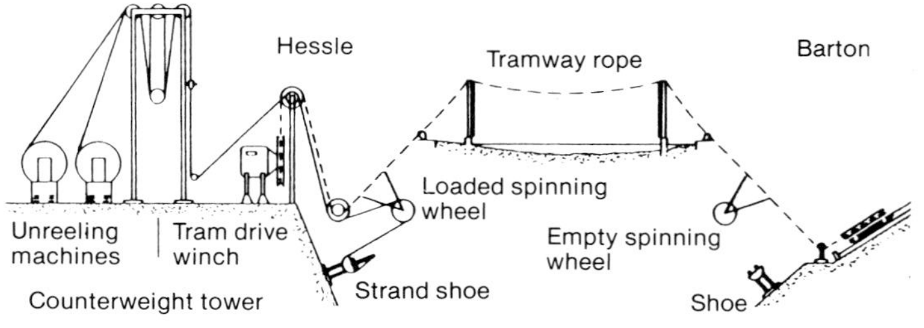


*Figure 6*
*Cable spinning for the Humber Bridge.*

The cables were of parallel wires, 5 mm in diameter, spun in position between the anchorages. In all, 66 000 km of wire were used. After spinning, the two cables were coated with red lead and wrapped before painting.

*Figure 7*
*Assembly yard for the deck sections for the Humber Bridge.*

The box sections for the deck were fabricated at a yard 2·5 km from the bridge site, and were floated on pontoons upstream for hoisting and welding into position in the bridge.

*Figure 8*
*Slipforming the concrete towers of the Humber Bridge.*

Unlike the earlier suspension bridges built in Britain, which have steel towers, these towers are of slipformed concrete and this proved to be a rapid and economic form of construction.

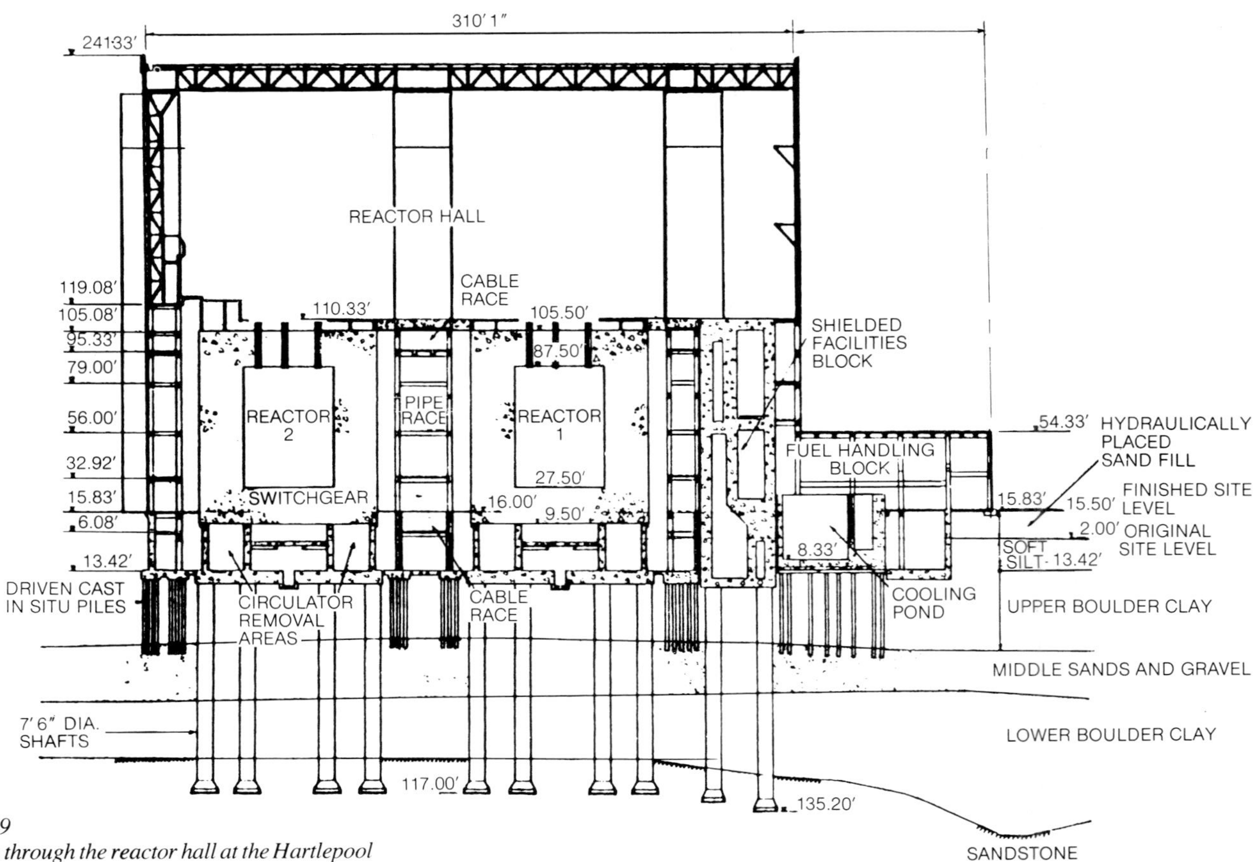


*Figure 9*
*Section through the reactor hall at the Hartlepool Nuclear Power Station.*

The Hartlepool station is the fourth of the nuclear power stations to be built in the UK with advanced gas cooled reactors. There are two reactors with a combined capacity of 1320 MW housed within a single building complex which also accommodates the turbogenerators and fuel handling and other services. The structure of the main reactor hall, which is 81 m long and 43 m wide, is comprised of six external hollow concrete columns 8·5 m × 7 m housing the lifts and supporting the roof and crane gantry.

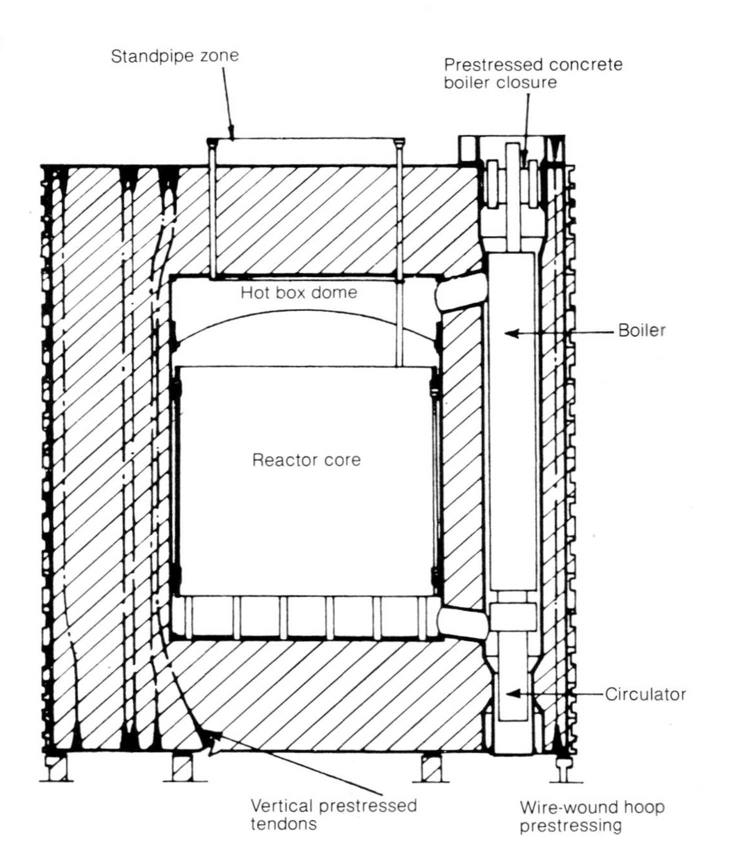


*Figure 10*
*Cross-section through the prestressed concrete pressure vessels at Hartlepool showing the prestressing tendons and boiler pods.*

The pressure vessels are stressed with vertical tendons and horizontal wire windings, applied by a specially developed wrapping machine; they are 29 m high and 26 m in diameter externally and, with their contents, weigh 40 000 tons each.

*Figure 11*
*The soffit shutter to the bottom cap of one of the reactor vessels at Heysham, showing the position of the boiler pods. The vessels at Heysham are similar to those at Hartlepool.*

protracted timescale nor the current arguments about its economic viability can detract from what is a major achievement in bridge engineering.

The building of electricity-generating stations had been concentrated increasingly on larger individual installations, and so fewer were built during the decade than before. Forecasts of future power requirements were also cut back, since demand had been overestimated and was later to fall away as industrial output declined. Nevertheless, some important plants were completed or were under construction during the period. They included coal- or oil-fired, nuclear and hydroelectric stations. The most sophisticated of the engineering structures in these installations are probably the prestressed concrete pressure vessels used to contain the reactors of the nuclear stations. The early reactors had been housed in steel pressure vessels, built using boiler fabrication methods, and had been surrounded by biological shields of mass concrete. In the later Magnox stations, prestressed concrete was used to provide a combined pressure vessel and shield, as pioneered in France over 20 years ago at Marcoule. The advanced gas cooled reactor stations at Hartlepool and at Heysham, now almost completed, each have prestressed concrete pressure vessels designed to contain both the reactors and their associated boilers. This arrangement is regarded as providing sufficient safeguards for the general public to enable nuclear stations to be sited near centres of population. Each of the stations has an installed capacity of 1320 MW generated by two reactors, which requires the pressure vessels to be designed for an internal pressure of a little more than 40 atmospheres with a mean internal surface temperature of the concrete reduced to 60°C by water cooling. A notable feature of the design of these vessels was the requirement that the boilers should be inserted after the completion of the vessels and should later be removable for maintenance, if required. Provision was therefore made for special plugs to be

*Continued on page 159*

*Figure 13*
*Aerial view of site of the underground car park at the House of Commons, London, looking east.*

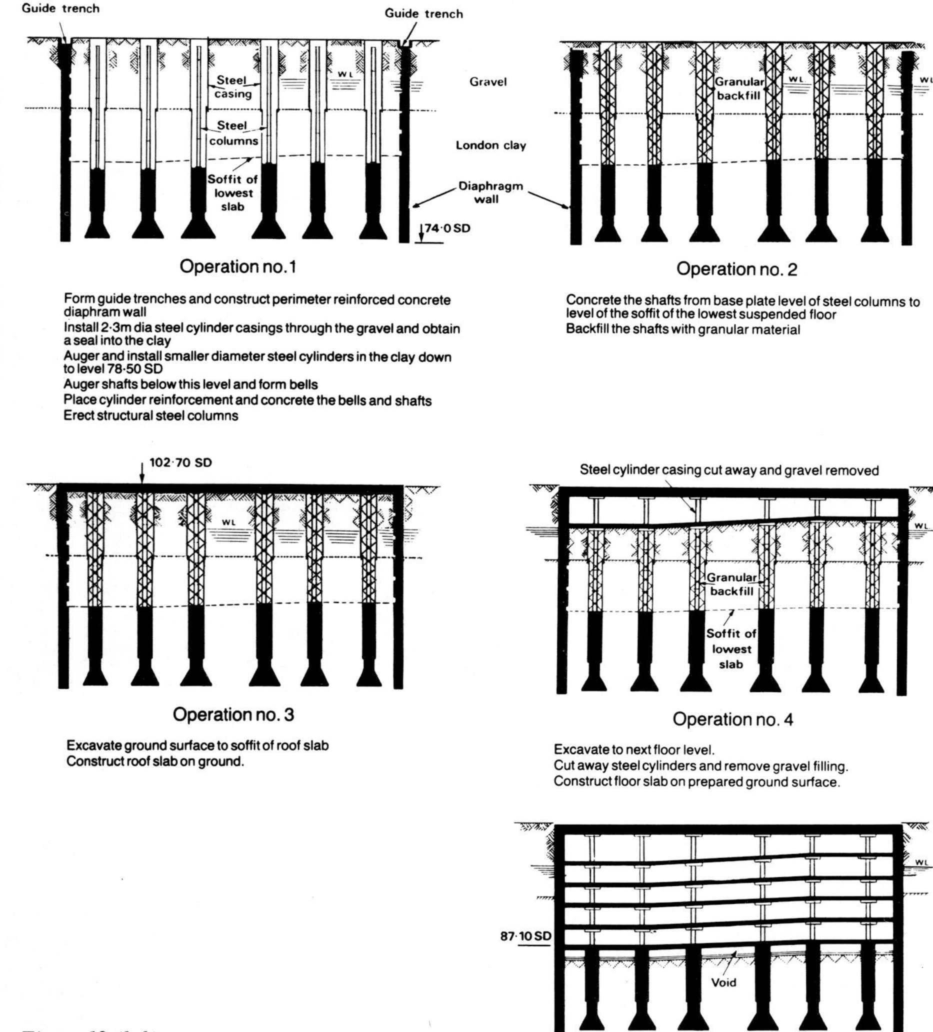

Guide trench
Guide trench
Steel casing
Steel columns
Soffit of lowest slab
WL
Gravel
London clay
Diaphragm wall
74·0 SD
Operation no. 1
Form guide trenches and construct perimeter reinforced concrete diaphram wall
Install 2·3m dia steel cylinder casings through the gravel and obtain a seal into the clay
Auger and install smaller diameter steel cylinders in the clay down to level 78·50 SD
Auger shafts below this level and form bells
Place cylinder reinforcement and concrete the bells and shafts
Erect structural steel columns
Granular backfill
WL
Operation no. 2
Concrete the shafts from base plate level of steel columns to level of the soffit of the lowest suspended floor
Backfill the shafts with granular material
102·70 SD
WL
Operation no. 3
Excavate ground surface to soffit of roof slab
Construct roof slab on ground.
Steel cylinder casing cut away and gravel removed
WL
Granular backfill
Soffit of lowest slab
Operation no. 4
Excavate to next floor level.
Cut away steel cylinders and remove gravel filling.
Construct floor slab on prepared ground surface.
WL
87·10 SD
Void
Operation no. 5
Continue this procedure on successive floors downwards.


*Figure 12 (left)*
*The National Westminster Tower, London, during construction.*

*Figure 14*
*Construction procedure.*

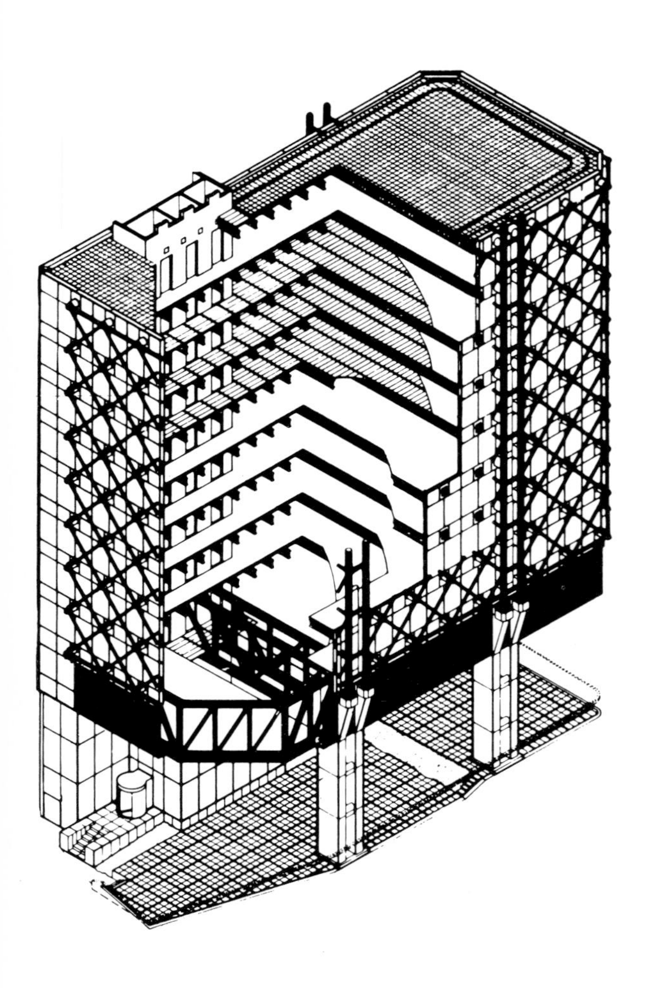

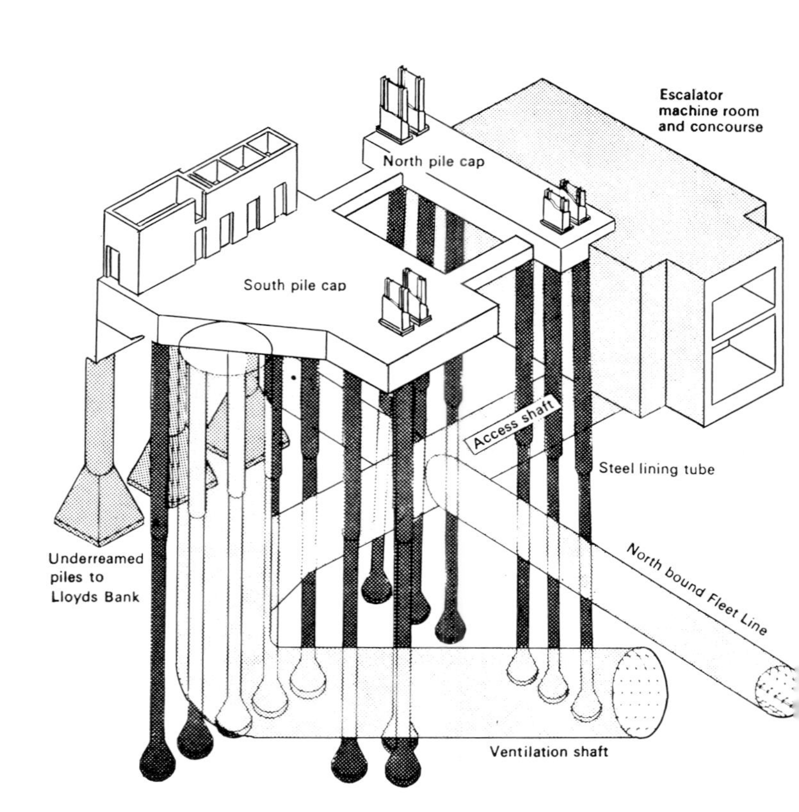


*Figure 15*
*Bush Lane House, London.*

*Figure 16 (right)*
*General view of the Pompidou Centre.*

Following a decision by the French President, a competition was announced early in 1971 for the design of a Centre in the heart of Paris to house contemporary arts. The result was a unique building, known formally as the Centre National d'Art et de Culture Georges Pompidou. The primary structure carrying the vertical loads consists of 12 identical steel frames with two braced end frames giving the building a length of 166·4 m and a width of 60 m. The secondary structure, which braces the building, incorporates prestressed concrete diaphragm floors, while the tertiary steel infills the main structure with smaller-scale structures, staircases, and lift towers. Special problems were created by the need to provide the exposed steel structure with the degree of fire resistance required for a large public assembly building. These were solved in a variety of ways which included filling the main tubular columns with water and the use of sprayed vermiculite.

incorporated in the top cap. These unique requirements were investigated thoroughly in comprehensive series of model tests undertaken as part of the design process.

In the housing field, the substantial reduction in requirements accompanied by the return to favour of brickwork at the expense of precast concrete was offset, in the first half of the 1970s, by an increase in other fields of activity, such as the construction of hospitals, factories, offices, multistorey carparks, exhibition halls, and arts and leisure centres, where prefabrication continued to make an important contribution. The abandonment of tall buildings for local authority housing, a form of construction that had originally been widely welcomed by architects, planners, and administrators, did not discourage the building of tall blocks for offices and even some hospitals, which included the National Westminster office building, reputed to be the tallest in Europe, and the Guys Hospital tower block.

A number of new ideas for the use of materials in structures and for methods of construction were explored in a wide variety of buildings. These ranged from the underground carpark in Palace Yard, Westminster, where the close proximity of the river and of historic buildings created special problems, to the office building, Bush Lane House, where much of the structure was a grid of stainless steel tube filled with water to provide the fire resistance required. Several of the buildings during this period merit special mention: The Centre Pompidou in Paris, the Sainsbury Centre for Visual Arts at the University of East Anglia (both of which make use of the steel skeleton for their visual appeal), and the Grandstand at

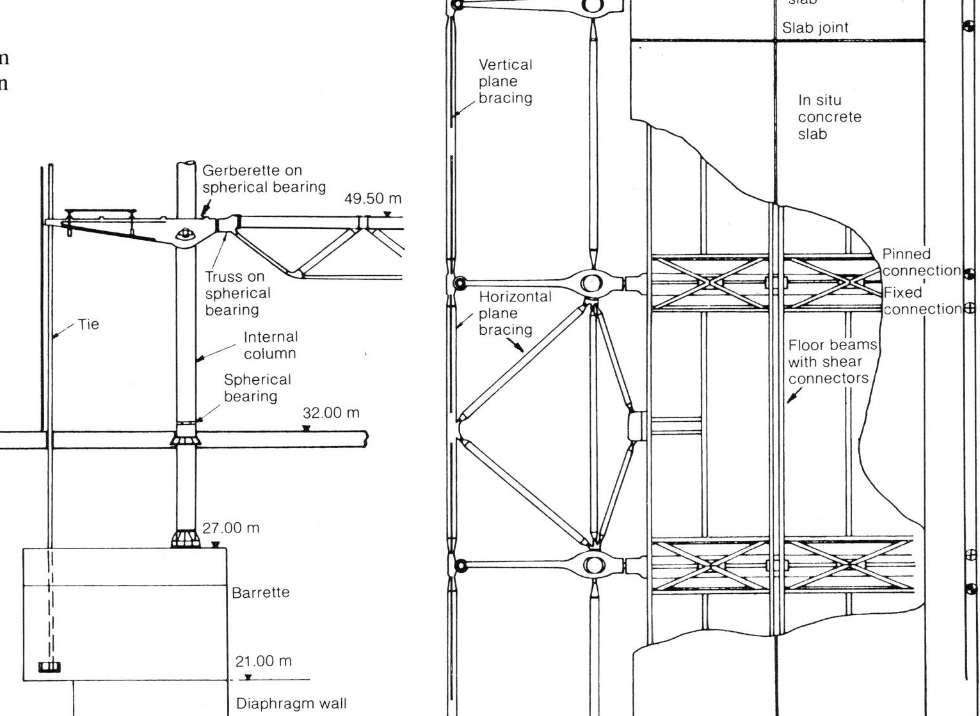


*Figure 17*
*Pompidou Centre, details of primary and secondary steel.*

More than half of the steel used was in the form of cast, forged or rolled sections over 60 mm in thickness, and special precautions were therefore taken to eliminate the risk of brittle fracture.

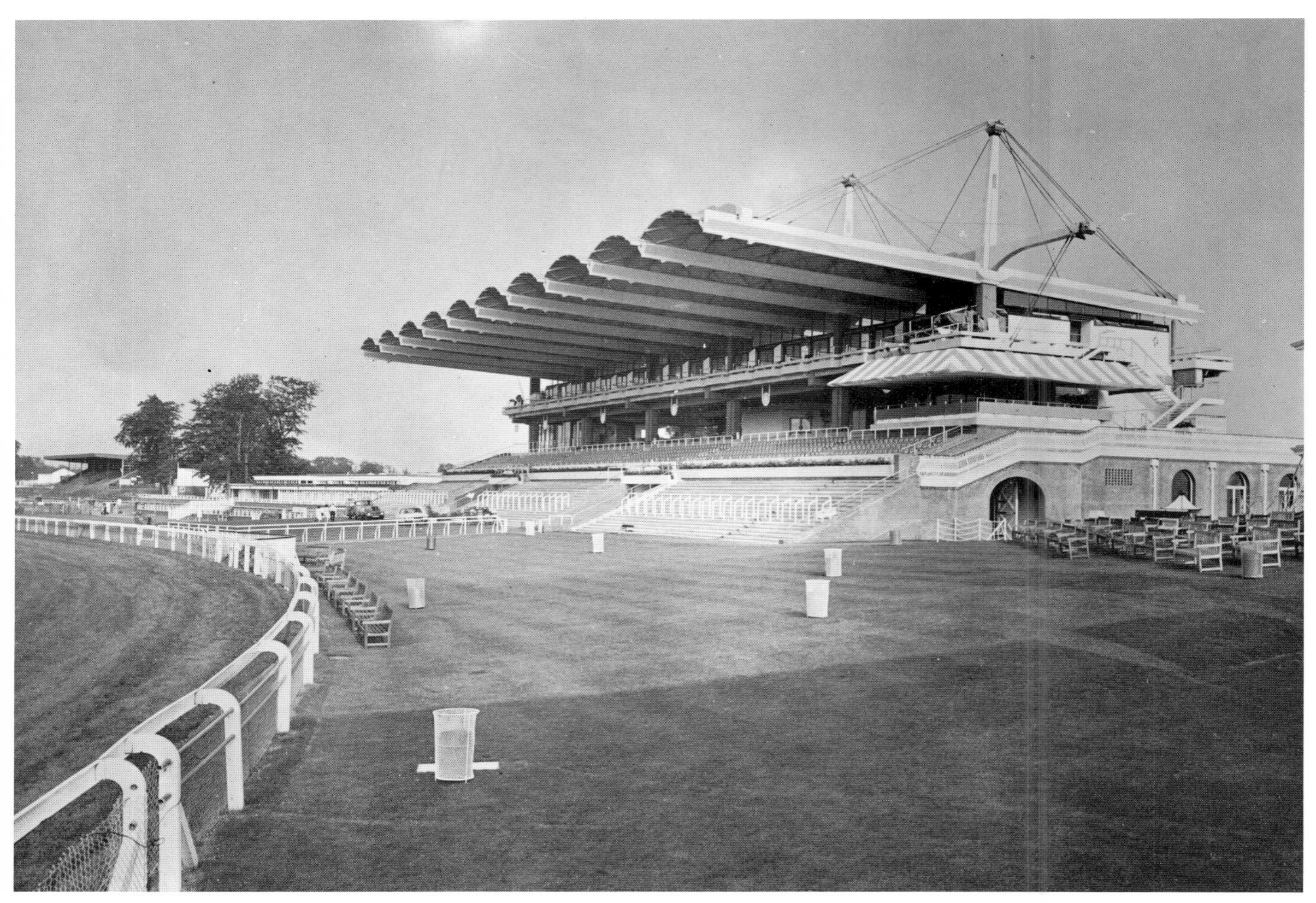

*Figure 18*
*Goodwood Grandstand nearing completion.*

The design of the grandstand at Goodwood was a direct development of earlier grandstands at Sandown Park and Calgary. The main roof structure consists of six precast concrete pylons which support cable-stayed roof beams, and these in turn carry lightweight ribbed concrete shells. The cables were of stainless steel wire. Since cantilever roofs of this kind are susceptible to wind excitation, the design ensured that resonance was avoided. The main frame structure consists of precast H-frames with precast prestressed concrete floors. Speed of construction was an important factor in the choice of the design since demolition of the existing stand and its replacement had to be completed between race meetings in 1979 and 1980.

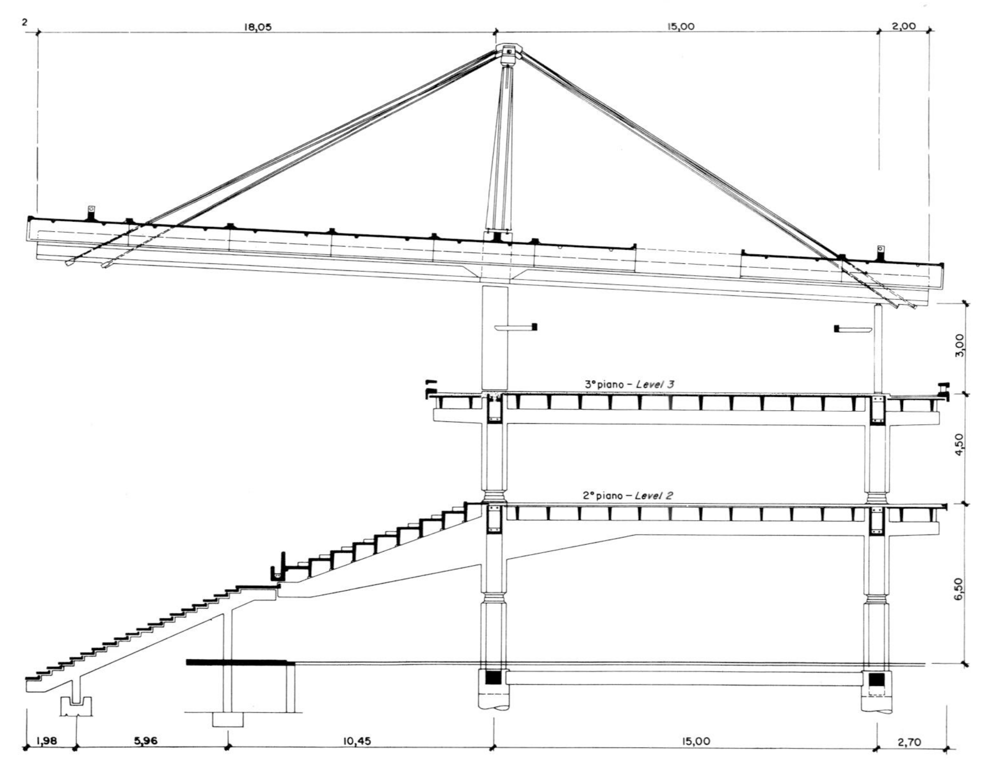


*Figure 19 (right)*
*Cross-section of the Grandstand.*

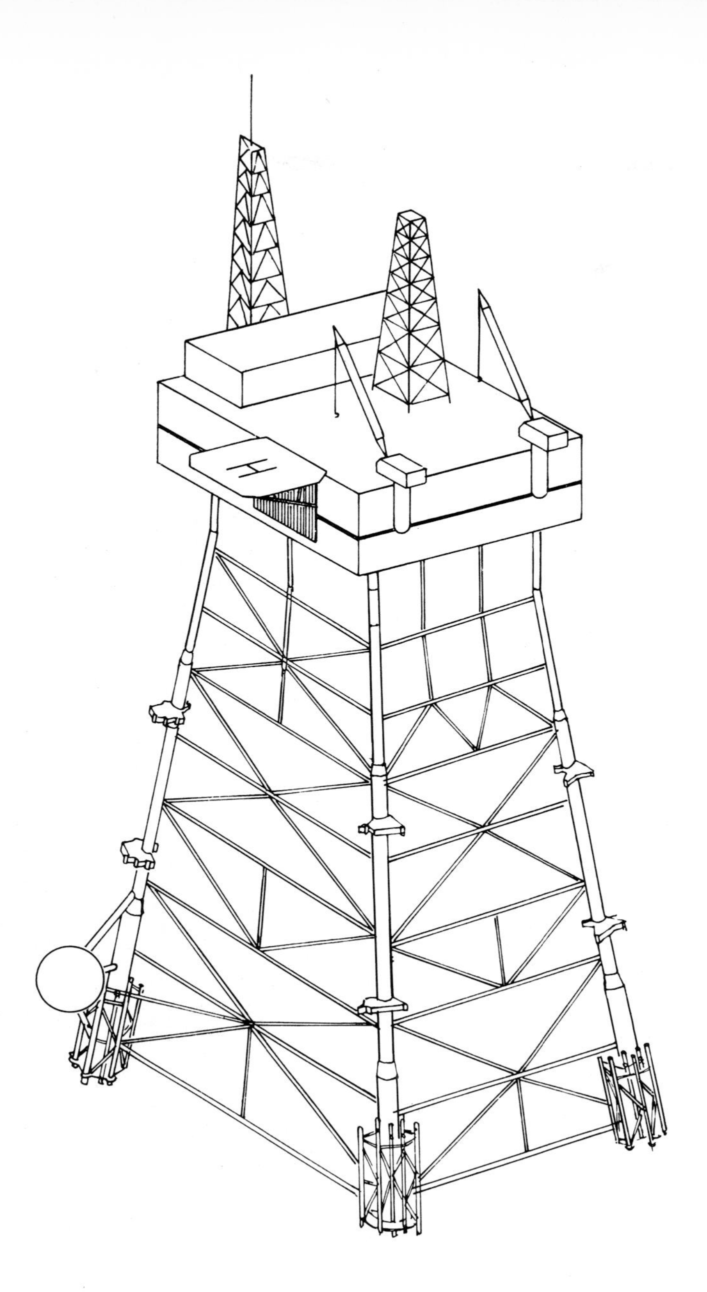


*Figure 20*
*Highland One – a steel offshore structure.*

At the time of its installation in August 1974, Highland One was the largest steel offshore rig. It was assembled with prefabricated nodal joints, which facilitated their heat treatment, firstly into subassemblies which then formed the complete structure in a graving dock at Nigg Bay in Scotland. The rig was then floated out on its side using special flotation tanks for placing in the Forties Field. From start to finish, including the construction of the shore complex, the whole operation was completed in 30 months.

Goodwood (the most recent of a series of similar structures), which explored various solutions for satisfying the requirements of their special function, the environment, and rapid construction.

Experience of the recovery of gas and oil from offshore sources had been confined, in America and the Middle East, to working in relatively shallow and calm water close to the shore, so that when it became economically desirable to exploit the hydrocarbon resources beneath the North Sea, the procedures used and the installations needed required extrapolation of that experience to solve the new problems presented. The solutions had to cater with depths of water between 100 m and 200 m, with wave heights of 30 m, and wind speeds in excess of 50 $m/s^2$, and they were required with great urgency. The earliest rigs were of tubular steel construction following previous practice; the largest of these to be built in Britain was the Highland One rig, which was built at Nigg Bay in Scotland and floated out to the Forties Oil Field 166 km ENE of Aberdeen where it was installed in August 1974. By 1970 it had been recognised that a concrete gravity platform could provide for storage of hydrocarbons on the seabed and could also be economically viable. The first of these to be constructed in Britain was the gas

*Continued on page 167*

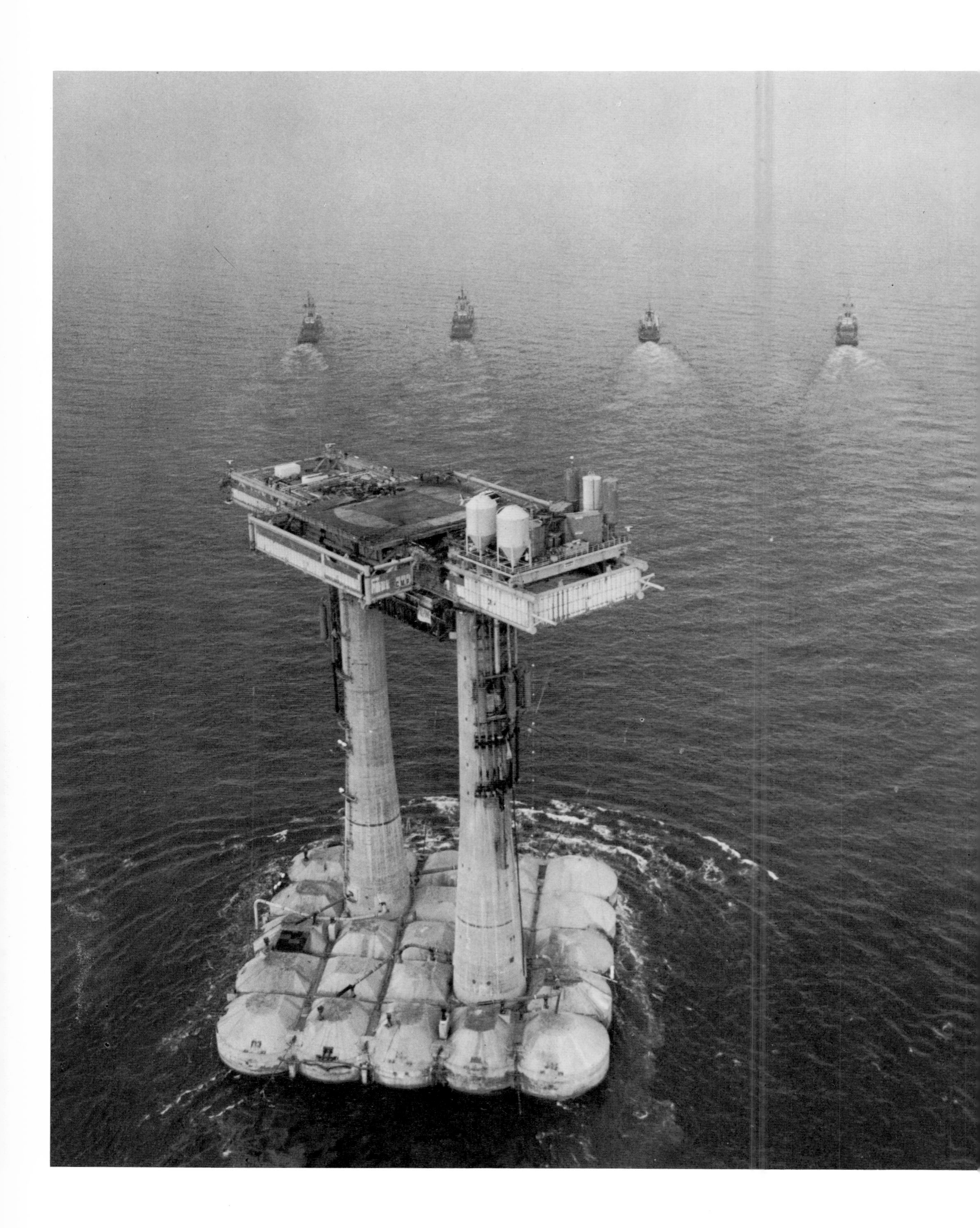

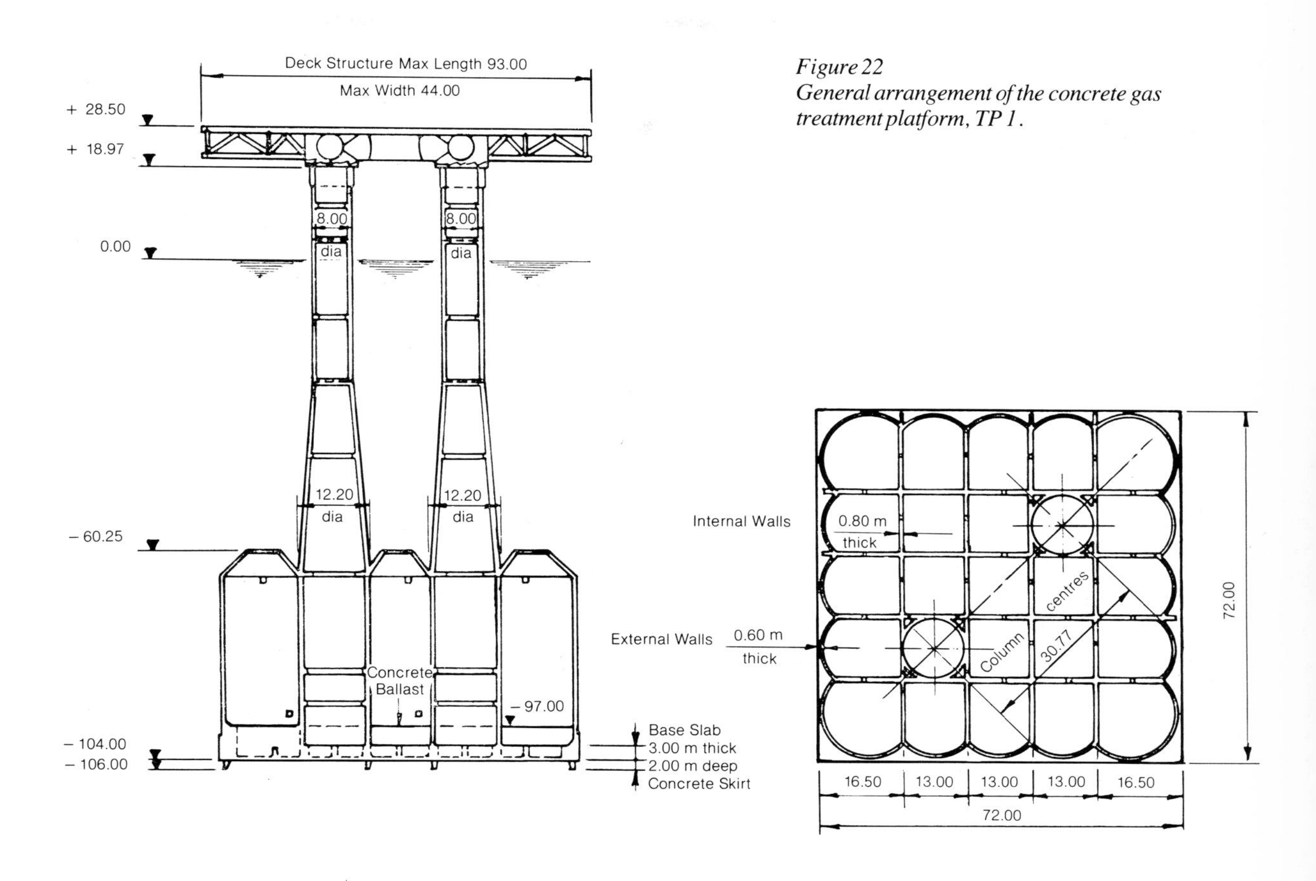


*Figure 22*
*General arrangement of the concrete gas treatment platform, TP 1.*

*Figure 21 (left)*
*TP 1 leaving Loch Striven.*

Gas treatment platform, TP 1, was designed in Paris and was the first concrete platform to be built in Britain. It is one of a group of platforms installed in the Frigg Field for the recovery of North Sea gas, which is delivered by pipeline to the St. Fergus shore terminal in Aberdeenshire, 360 km away. The structure comprises a concrete cellular caisson approximately 72 m square and 44 m deep supporting two concrete columns 12 m in diameter and 83 m high, which carry a structural steel deck. The overall weight of the structure, including all installed pipework and equipment, amounted to 166 000 t. It was positioned in the North Sea just over 2 years after the commencement of the design.

*Figure 23*
*Slip form work on TP 1 in shore basin.*

*Figure 24*
*The Ninian central oil production platform under construction.*

The largest of the concrete gravity platforms so far built is the central oil production platform for the Ninian Field, which was towed out from Scotland in 1978. It has a circular base of about 140 m in diameter and a height-to-deck level of about 170 m.

*Figure 25 (right)*
*An artist's impression of the Ninian central platform on station in the North Sea.*

*Figure 26*
*The Thames Barrier*

The Thames Barrier, built at an estimated total cost of £450M, became operational at the end of October 1982. Its construction, which has taken about 10 years, followed some 20 years of deliberation and study after the floods of January 1953. It will secure London against flooding as a result of the development of storm surges in the North Sea for more than the next half century.

treatment platform, TP 1, installed in June 1976. More recently, the largest of all the gravity platforms built in the decade, the Ninian central platform, was towed out from Scotland and installed in 1978. Apart from the very severe environmental conditions that these structures are required to withstand, their construction presents special design problems, since each phase of construction and installation must be considered from that commenced on shore and continued afloat after launching, the towing-out operations, to the final phases of installation and anchorage in position offshore. Of all the achievements in structural engineering during the 1970s, those in offshore construction have been the most demanding in the technical skill and perseverence required of the engineers involved.

Probably the most significant structure to be completed in the early years of the 1980s is the Thames Barrier at Woolwich, which became operational at the end of October 1982 and was first used to protect London from flooding during a severe storm in January 1983. The initial planning of the barrier stemmed from the disastrous floods of 1953 when parts of the eastern coastal areas of England, particularly East Anglia, Canvey Island and the lower reaches of the Thames, as well as large areas in Holland were inundated. The flooding originated from the combined effects of an expected Spring high tide and a storm surge caused by a severe depression in the North Sea area. Fortunately the flow in the Thames was

*Figure 27*
*One of the box-girder sector gates, which weighed up to 1400 t, in a horizontal position above the water during final adjustments.*

The gates, built on Teesside, were welded to comply with the Merrison standards for box-girder bridges.

unusually low for the time of year and flooding in London was confined to streets in West Ham. A number of instances of flooding have been recorded throughout history and the likelihood of recurrence has increased, partly as a result of lowering of land levels, and recently the high tide level for London has been increasing by about 1.0 m in 130 years.

The remedial measures have included the raising of flood banks and controlling the flow of rivers which join the Thames downstream of Woolwich where the Thames Barrier has been built. Account was taken in designing the barrier of the likely cost to London of serious flooding, estimated as being as much as £3bn, and this led to the adoption of a tide level for design corresponding to what might be expected once in a 1000 years at the year 2030. The final form of structure chosen, illustrated in Figures 26 and 27, provides four main channels through the barrier with six smaller openings, all of which can be closed by rising box-girder sector gates pivoted at piers constructed on the river bed. Normally the gates, the four largest of which are 61 m in length, are housed in precast concrete cills, the largest weighing 10,000 tons, positioned by electrically driven hydraulic rams and can be raised to the nearly vertical operating position by electrically driven hydraulic rams and can be raised further through a total of 180° clear of the water for maintenance; in the event of mechanical breakdown, a secondary system for driving the gates can be brought into operation. This unique structure drawing on a variety of engineering skills and craftsmanship will provide the protection of London against flooding well into the 21st century.

# Editorial comment

Richard Collins

## The impact of science on structural engineering

The great advances in structural engineering described in this book have been achieved as a result of a number of interacting factors. Structural engineers and their close associates, the architects, are responsible for providing most of the basic fixed physical assets of urban civilisation in the form of buildings, bridges and other structures used by the public. These structures are expected to be safe, efficient, economical, and to have a life measured in many decades or even centuries. These overriding requirements have always been a challenge to the ingenuity of the designer which has resulted in new and improved methods.

There are also, however, other sources of innovation. For many centuries prior to the Industrial Revolution, buildings and other structures were designed largely by 'rules of thumb' based on past experience but the Industrial Revolution, which itself imposed new demands, also provided new solutions to some of the problems and new and more efficient materials. The Industrial Revolution was, to some extent, the result of the growth in interest in science during the 18th century and, in the 19th century, science gradually but increasingly had a direct influence on all branches of engineering and industry.

During the early years of the century, those concerned with the design of structures relied mainly on practical experience and their own inventiveness and it is to their credit that a number of their structures are still in use. It was, however, not long before they began to make experiments to test, in advance, the effectiveness and safety of the designs they proposed to use and, as the century progressed, scientists began to undertake research having a direct relevance to the design and construction of structures. Advances were also made in the field of mathematics which helped structural engineers to make more reliable calculations of the stresses and strains in the structures they designed.

This growing relationship between engineering and science advanced slowly during the early years of the 20th century and it was not until the end of the First World War that the major break-through occurred. The War had shown that German industry had been much more successful than British industry in the exploitation of science and, soon after it ended, the British Government established the Department of Scientific and Industrial Research (DSIR) to encourage the use of scientific research by industry. The DSIR itself established several industrial research laboratories, including the Building Research Station (now Establishment) and made funds available for research in the universities and for industrial research associations which could be set up by any industry willing to contribute to the cost.

The role of the DSIR has since been taken over by various other Government departments but, during its lifetime, it created a massive increase in the volume of industrial research, especially in the field of construction, which has had a great effect on the work of the structural engineer. Research on subjects of concern to the structural engineer is now undertaken in several Government laboratories, notably the Building Research Establishment and the Transport and Road Research Laboratory, by several industrial research associations, of which the Construction Industry Research and Information Association is directly supported by many structural engineers, by almost every university, and by many polytechnics. Much research is also now undertaken by individual firms of designers, the larger contractors, and the producers of materials and equipment. This work is of special importance because it facilitates the application of the results of all research and creates links between the profession and industry and those engaged in research elsewhere. The overall effect is a continuing revolution in the design and construction of structures, some of the possible results of which are discussed in the next chapter.

# The future

Edmund Happold

E. Happold BSc, FEng, FIStructE, FICE, FCIoB, HonFRIBA

Edmund Happold is Professor of Building Engineering at University of Bath and Senior Partner Buro Happold Consulting Engineers.

He was educated at Leeds Grammar School, Bootham School, York and University of Leeds.

He started in construction industry on a Sir Robert McAlpine building site; worked for consultants in both Britain and the U.S.A. Worked on a wide range of engineering projects including being one of the winning team of the Centre Pompidou competition, the Vauxhall Cross Competition and others.

His hobby is long span structures and his research group on air supported structures is internationally famous.

He is senior partner in a practice known for its design of innovative structures including airship frame design, bicycle design, buildings, tunnels, pneumatic flood preservation control systems etc.

Awarded two Oscar Faber medals, a Guthrie Brown medal and Henry Adams award of the Institution of Structural Engineers; Murray Leslie medal of the Chartered Institute of Building. Member of the Fellowship of Engineering and an Honorary Fellow of the Royal Institute of British Architects.

To be successful in futurology is extremely difficult – a dangerous extension of one's work as a designer. One tries to take history and to extend it by analogy; in effect, like structural engineering itself, to take past experience – largely of needs and behaviour – and predict performance. There seem to be three main fields where structural engineering skills are of use.

The first is within the field of civil engineering, for the design and construction of bridges, dams, water retaining structures, and so on. As this book has shown, this section of the profession is an extremely old one, and grew out of a knowledge of construction methods. Everyone is aware that the Romans developed their empire by their roads and public works programme. The design approach was entirely empirical: stones were placed on top of one another; they stood up or they fell down. Roman engineers experimented, observed, and then imitated.

The use of scientific theory as a method of predicting the performance of structures did not start until the mid-17th century and did not really expand until the mid-18th. For example, around 1760 John Smeaton carried out a range of experiments from which he developed theories that enabled him to predict the performance and efficiency of different types of water mill and windmill. This ability to quantify the performance of a design before it is constructed, is an important quality of engineering. It enabled Smeaton, among others, to sell his time as a consultant designer, making him a forerunner of those many British consulting engineering firms who successfully work across the world.

In civil engineering the purpose of the structure is usually specific and the scale of construction is large. In the 18th and 19th centuries the consulting civil engineer's position was dominant; he defined what was possible to construct and controlled its construction. Most 19th century engineers were excellent draftsmen – Telford was an architect before he became a civil engineer; Brunel could have been one – and extremely practical, as well as skilled at developing theory. In deciding what is constructed nowadays, power has largely passed to economic planners, but control of design and construction still lies with civil engineers, largely because they are the only ones who know how to produce an economic solution. The scale of the problems they solve is so large that they, as a profession, still control their own destiny.

The second field is that of structures for buildings. While the type of building that can be built has been dictated largely by the structure, the purpose is usually a complex one of functional performance and the satisfaction of emotional needs. Until the 19th century, most building design was carried out by architects who were also engineers; because what could be built came from a relatively small choice of building materials, this was not difficult. Changes in building design were as much influenced by human comfort (the development of cheaper glass allowing larger windows, the development of gas for lighting requiring raised ceiling heights, etc.) as by fashion changes in buildings for the rich, usually starting from the revival of some historical style (Georgian building developed from the Doric style of ancient Greece, Victorian Gothic from medieval building, etc.). As architects started to be educated formally, this education took the form of strong training in drawing solutions based on previous solutions, together with learning how to control and manage the building process. By the end of the 19th century, primarily because of the development of new materials (structural steelwork, reinforced concrete, etc.) together with the demand for larger buildings, structures could no longer be designed by architects. Most types of modern building structure were developed by design-and-construct firms, often of foreign origin, selling special forms of construction and who were selected by tendering after the planning of the building was carried out. So, while it became impossible to build a major building without involving a structural engineer, the latter was viewed very much as a tradesman and had little direct say in the design and no relationship to the client. But he did have a very direct knowledge of where the costs lay in the construction of structure. Many of today's leading designers started in such firms.

The Second World War initiated large changes. Central and local government became the major clients for building work. Architects moved into public service to control, and often design, this work. Public accountability demanded clear documentation before tendering and the rather messy interface in structural design between architect and contractor had to change. Public clients were also willing to pay the fees of additional consultants without reducing the architect's fee. A generation of consulting engineering firms therefore grew up, devoted to structural engineering consultancy, though usually appointed by the client on the advice of the architect and acting as a service to that architect. There is real conflict in this relationship. The architect sees his role as a design polymath and the structural engineer as a service to him. The best young structural engineers, with the technology from a university education now at their disposal to enable innovation, start by trying to convert architects to welcome technological innovation but more often end by trying to move over to working in civil engineering. In the public's eyes, architects have the reputation of being 'creative designers' and engineers that of 'executors'.

The third field of structural engineering is that of 'mechanical' structures, which includes boats, cars, aircraft, space vehicles, medical engineering, etc. Here the purpose of the structure is usually transportation and the element of fashion is less important than it is in the design of a building. The ergonometric, power and control systems and the structure are usually of equal importance. This field is, and has been for some time, subject to rapid technological development and is almost entirely industrialised and controlled by design and manufacturing firms, though considerable subconsultancy goes on. It is an area of structural design in which some of the most exciting structural design problems of the future lie.

The strength of British structural engineering has been the type of person attracted to it and their values and education. Unlike the continent of Europe, our education and training systems have not been determined by Government authority but by the professional institutions, the membership of which includes clients, designers, contractors, teachers and researchers of the industry. Until the end of the 19th century, education was 'effected by a simple course of apprenticeship, usually with a premium, to a practising engineer during which the pupil is supported by taking part in the ordinary business routine, to become gradually familiar with the practical duties of the profession'. Gradually, more formal theoretical education was developed and now all qualified engineers have to be educated to the equivalent of university degree standard; but the strong emphasis on training in practical application remains and will continue to remain in the future. The rate of growth of theoretical knowledge has been enormous, though, and it is hard to believe that the education period and the growth of specialisations will not increase as the body of knowledge in subjects such as aerodynamics, materials science, geotechnics, hydraulics, etc., continues to grow.

There is also an awareness that, while a knowledge of scientific theory is essential to predict physical behaviour, the main role of the engineer is to design – to make decisions as to what is to be built and how. In recent years, there has been a decline in the teaching of how to evolve a design, to look at it and bring its various elements into balance, and then to explain it to others. Structural engineering is an art, perhaps best learnt by understanding the qualities in previous designs, developed by actually engaging in designing and expounded to non-engineers by explaining to them the assumptions or qualities of the products.

Certainly, the need for good structural engineering will grow. As the member of the building design team trained in methods of understanding physical behaviour, the engineer is likely to take over those elements of a building's performance that require such knowledge. In fact, at present, structural engineers not only analyse and size the structure and carry out the detail design of those parts, while services engineers determine the heating, ventilating, and other service needs, but it is usually structural engineers within subcontracting firms who currently design such building elements as cladding, windows, and the like. It is only because engineering, in its modern form, came late into building that the social structure of the industry so far does not allow recognition of its contribution and creativity. It is hard to believe that this will continue, since value is what is required and the engineer's creative contribution is essential to achieve this.

Change in most industries is slow. Construction is both labour- and materials-intensive, so change is often extremely slow. There is no doubt that, for most structures, the traditional inorganic materials such as stone, brick, steel, and concrete, will continue to be used, together with the traditional methods of constructing with them. Not only are the constituents of the materials readily available in most parts of the world, but the skills needed in constructing in these materials are easily handed down, within the local society. What will be needed of engineers is, firstly, a better understanding of how to achieve comfortable conditions internally with a minimum use of energy by the form and materials of their design and, secondly, to design construction systems that are appropriate to the labour, materials, plant, and money, that are available. These are the needs that engineers have to satisfy worldwide; they are not dramatic, they will not change the scale of structures, but they will, hopefully, provide better living and working conditions in a world where a part of the population still lives in abject poverty.

*Figure 1*
*Resources: The Emptying Storehouse*

So most of the developments in structural engineering will not be dramatic. For a new material, or even a new construction method, to come into general use requires enormous impetus. The building professions are extremely conservative, public acceptability even more so. Even in the period of very fast growth in materials science in the last few decades, developments in the construction industry have been slow and usually taken from other areas of engineering.

G. Mensch has written about the time-gap between an invention and its emergence as innovation in industry, and this period has been a declining one. The gap was 52 years in 1802 to a predicted 24 years in 1980. He further contends that there are waves of innovation about every 55 years, the centre of the next wave predicted being 1992. This means that some 80% of the inventions that will form the next innovation wave exist already, but because the time constant for market penetration is about 50 years, one's awareness of the success of an innovation may be delayed considerably.

We therefore have to look at the research and invention of the recent past to guide us into the innovations of the future. The limitation for any new material or type of structure is not only its invention but the codification of an understanding of how it behaves, i.e. the way the wind puts load on it, the amount it will deform, and the determination of what is acceptable deformation, the ways in which it can fail, how it deteriorates over time, and so on. This, of course, can be done by building a prototype and testing, and for a small structure that is designed for series production, such as a car, this is commonly done. But for most building structures, the size, the number, the cost, and the time element, are such that the client wishes to be as sure as possible before he commits himself to manufacture.

Structural engineering is still very much in its infancy. But just as the invention of cheap processes of manufacture of steel that could carry tension revolutionised the size of structure that could be built, the invention of the computer is revolutionising our ability to predict structural performance. Not only is the computer a marvellous store for information but it can manipulate data at an incredible rate. This has meant that engineers have quantified loadings in much more detail and are now able to treat many structures as dynamic problems rather than static ones.

We also now understand that the conditions that we design for can be looked at in more depth. We design not only for the wind, snow and temperature changes but also radiant energy, the acoustic environment, and so on. In the last century the structural engineer found that his problem was not just the strength of his structure that was important, but its resistance to rusting. Similarly, today, we realise that it is not just the maintenance element of the cost in use of a structure that is important but also the energy required to operate and maintain such a structure which broadens the problem.

Analysing the performance of any structure is still extremely difficult. It depends on the prediction of its material efficiency. The earliest method of measuring material efficiency was strength in compression or tension, but this was appropriate only to certain types of structure resisting certain types of load. Then the concept of strength was developed and, more recently, an understanding of fatigue. Tests were invented to try to ensure that the materials used in a construction were the same as assumed in the analysis of the materials behaviour. Such tests were then used in a method of analysis that depended for its accuracy on a simplified loading assumption. The need for simplicity induced a tendency to design crudely.

Engineers start by trying to use homogeneous materials. If they are not available, they try to use only those that are well understood empirically. They are generally guided by Hooke's Law which assumes that the force in a member always has a constant relationship to its extension and then work on principles of small strains and deflections. Yet they are aware that the use of materials in combination can produce better structural qualities and that non-Hookean characteristics can be very desirable. Reinforced concrete not only provides strength in compression and bending but also provides good mass and damping characteristics, as well as excellent fire resistance and weathering qualities. Prestressed concrete emphasises the tensile qualities of steel wire. The plasticity of mild steel provides great safety characteristics.

Yet our methods form a mosaic, evolved at different times, which we use because we have learnt them and they work. We are probably near a time when a whole new method of predicting material behaviour in structures could be evolved by physicists which could integrate the effects of deterioration over time with those of strength and deformation. Some of this applies already and the understanding of strain energy and how this strain energy is converted during fracture has made fracture mechanics a major predictive method. Yet the theory is still relatively elementary, and the amount of strain energy released in composite structures is not necessarily taken up as the work of fracture. We begin to understand why the increased strengths of certain materials, bound together with appropriate matrices, can give useful and wide-ranging qualities.

There may, or may not, be an energy shortage. Certainly, cheap steel and cheap cement are products of cheap coal and oil. Yet there is a shift in the relative costs of different sources of energy as the stored forms of energy from the sun, such as oil and coal, are depleted. There is also a depletion in supplies of the basic forms of inorganic materials such as iron, copper, lead, etc. (*Fig. 1*). So we become more interested in those organic materials that are produced by energy from the sun. In fact, organic materials will become more and more important. And just as 200 years ago those who resisted change expressed horror of iron and steel as 'inhuman' materials, today people say the same about plastics. Yet they will be increasingly important, and we will have to come to understand better the characteristics we require – strength, toughness, imperviousness, mass, good insulation, translucency or whatever – and how, by combination, to achieve them.

We have started to study structures in nature because they have to be totally appropriate: mistakes become extinct. Such structures are extremely complex chemically; basically made up of polymers, water, and calcium salts, but with many other trace elements, made up as composites. The predominant form is the cylinder, some stiff and some flexible. It is the way in which these composites are formed and their characteristics that are so interesting. Firstly, many of them start deforming easily under load so allowing load distribution and they then become progressively stiffer. This strain-dependent stiffness and the visco-elastic nature of the polymeric tissue make them of great interest. Secondly, orientation of the fibres is such that bodies in nature can bend without kinking and this has immense potential in the design of structures; (*Fig. 2*) just as small plants, like grasses, get

*Figure 2*
*Cross layering of sheets of orientated polymers enabling bodies in nature to bend without breaking.*

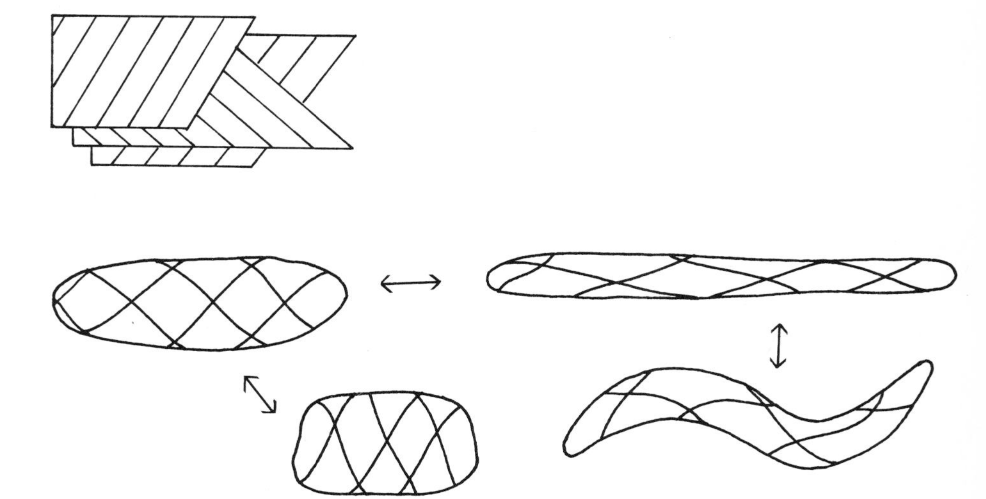

*Figure 3*
*Transparent air supported roof providing intermediate climatic space for the Canadian semi-artic. Designers: Fullerton, Buro Happold, Otto & Newby.*

*Figure 4*
*Part of the French solar farm system.*
*Temperatures up to 6300°F have been achieved.*

trodden on and recover. The development of 'safe' structures, as regards both the materials and the structural systems used, will go much further to reducing, even eliminating, the dangers of structural collapse.

In his structures, man has always wanted to rise higher, span further, and enclose more space. It is hard to believe these ambitions will not continue. Already we can design a 40-acre single-span dome to cover the centre of a city in the semi-arctic at an economic cost (*Fig. 3*). The great change in power generators is the constant reduction in size. Yet the new machines we will use to concentrate energy, be they from wind, sun (*Fig. 4*), or water, will be as different from those of the past as the atomic power station is from the old town gas-plant. Just consider the needs of structures in space (*Fig. 5*). As energy, materials, and labour, become more expensive, so the structural engineers will have to develop new solutions.

At best, these new structural solutions will be art in that they extend the way we see and feel about things, and they will stimulate our senses as well as satisfy our material needs. The problems structural engineers solve cut across all our lives. Structural engineering is immensely satisfying because it is an art grounded in social responsibility.

*Figure 5*
*The immense problems of structures in space.*

# A History of the Institution of Structural Engineers 1908–1983

Cyril Morgan

C.D. Morgan OBE, FCIS.

Educated at Sloane School, Chelsea and qualifying as a Chartered Secretary after studies at the City of London College, Cyril Morgan's appointment, as a non-engineer, to be Secretary of the Institution of Structural Engineers in 1961 was a break with tradition.

He served, 1939-1945, with the KRRC and The Buffs, seeing active service in North Africa and Italy; he was awarded the Territorial Decoration (TD) in 1945.

In 1948 he became the first full-time Secretary of the then-recently-formed Institute of Road Transport Engineers and, from 1953-1961, was Secretary-Director of the British Road Federation.

Cyril Morgan received the OBE in 1970 for services to structural engineering and regards it as a special privilege to be an Hon. Fellow of both the Institute of Road Transport Engineers (1953) and of the Institution of Structural Engineers (1983).

From around 1897, the British Fire Prevention Committee, which included architects, surveyors, engineers and others concerned with the safety of buildings, had been testing the fire resistance of various building elements, particularly floors and including those of reinforced concrete construction. In 1906 this Committee appointed a Special Commission on Concrete Aggregates and in the same year the Royal Institute of British Architects set up a Reinforced Concrete Committee to inquire into the proper conditions for the use of reinforced concrete in buildings and other structures. The first report of this committee was published in the RIBA Journal of 15 June 1907.

This activity resulted in one of the firms which was marketing a proprietary system for reinforcement proposing that other similar producers should form some kind of organisation. But Edwin O. Sachs, Chairman of the Fire Prevention Committee, took the view that a trade association perpetuating the limitation of design in concrete to a variety of 'systems' based on patents was undesirable and that if reinforced concrete was to be developed freely in accordance with principles known to any competent engineer, a different kind of association was needed. Thus, in the Smoking Room of the Ritz Hotel on 21 July 1908 the first Council meeting of the Concrete Institute was held. The Earl of Plymouth accepted the office of Founder President and took the Chair; he was supported by Sir Henry Tanner, Chief Architect of the Office of Works as Vice-President, Mr. E.P. Wells was Hon. Treasurer and the indefatigable Edwin O. Sachs was Chairman of the Executive Committee. The Council resolved to incorporate the Institute as a technical society and approved a programme of meetings and discussions for the following months. On 22 February 1909 the Concrete Institute was formally incorporated as a company limited by guarantee. Its principal objects were defined as:

(i) to advance the knowledge of concrete and reinforced concrete and direct attention to the uses to which these materials can best be applied and

(ii) to afford the means of communication between persons engaged in the design, supervision and execution of works in which concrete and reinforced concrete are employed (excluding all questions connected with wages and trade regulation).

Membership was open to all those professionally or otherwise engaged in the field of concrete. The first 500 enrolled were to pay an annual subscription of one guinea; all after to be charged two guineas a year with firms and public authorities enrolled as 'special subscribers' at 5 guineas pa.

The new Institute was in action almost at once. A meeting of the Executive held on 10 December 1908 was attended by Mr W. E. Riley, FRIBA, Superintending

Architect to the London County Council. He explained amendments which the Council was seeking to make to the London Building Acts (1894-1908). The Acts then in force made no provision at all for the use of reinforced concrete nor allowed any reduction in the thickness of external walls even if they were relieved of all load by a frame of structural steel or reinforced concrete.

In the months that followed the Concrete Institute was busy both in submitting drafts of clauses for the new Bill and preparing a petition to Parliament protesting against certain of the County Council's other proposals. When the London County Council (General Powers) Act became law on 16 August 1909 it embodied an appeals procedure and the young Institute was named as one of the bodies to be consulted by Statutory Authorities when regulations affecting the stability of buildings were under consideration. The Institute was also invited by the RIBA to nominate two members to their Joint Committee on Reinforced Concrete whose Second Report, issued in 1911, became a standard guide for British designers in that material.

These are the cornerstones upon which the Institution of Structural Engineers was founded. By October 1912 consideration was being given to expanding the purpose of the Concrete Institute to cover structures of all kinds, 'structures' being defined as 'those constructions which are subject principally to the laws of statics as opposed to those subject to the laws of dynamics and kinematics such as engines and machines'. The wider purpose was agreed and the title of the body was extended to become 'The Concrete Institute: an Institution of Structural Engineers, Architects, etc.'

Mr E.P. Wells served as President from 1912-1914 and it was during his term of office that the Institute Library was founded. Plans were developed for qualifying examinations for membership which, it was intended, should be introduced in 1916. In the event, the first examinations were delayed until 1920 because of the First World War. In the 1914-1918 period the Research Committee continued to be active, leading to the publication of the first of the long series of authoritative reports published by the Institution; in 1918 the report *Recommendations to Inspectors, Clerks of Works and Foremen concerning the execution of reinforced concrete works* appeared, followed in 1919 by the *Report of the Joint Committee on loads on highway bridges* and *Mnemonic notation for engineering formulae*.

These early examples of published reports illustrate a capacity, which has been maintained over the whole of the past 75 years, for the Institution to bring together structural designers from Government, public service, private practice, and the manufacturing and contracting industries to produce material to guide and extend the practice of structural engineering.

In 1921 the first *Year Book* appeared and in January 1922 the periodic *Transactions* were replaced by a monthly journal which, in 1924, took the title *The Structural Engineer*.

At a Council meeting of the Concrete Institute on 28 September 1922 it was resolved to change the name to the Institution of Structural Engineers; the first Council and officers of the newly-named body took office in 1923 when total membership was some 1330. Branches of the new Institution were quick to form – in Lancashire and Cheshire in 1922, Western Counties in 1923 followed in succession by the Yorkshire, Midland Counties, South Western Counties, Wales and Monmouthshire and Scottish Branches in the period 1924-1931. In 1937, a Branch was formed in South Africa to become the only Overseas Branch of the Institution to continue into the 1980's. After the Second World War further Branches were established in the Northern Counties, Northern Ireland, the Republic of Ireland, Southern Counties, East Midlands, East Anglia and Bedford and surrounding areas – to bring the total to 15. It is through the work of the elected Committees of these Branches, whose Chairmen and nominated representatives attend regularly the meetings of Council and its Standing Committees, that the Institution keeps in touch with, and pursues policies reflecting the views of, members at large.

In 1928 the President of the Institution was the UK delegate in Vienna for the International Congress on Bridge and Structural Engineering thus forging a link which has held for more than 50 years and which has resulted in the Institution holding the secretariat of the British National Committee of the International Association for Bridge and Structural Engineering.

By the early 1930's membership had reached 3000 and the standing of the Institution had been established; its nominees served on the Committee of the Building Research Board which produced in 1933 the *Code of Practice for the use of reinforced concrete in building* – an early example of the many dozens of official British and International Standards and Codes to which members of the Institution have contributed as formal representatives. The qualifying examinations were amended to include a compulsory paper – *Structural Engineering Design and Practice*. Against this background the Institution successfully petitioned for a Royal Charter which was granted in perpetuity by HM King George V in March 1934. The Charter President was Major A. H. S. (later Sir Arnold) Waters, VC, DSO, MC who, by leading the Institution again in 1942-44 has been the only one of the 61 Presidents since 1908 to serve two separate terms of office.

Between 1934-1939 the Institution grew in size and authority. Membership increased to around 4000; Branch and Section programmes of meetings provided opportunities for members everywhere to meet together to update their knowledge and skills; Ordinary Meetings, Symposia and Conferences supplied the material for reports and monthly issues of *The Structural Engineer*. Institution reports appeared regularly – the *Report on steelwork for buildings – Part I – Loads and Stresses* (1933); *Part II – Formulae for the computation of stresses* (1938); *Bearing plates for girders* (1932); *Water retaining structures* (1934); *Welded structures* (1935). As Professor Sir Alfred Pugsley, OBE, FRS (President 1957-58) wrote in the Golden Jubilee issue of *The Structural Engineer* (July 1958):

> '... time and again our members seem not only to have been in the forefront of new developments but also to have interested themselves in what appeared to their seniors in the engineering world as unprofitable novelties or lost causes, and yet helped these forward to become major weapons in the structural armoury ...'

The outbreak of war in 1939 found members serving on the Government Committee on Air Raid Precautions. The Institution collaborated with the War Office, the Ministry of Labour and the Ministry of Home Security in respect of the recruitment and employment of engineers in the forces and in civilian war time occupations requiring qualified structural engineers. October 1940 brought tragedy when the recently-appointed President, Captain Murray Buxton was killed in a London air-raid.

In 1942-43 the then Ministry of Works and Planning set about the compilation of a comprehensive series of Codes of Practice for civil engineering and building. The Institution was appointed to take charge of work on load-bearing superstructures and earth retaining structures. In 1954 a Council for Codes of Practice was established within the British Standards Institution which, by agreement with the Ministry of Works and the professional institutions, became responsible for the drafting of these Codes and their publication. The Institution, however, remained responsible for servicing the revelant structural Code committees until 1968 when it was decided in view of ever-increasing costs in money and resources, that these duties should pass to the BSI to allow the Institution to use its own funds for the production of further *ad hoc* reports pointing the way to fresh developments in structural engineering practice.

The war years were significant also for the review undertaken of the qualifying examinations of the Institution. Syllabuses were revised and examinations were set to the new rules in 1944. In that year, a Chair in Concrete Technology was founded at Imperial College. By the date of the Golden Jubilee of the Institution in 1958, further changes had been introduced into the Part 1 and Part 2 examinations; a Chair in Structural Engineering had been established at the University of Witwatersrand, Johannesburg (in 1952) and another (in 1957) at Manchester College of Science and Technology (now UMIST); the City and Guilds College, London, founded a further Chair in Engineering Structures in 1958 and the Institution was directly responsible for funding for five years from 1961 a Chair in Structural Engineering at the University of Southampton. At the time of writing these precedents are being followed by an effort, in 1983, to fund a Chair of Structural Design at the University of Leeds.

The 50th anniversary of the Institution in 1958 was a time for congratulation, stock-taking and planning for the future. The messages of congratulation from all over the world confirmed the high reputation achieved in the first half-century. The celebrations attended by civic representatives and members of sister professions in towns and cities throughout the United Kingdom and overseas demonstrated the recognition given both to the Institution and – more important – to its members. The 1950's and 1960's were decades of hope and excitement that the new technologies could bring greater opportunities for improving the efficiency and economy of structural engineering.

Certainly the volume of structural engineering opportunity in the years that followed can seldom have been greater – new industrial development, New Towns, reconstruction of bombed inner city areas, slum clearance, high-rise residential blocks, countless overbridges on 1200 miles of motorway and the design and construction of the series of great estuarial bridges. Throughout, the Institution served its members – 8500 in 1960, 13500 in 1970, 14000 by 1980 – by meetings and discussions, by papers published in *The Structural Engineer,* by reports such as *The use of digital computers in structural engineering* (1961); *Report on concrete practice* (1963); *Composite construction in steel and concrete* (1964); *Report on the use of high alumina cement in structural engineering* (1964); *Falsework* (1971); *Design and construction of deep basements* (1975) and many others. With hindsight the work of the Institution in this period conjures the same mental image as does the dramatic device of a ship's rail carrying a lifebelt marked 'SS Titanic'. A feeling reinforced by the major conference organised by the Institution in 1966 under the title 'Industrialised building and the structural engineer', the extensive papers and discussions from which were published in the following year.

The lessons were there to be learned; many profited but not all. A few weeks after the Institution had celebrated its Diamond Jubilee in March 1968 when a message of congratulations and good wishes was received from HRH Prince Philip, an Honorary Fellow, there occurred on 16 May 1968 an event that tested the whole fabric of the Institution and, paradoxically, finally established its authority in the field of structural engineering in the United Kingdom. The event was the gas explosion which resulted in the collapse of one corner of a new, 23-storey block of flats in Plaistow, East London – Ronan Point. A number of persons were killed and injured and more than 80 families made homeless. The Minister of Housing and Local Government was in touch with the Institution within hours of the disaster and within a week a Tribunal of Enquiry was set up under the Chairmanship of Hugh Griffiths, QC., Recorder of Cambridge, with Sir Owen Saunders of Imperial College and Sir Alfred Pugsley, OBE., (Past President) as its members. The publication of the report of the Tribunal on 6 November 1968 illustrated both the power of the communications media and the ability of the Institution to respond. The report made far-reaching recommendations with regard to the design of tall buildings of large panel construction and for the appraisal of existing blocks. Something akin to public panic followed. Mr L. R. Creasy, CB., OBE., then Director of Central Services, Ministry of Public Building and Works and subsequently (1973-74) President of the Institution, was appointed principal technical adviser to the Minister of Housing and Local Government, the Rt. Hon. Anthony Greenwood, MP. Mr Creasy was instrumental in bringing the Institution into consultation with Ministry engineers and others concerned with preparing technical recommendations arising from the findings of the Report of the Tribunal. The Ministry's advice – Circular 62/68 – was circulated to local authorities on 15 November and sent by the Institution to each of its members on 19 November 1968. Two further Guidance Notes were prepared by the Institution – *Structural stability and the prevention of progressive collapse* and *Notes for guidance on the interpretation of Government circular 62/68*. Both were completed and were in the hands of members by Christmas 1968 and were formally endorsed by the Government when they were later sent by the appropriate Departments to all local authorities.

The Ronan Point collapse and its consequences are chronicled because the episode was, in effect, a 'test to the limit' of the expertise and attitudes that the Institution had fostered over the previous 60 years. In the event, through the efforts of those closely involved and of members generally, Government, local authorities, industry and the public at large developed a new awareness of the practice of structural engineering. It became recognised that 'as safe as houses' was no more than an idiom and that, despite modern technology, structural design was an imprecise field of science. Instead of blame came respect; respect that grew as the Institution and its members contributed to solutions to the succession of problems that made headlines over the next decade – box girder bridge design (1971); high alumina cement concrete (1973); calcium chloride attack (1976); stability problems of Airey houses (1981).

In parallel with these preoccupations in its own discipline, the Institution developed an increasing influence in the broader field of engineering. In 1962 it joined the Royal Institute of British Architects, the Royal Institution of Chartered Surveyors and the Chartered Institute of Building to study, under the Chairmanship of Sir Noel Hall, the encouragement of joint training for the construction industry professions. The Noel Hall Report was published in 1965.

In 1961 inter-Institutional discussions were opened which resulted, a year later, in the formation of the Engineering Institutions' Joint Council – a voluntary coming-together of 13 chartered engineering institutions to tackle problems of common interest for the engineering profession. With Government backing EIJC was granted a Royal Charter on 3 August 1965 as the Council of Engineering Institutions. Throughout the chequered history of this organisation over the next 18 years, numbers of members of the Institution served on its Board and Standing Committees, following the example of endeavour to improve standards and unify the profession set by F. R. Bullen (President 1961-62) who, during the formative years 1962-66, was Institution representative on the Board of EIJC/CEI, first Chairman of the General Purposes and Finance Committee (1962-64) and Chairman of three other major Committees of EIJC/CEI. Senior members of the Institution gave equally devoted effort to the wider needs of the profession; in 1983 Dr W. Eastwood (President 1976-77) became the Chairman of the CEI in the period when arrangements for its registration functions to be transferred to the new Engineering Council were a major preoccupation.

The failure of the CEI to fulfil early hopes must be attributed to the inability of its member institutions to learn to work effectively together. Among its successes must be numbered the establishment of common academic standards, common training requirements and post-training qualifying processes leading to admission to the register of Chartered Engineers – later extended, in February 1971, by a definition of standards and the establishment of registers for Technician Engineers and Engineering Technicians.

These developments were reflected in the policies of the Institution. By 1969 its Part 1 examination and recognition of exempting qualifications at that level were ended in favour of the CEI Part 1 examination. The last Institution Part 2 examination was held in 1970 and thereafter corporate membership by examination was attained only by passing the post-training Part 3 examination after completing CEI Parts 1 and 2 examinations or obtaining an appropriate engineering degree exempting therefrom. This change from recognition of part-time study as the normal route to corporate membership to requiring studies to graduate level and beyond was reflected in the numbers on the Roll of the Institution over the decade 1971-1981. Total membership at the start exceeding 13500; by 1976 it had dropped to 13200 but had recovered to more than 14500 by 1981 – including at that date some 600 registered Technician Engineers. These had qualified as Associate-Members under Bye-Law revisions that had been approved by the Privy Council on 21 October 1975.

The Institution held firm convictions as to the measures needed to achieve a strong and unified profession in the United Kingdom – convictions which were respected but not necessarily shared by its colleagues in the Institutions of Civil and Municipal Engineers with whom close ties developed from 1966 onwards. The three chartered institutions formed the 'construction group' within the CEI where, whatever differences may have been revealed in pre-meeting discussion, a common policy was invariably presented in matters relating to the broader interests of the profession. It was in this spirit that the Institution reluctantly accepted the 1978 revisions to the Royal Charter and Bye-Laws of the CEI which admitted every registered Chartered Engineer into membership alongside the (by then) 16 chartered engineering institutions who were given 'corporation member' status. The revised constitution, however, was given little opportunity to demonstrate its effectiveness. Following a call for a radical reorganisation of the engineering institutions published by the Presidents of the Institutions of Civil, Electrical and Mechanical Engineers in August 1974 and representations made to Members of Parliament by those associated with a number of non-chartered societies in the field of engineering, the Secretary of State for Industry announced in July 1977 that a Committee of Inquiry into the organisation of the engineering profession would be set up under the Chairmanship of Sir Monty Finniston.

In the period 1978-1980 the Committee of Inquiry gathered evidence from every quarter. The Institution, in its submission, stressed the need to maintain academic and training standards at the highest level and to strengthen the effectiveness of the registers for chartered and technician engineers as maintained by the CEI. The Institution declared itself unimpressed by claims for some form of statutory registration for engineers and suggested that 'licensing' as a restriction of function should be introduced only if such a measure could be demonstrated to be in the public interest.

The Finniston Committee Report, published in January 1980, called for extensive reforms of public attitudes to engineering and proposed a number of measures to promote the 'engineering dimension' and improve the education and training of British engineers. After considerable discussion and widespread consultation the Government, in 1981, announced its intention to set up an Engineering Council under a Royal Charter, to act as the registration body for the profession and as the 'engine of change' called for by the Finniston Committee Report. Initial Government funding of £3m was promised. Among the members of the new Council nominated by the Secretary of State was Sir Alan Harris, CBE., (President 1977-78). Under the Chairmanship of Sir Kenneth Corfield the new Council had, by the end of 1982, established contact with all the Institutions and societies in membership of the CEI or its associated Boards for Technician Engineers and Engineering Technicians and was planning the development of the Council's own registers and fields of operations. The CEI had taken steps formally to surrender those of its powers and awards of title essential to the achievement of the intentions of the Government as evidenced by the Royal Charter of the new body.

Thus in its 75th year the Institution, pre-eminent in its own field, stands alongside the Institutions of Civil and Municipal Engineers as the 'core' of the 'construction group' of the Engineering Council, prepared again to work, in the public interest, to achieve a wider unification of the engineering profession and an enhancement of its contribution of the well-being of the nation at home and overseas.

A more detailed account of the formation, work and growth of the Institution between 1908-1958 can be found in the contribution 'The History of the Institution of Structural Engineers' by Dr. S. B. Hamilton (President 1954-55) published in the Golden Jubilee issue of *The Structural Engineer,* July 1958.

Accounts of events in each of the years following that date exist in the Annual Reports of the Council of the Institution 1958-1982.

Copies of these sources are available for reference in the Library of the Institution at 11 Upper Belgrave Street, London SW1X 8BH.

**November 1982**

# Selected further reading

This list is highly selective. It is limited to books in print or readily available through good libraries. Inevitably, therefore, there are gaps in some areas.
The serious student will have to consult other, more specialist, publications whatever his period of interest. Up to about 1860 these will usually be other books, such as the accounts by Smeaton, Telford, and Stephenson of the building of the Eddystone Lighthouse, the Menai Suspension Bridge, and the Britannia Bridge. After that date they are more likely to be articles in the technical press or papers presented to the professional institutions and published in, for instance, the Structural Engineer and the Proceedings of the Institution of Civil Engineers. One further group of important sources is the series of reports of Commissions of Inquiry into serious failures, from the Dee Bridge collapse in 1847 to Ronan Point in 1968. References to this much more extensive literature will be found in many of the books listed below, most comprehensively in the first.

## Introduction

General studies of the history of structural engineering

**Developments in structural form**
R. J. Mainstone
Allen Lane, London, and MIT Press, Cambridge, Mass., 1975 (reprinted Allen Lane/ Penguin and MIT Press, 1983)

**A history of technology**
C. Singer and others (editors)
Clarendon Press, Oxford, vols IV, V, and VII, 1958-78 (articles on building and on bridges by Hamilton, Shirley Smith, Berridge, and Mainstone)

**A history of civil engineering**
H. Straub
(translated by E. Rockwell), Leonard Hill, London, 1960

**The Structural Engineer: The Jubilee Issue.**
Institution of Structural Engineers.
London, July 1958 (covers the years 1908-58)

Materials and Construction

**The British building industry**
M. Bowley
Cambridge University Press, London, 1966

**A history of building materials**
N. Davey
Pheonix, London, 1961 (chiefly for the earlier periods)

**The new science of strong materials**
J. E. Gordon
Penguin, Harmonsworth, 1976 (for recent developments)

**A note on the history of reinforced concrete in buildings**
S. B. Hamilton
National Building Studies, Special Report No.24, HMSO, London, 1956

**A short history of the structural fire protection of buildings**
S. B. Hamilton
National Building Studies, Special Report No.27, HMSO, 1958

**Prefabrication. A history of its development in Great Britain**
R. B. White
National Building Studies, Special Report No.36, HMSO, London, 1965

Structural theory

**History of strength of materials**
S. P. Timoshenko
McGraw-Hill, New York, 1953

Bridges

**Bridges of Britain**
E. de Maré
Batsford, London, 1975

**A span of bridges**
H. J. Hopkins
David & Charles, Newton Abbot, 1970

**The architecture of bridges**
E. Mock
Museum of Modern Art, New York, 1949

Buildings and Architecture

**Theory and design in the first machine age**
R. Banham
Architectural Press, London, 1960

**Space, time and architecture**
S. Giedion
Harvard University Press, Cambridge, Mass., 5th edn, 1967

**Towards a new architecture**
Le Corbusier
(translated by F. Etchells), Architectural Press, London, 1927

**Contemporary structure in architecture**
L. Michaels
Reinhold, New York, 1950

Engineers and their works

**Thomas Telford: Engineer**
A. Penfold, editor
Thomas Telford, London, 1980

**The works of Isambard Kingdom Brunel**
Sir A. Pugsley, editor
Institution of Civil Engineers and University of Bristol, London, 1976

**Isambard Kingdom Brunel**
L. T. C. Rolt
Longmans, London, 1957 (reprinted Penguin, 1970)

**Thomas Telford**
L. T. C. Rolt
Longmans, London, 1958 (reprinted Penguin, 1979)

**George and Robert Stephenson**
L. T. C. Rolt
Longmans, London, 1960 (reprinted Penguin, 1978)

**John Smeaton FRS.**
A. W. Skempton, editor
Thomas Telford, London, 1981

## 1780-1850 and 1850-1890

**A History of Technology**
Singer, Holmyard, Hall & Williams, editors
Relevant chapters in Volume IV (1750-1870) and Volume V (1850-1900), Oxford University Press 1958

**Developments in Structural Form**
Rowland Mainstone
Allen Lane 1975

**History of Strength of Materials**
Stephen P. Timoshenko
McGraw-Hill 1953

**The Works of Sir Joseph Paxton 1803-1865**
George F. Chadwick
The Architectural Press 1961

**The Works of Isambard Kingdom Brunel**
Several authors
edited by Sir Alfred Pugsley
Institution of Civil Engineers 1976

**Thomas Telford: Engineer**
Several authors
edited by Alastair Penfold
Thomas Telford Ltd. 1980

**The Life of Robert Stephenson FRS**
J. C. Jeaffreson
(with technical chapters by William Pole)
Longmans 1864

**Isambard Kingdom Brunel**
L. T. C. Rolt
Longmans 1957

**Thomas Telford**
L. T. C. Rolt
Longmans 1958

**George and Robert Stephenson**
L. T. C. Rolt
Longmans 1960

**The Railway Navvies**
Terry Coleman
Hutchinson 1965, Penguin Books 1968

**Thomas Brassey: Railway Builder**
Charles Walker
Frederick Muller 1969

**Lives of the Engineers**
Samuel Smiles.

## 1890-1910

**Why Engineers Should Study History**
Dr. S. E. Hamilton, OBE
Newcomer Society 1956

**Developments In Structural Form**
Roland J. Mainstone

**Evolution of the Steel Building Frame**
Professor A. W. Skempton
Imperial College Library

**One Hundred Years of Steel Framed Structures: Developments and Achievements**
Institution Library

**W. B. Wilkinson (1819-1902) and his place in The History of Reinforced Concrete**
Joyce M. Brown, M.A.
Newcomen Transactions: Vol XXXIX

**The Cement Industry 1796-1914: A History**
A. J. Francis

**A Note On The History Of Reinforced Concrete In Buildings To The Year 1900**
Institution Library

**A Reprieve For Weaver's Mill**
Patricia Cusack
Journal "Concrete" March 1976

**Science And Building: Structural And Environmental Design In The 19th And 20th Centuries.**
H. J. Cowan

**The MacMillian Encyclopdia Of Architecture And Environmental Change.**

**Robert Maillart's Bridges: The Art Of Engineering**
David P. Billington

## 1910-1939

**Architecture of Bridges**
Elizabeth B. Mock
Museum of Modern Art

**Bridges of Britain**
Eric de Maré
Batsford

**Contemporary Structure in Architecture**
Leonard Michaels
Reinhold

**European Architecture in the 20th Century**
Arnold Whittick
Grosby Lockwood

**Guinness Book of Structures**
John H. Stevens

**History of Architecture, 18th edition.**
Sir Bannister Fletcher
Athlone Press

**Key to Modern Architecture**
York & Penn, Blackie

**Robert Maillart**
Max Bill
Pall Mall

**Science & Building**
Henry J. Cowan
Wiley Interscience

**Structures**
J. E. Gordon
Pelican Books

**New Science of Strong Materials**
J. E. Gordon
Pelican Books

## 1939-1955

**The Civil Engineer in War**
Institution of Civil Engineers. Symposium of papers on wartime problems 1948.

**Space Frames and Stressed Skin Construction**
F. J. Samuely
Royal Institute of British Architects Journal
March 1952

**Some Recent Experience in Composite Precast and Insitu Concrete Construction with particular reference to Prestressing**
F. J. Samuely
Institution of Civil Engineers February 1952 — Structural Paper No.30

**The Structural Engineer**
Jubilee Issue 1958

**Prestressed Concrete**
K. Hajnal-Konyi
Architects Year Book No.3 1949

**Recent Developments in Prestressed Concrete Construction with resulting Economy in the Use of Steel**
T. J. Gueritte
With a technical appendix by
Dr. K. W. Mautner.
Institution of Structural Engineers Journal July 1940

**Aircraft Structures**
A. G. Pugsley
Institution of Structural Engineers Journal
January 1941

**The Mulberry Invasion Harbours**
Major W. J. Hodge
Institution of Structural Engineers Journal
March 1946

**Shell Concrete Construction**
F. S. Snow
Institution of Structural Engineers Journal July 1947

**Developments in the Design of Welded Steel Structures**
H. V. Hull
Institution of Structural Engineers Journal
August 1945

**Reinforced Concrete**
Ove Arup
Architects Year Book 1945

**Structural Steelwork**
K. Hajnal-Konyi
Architects Year Book 1945

## 1955-1970

**The Severn Bridge superstructure**
Associated Bridge Builders Ltd
Studio G, Yorkshire, 1966

**Modern architecture in Britain; selected examples of recent building**
T. Dannatt
Batsford, 1959

**A broken wave. The rebuilding of England 1940-1980**
L. Esher
Allen Lane, 1981

**Forth Road Bridge superstructure**
Forth Road Bridge Joint Board
The Board, 1964

**Aims of structural design**
Institution of Structural Engineers
ISE, 1969

**New architecture of London; a selection of buildings since 1930**
S. Lambert
British Travel and Holiday Association in collaboration with the Architectural Association, 1963

**Guide to modern buildings in London 1965-75**
C. McKean and T. Jestico, editors
Warehouse Publishing Ltd., 1976

**Developments in structural form**
R. J. Mainstone
Allen Lane, 1975

**Building systems, industrialization, and architecture**
B. Russel
John Wiley, 1981

**The Art of Structural Engineering**
P. Dunican
ISE, 1966

## 1970-1983

Reports of the Institution of Structural Engineers:

**Aims of structural design**
August 1969

**Design for industrial production**
November 1971

**Communication of structural design**
April 1975

**Design and construction of deep basements**
August 1975

**Criteria for structural adequacy of buildings**
March 1976

**Structure-soil interaction**
April 1978

**Structural joints in precast concrete**
August 1978

**Inspection of building structures during construction**
April 1983

Jointly with the Concrete Society:

**Fire resistance of concrete structures**
August 1975

Jointly with the Institution of Highway Engineers:

**Design recommendations for multi-storey and underground car parks**
February 1976

Institution Symposia on:

**Stability of low-rise buildings of hybrid construction**
July 1978

**Structural failures in buildings**
April 1980

Institution Colloqium on:

**Computer produced drawings in structural engineering**
Structural Engineer, (5 papers) November 1980

**Civil engineering aspects of Heysham nuclear power station**
K. A. O'Connor
ProcICE, Part 1, 1975 *58,* August 377-393

**Hartlepool power station: major civil engineering features**
F. W. Coates and R. S. Taylor
ProcICE, Part 1, 1976 *60,* February 95-121

**Design and construction of the Centre National d'Art et de Culture Georges Pompidou**
P. B. Ahm, F. G. Clarke, E. L. Grut and P. Rice
ProcICE, Part 1, 1979 *66,* November 557-593

**The design and analysis of grandstand structures**
J. Bobrowski, B. K. Bardhan-Roy and T. Maciag
Struct Eng, 1974, *52,* (February) 2 37-56

**TP1: The construction of gas treatment platform no. 1 for the Frigg Field for Elf-Norge A/S**
J. A. Derrington
Struct Eng, 1977 *55,* (February) 2 61-73

**Humber Bridge**
New Civil Engineer Supplement, May 1981

**Thames Barrier**
New Civil Engineer Supplement, November 1982

## The Future

**John Smeaton FRS**
edited by A. W. Skempton
Thomas Telford Ltd 1981

**The British Building Industry**
Marian Bowley
Cambridge 1966

**Report of the education and status of civil engineers in the United Kingdom and in Foreign Countries**
Council of the Institution of Civil Engineers 1870

**Mechanical Design in Organisms**
S. Wainwright, W. Biggs, J. Currey and J. Goseline
Arnold Edward 1976

**Life in the future. Prospects for Man and Universe.**
Malcolm Ross-Macdonald
Aldus Books. Jupiter Books, London

**Das technologische Patt**
G. Mensch
Umschau Verlag, Frankfurt, 1975

# Glossary

This selected glossary is intended as a help to the non-technical reader. Exact technical definitions may be obtained from published glossaries.

**abutments**
a support of an arch or bridge, which usually resists a horizontal force from an arch, as well as its weight

**arch**
a structural element curved in profile, capable of supporting loads largely by internal compression

**auger shafts**
holes drilled in earth

**bascule bridge**
a lifting bridge, viz Tower Bridge

**biological shields**
barriers protecting organic life from harmful radiation

**box beams**
a hollow, square or rectangular girder or beam

**braced roofs**
a 2 dimensional braced roof has an open assembly of interconnected linear structural elements which form a structure which has length and height and secondary bracing; a 3 dimensional braced roof is an assembly of interconnected linear structural elements which produce a structure which has length, height and width

**bulls-eye light**
a small circular or oval window or opening

**caisson foundations**
a cylindrical or rectangular structure for keeping soft ground and water from flowing into an excavation, which sinks as the foundation is excavated

**cantilever**
a beam which is built-in and held down by weight or otherwise secured at one end and hangs freely at the other

**capitals**
moulded, crowning feature of a column

**cartesian coordinates**
coordinates measured perpendicularly from fixed axes of reference which are at right angles to each other, such as in an ordinary graph

**casein glues**
glues made from milk

**cellular**
a structure with deep indentations that amount to no more than 20% of its volume

**CLASP**
Committee for Local Authorities Special Programme

**coffer**
a panel in a ceiling strongly recessed to make a decorative pattern

**concrete shell**
a relatively thin curved plate-like structure, typically a low rise dome

**continuous beams**
multi span beams with a bending strength at their points of support comparable to that at mid-span or single span beams fixed rigidly at their ends. In general continuous beams are stiffer and can support more load than comparable sections with simple vertical supports at the end of each span

**crack propagation, theory of**
a theory of determining the stress at which a crack will develop within a material

**cramp**
a metal U-shaped bar which holds ashlars (a square hewn stone, or stone wall) to each other or to a steel or concrete beam

**creep**
deformation that occurs over a period of time without any increase in load

**curtain wall**
a non load-bearing external wall between columns or piers, not always carried on the floor on which it rests

**damping**
a force which tends to reduce vibration as friction reduces ordinary motion

**decentering arches**
removing the temporary scaffolding and other falsework after completion of construction

**deck**
a flat roof or quay, jetty or bridge floor, generally a floor with no roof over

**diaphragm slabs**
a stiffening plate between main girders

**eccentric loading**
a loading, usually on a column, applied at a point away from the column centre

**elastic analysis**
an analysis of the stresses in a structure based on the elastic behaviour of the material which has the capacity to return to its original shape when the stress is removed

**ergonometric**
relating to people, particulary the design of machines, chairs, tables etc., to suit the body and to permit work with the least fatique

**equilibrium**
the state of a body which does not move

**eye-bar links**
the loops forged onto one end of a bolt

**filler joist floors**
a floor consisting of rolled steel joists spaced at intervals. The intervals may be filled with plain or reinforced concrete

**finite element analysis**
method of analysing the forces in a structure by assuming it is composed of a conglomerate of small finite pieces

**flying butress**
a butress which provides support, including lateral thrust, at a high level

**folded plate roof**
a roof made of relatively thin material which derives its strength from the folds

**galvanised**
dipped in molten zinc

**geodesic dome**
a spherical dome structure made up of short straight struts usually in a triangular formation

**geotechnics**
the study of the properties of soils and rocks

**gravity dam**
a structure that is water retaining by means of its shape and mass and is prevented from overturning by its weight alone

**gravity platform**
an oil platform which rests on the seabed, held down by its shape and mass

**grillage foundation**
a foundation which by virtue of its superimposed layers of beams, placed at right angles to each other, can distribute a concentrated load over an area. The beams are usually steel encased in concrete to provide protection

**helical reinforcement**
steel rod reinforcement bent into a spiral curve

**Hooke's Law**
the deformation in an elastic material is proportional to the load on it

**hoop tension**
the tension which occurs in the wall of a circular bunker or tank containing solid or liquid

**hyperbolic paraboloid**
a saddle shaped curve generated by a straight line moving over two other straight lines inclined to one another

**I beams**
a rolled steel joist, generally imlying one which is 'I' shaped

**influence coefficient**
a graph examining the effects of different loads on beams

**insitu**
constructed or carried out in the final location, referring most frequently to the casting of wet cement

**jack arches**
a brick or concrete arch springing from the bottom flange of a rolled steel joist or rail

**limit design**
see plastic design

**lines of thrust**
the locus of the points through which the resultant force in an arch or retaining wall passes

**loads (imposed)**
the weight carried by a structure

**matrix**
an array of coefficients of a series of linear equations

**membrane structure**
structures like tents or shells, which support loads through effectively uniform forces within the thickness of the material and depend for stability on their curved shape rather than any bending strength

**membrane theory**
a theory for designing a thin structural shell on the assumption that it is free from bending

**moment distribution**
an arithmetic method for designing statically indeterminate structures

**Newton**
the Newton is a metric measure of force and is equivalent to 0.225 lb force

**nodal joints**
a point in a framed structure where two or more members meet

**oblique arches**
an arch which is set obliquely across the two parallels which it joins

**pilasters**
a rectangular pier, sometimes fluted, projecting from the face of a wall, having a cap, shaft and base

**piled foundation**
a foundation by which loads from the structure above are carried down (by means of long struts of timber steel or concrete which are either driven into the soil or cast in preformed shafts) to a depth where the sub-soil can support these loads

**piles**
usually vertical, driven into or cast into the ground, carrying vertical and/or horizontal loads

**plastic design**
design of steel or reinforced concrete frames on the assumption that plastic hinges form at points of maximum bending moment

**plasticity**
behaviour of a material which deforms under stress but does not have the capacity to return to its own shape when stress is removed

**polymers**
organic compounds including many synthetic resins. They have large molecules containing many hundreds of smaller molecules of the same compound linked in chains

**pontoons**
a vessel, generally flat bottomed, for carrying plant or materials, or for carrying part of a floating bridge

**portal frames**
building frames whose stability depends on the stiffness of joints between beams and columns without aid from bracing walls or any diagonal struts or ties

**prestressed concrete**
concrete in which cracking and tensile forces are elminated or greatly reduced by artificially building-in compression forces

**purlins**
horizontal beams in a roof at right angles to the principal rafters and carried on them

**reinforced concrete**
concrete containing reinforcement of mesh or steel rods

**resonance**
condition where the natural frequency of two or more bodies causes harmonic oscillation, undesired between machines and structures

**retarders**
an admixture which slows up the setting rate of concrete

**sheet piling**
a retaining structure usually constructed by driving interlocking preformed steel sections into the sub-soil

**shell roof**
a relatively thin structural membrane with a singly or doubly curved surface

**shuttering**
the part of formwork which is either in contact with the concrete or has the form lining attached to it

**side thrust**
a horizontal force

**slipform concrete**
a narrow section of formwork in slab or wall shuttering that can easily be jacked up as the concreting proceeds

**soffits**
the under surface of a cornice, stair, beam, arch, vault or rib

**soil mechanics**
the science and art of predicting the behaviour of different sub-soil types in relation to the loads applied by a variety of different structures

**spandrel**
triangular space between an arch and the road carried by the arch

**splayed**
bevelled or rebated edges

**springings**
the intersections at each side of an arch between its lower surface and the faces of the walls or piers that support it

**stanchion**
a vertical steel strut

**stay**
a tie-bar or diagonal brace to prevent movement

**strain**
distortion of a structural material produced by an imposed stress

**stress**
force put onto a subject divided by the area which carries the force

**sway**
sideways movement of a structure

**tension coefficient, method of**
a method of expressing the nature and direction of forces in a structure as ratios of coordinates x.y and z at right angles to each other

**tensometer**
a device for measuring small elastic strain

**thermal movements**
movement due to expansion or contraction caused by temperature change

**thermal welding**
heat welding

**thermo setting resin glues**
resin glues which only set with heat application

**tie-rods**
a member carrying tension, generally steel, often threaded

**trace elements**
an indication of the presence of a minute amount of some constituent in a compound, a quantity so minute as to be inferred but not actually measured

**transept**
the transverse part of a cruciform church considered apart from the nave

**trapezoidal box deck**
quadrilateral arrangement of hollow girders to form a floor

**trajectories stress**
lines joining points of equal stress

**truss**
an open assembly of interconnected linear structural elements designed to act as a strut, tie or beam

**tubular bridge**
bridge made from hollow steel tubes

**undulation**
a wave-like curve or a series of these, a surface defined by such curves

**vault**
an arched masonry roof, generally with a smooth curved soffit, or a room or passage with an arched masonry roof

**vermiculite**
a mica, which when heated expands to form a very light insulating aggregate

**Vierendeel girders**
a girder composed of top and bottom members joined by verticals and connected together with rigid joints

**yieldline theory**
theory relating to permanent deformation which a metal takes when it is stressed beyond the elastic limit

# Index

This index refers to pages 5-180, italicised numerals refer to illustrative references.

# Acknowledgements


The publishers wish to thank the following people and organisations for their permission to reproduce photographs and illustrations belonging to them.
The publishers have made every endeavour to obtain permission for the use of illustrative material. Apologies are tendered to any owners whose copyright is unknown.

## Introduction

Figures 1, 2, 3, 4, 5, 6, 7, 8, 9, 10, 13, 15, 16, 17, 18, 19 and 21 R. J. Mainstone
Figures 11, 12, 14, 20, and 22 R. J. Mainstone from *Developments in Structural Form*

## 1780-1850

Figures 1, 17, 22, 23, 24, 29 and 30 James Sutherland
Figures 2, 4, 5, 8, 9, 12, 13, 14, 15, and 16 Institution of Civil Engineers PHEW Collection
Figures 3, 6, 10, 11, and 21 John Bancroft
Figure 7 Weinreb
Figure 18 The Times
Figure 19 Fotomas Index
Figures 25 and 26 Chatsworth Library
Figure 27 Country Life
Figure 28 Edward Diestel Kamp

## 1850-1890

Figures, 1, 2 and 12 James Sutherland
Figure 3 Fotomas Index
Figure 10 Eric de Maré
Figure 11 Professor A. W. Skempton
Figure 13 John Bancroft and James Sutherland
Figures 14, 15 and 16 Institution of Civil Engineers PHEW Collection
Figures 17 and 18 Institution of Civil Engineers/ University of Bristol
Figure 19 John Bancroft and Weinreb
Figure 20 Dr G. Booth
Figure 21 Ove Arup & Partners
Figures 22, 23, 24 and 25 John Bancroft

James Sutherland wishes to acknowledge the research of Professor A. W. Skempton in relation to Belper Mill and the Boat Store at Sheerness, and also to Dr L. G. Booth in relation to Brunel's Timber viaducts.

## 1890-1910

Figures 1, 2, 13 and 14, Institution of Structural Engineers
Figure 3 R. J. Mainstone
Figures 4, 5 and 6 Institution of Civil Engineers PHEW Collection
Figures 7, 8, 9, 10, 17, 18 and 19 Modern Building Record
Figures 11; 12 & 15 (Christopher Stanley) and 16 (Terence Soames) Cement and Concrete Association
Figures 20 and 21 Hampton Hill Studio

## 1910-1939

Figure 1 Kodak Museum
Figures 2, 31, 32 and 34 Architectural Press
Figures 3, 8, 9 and 11 British Architectural Library RIBA
Figure 4 Arnold Whittick from *European Architecture in the Twentieth Century*
Figures 5, and 6 Institution of Civil Engineers PHEW Collection
Figure 7 Freeman, Fox & Partners
Figures 10, 12, 13, 14, 15, 16, 17, 19, 20, 21, 23, 24, 25, 26, 27, 28, 29 and 30 Building
Figures 18 and 22 National Monument Record
Figure 33 Architectural Association
Figure 35 Van Nostrand Reinhold Publishing Corp

## 1939-1955

Figures, 1, 2, 3 and 4, Imperial War Museum
Figures 5 and 6 Cement and Concrete Association
Figures 7, 16 and 17 Sidney W. Newberry
Figure 8 Ministry of Works
Figure 9 Holland Nannen and Cubitts
Figures 10 and 14 F. J. Samuely & Partners
Figure 11 E. S. & A. Robinson
Figure 13 British Insulated Callenders Cables Ltd
Figure 15 Horsekey Bridge & Piggott Ltd
Figure 18 Timber Research and Development Association

## 1955-1970

Figures 1 and 19 Ove Arup & Partners
Figure 2 John Lang Construction
Figures 3, 11 and 15 Henk Snoek
Figure 4 Frederik Gilbert & Partners
Figure 5 Richard Einzig
Figure 6 GLC Photo Library
Figures 7 and 13 Colin Westwood
Figure 8 Frank Gadd
Figure 9 Freeman Fox & Partners
Figure 10 John Donat
Figure 12 British Telecom
Figure 14 British Insulated Callenders Cables Ltd
Figure 16 Sam Lambert
Figure 17 Architectural Press
Figure 18 British Airways

## 1970-1983

Figures 1, 14, 15, 20 and 22 Institution of Structural Engineers
Figures 2 and 3 Bryan & Shear Ltd
Figure 4 Metal Construction
Figures 5, 7 and 8 Freeman Fox & Partners
Figures 6, 12, 16 and 27 New Civil Engineer
Figures 9, 10, 11 and 17 Institution of Civil Engineers PHEW Collection
Figure 13 Aerofilms
Figure 18 Handford Photography
Figure 19 Howard Lobb & Partners
Figures 21 and 23 W. Ralston Ltd
Figures 24 and 25 Howard Doris Limited
Figure 26 J. R. Hatfield Powell

## The Future

Figures 1, 2 and 5 BPCC/Aldus Archive.
Figure 3 C. H. Wood (Bradford) Ltd.
Figure 4 Dr Georg Gerster, John Hillelson Agency Limited.

The picture researcher, John Bancroft, would like special mention to be made of Mr Mike Chrimes of the ICE Library who was so very helpful to him in his searches. And also to photographer Michael Denman MMPA, Haywards Heath.

Acknowlegements and additional information relating to structures where supplied by the Authors.

**Bush Lane House**
Client: City and West End Properties Ltd
Architect: Arup Associates
Engineer: Ove Arup and Partners
Contractor: Trollope and Colls Ltd (main)

**Computer drawing**
Client: Public Services Agency
Contractor: Genesys Ltd

**Cottage at Letchworth**
Engineer: A. J. Brodie, Esq

**Glenfinnan Viaduct**
Engineers: Simpson & Wilson

**Goodwood Racecourse**
Client: Goodwood Racecourse Ltd
Architect: Howard Lobb Partnership
Engineer: Jan Bobrowski and Partners
Contractor: James Longley and Co Ltd

**Hartlepool Power Station**
Client: Central Electricity Generating Board
Architect: Fredrick Gibberd and Partners
Civil engineering design and construction: Taylor Woodrow Construction Ltd
Principal contractor: The Nuclear Power Company (Whetstone) Ltd

**Heysham Reactor Vessel**
Client: Central Electricity Generating Board
Design and construction: British Nuclear Design and Construction Ltd

**Highland One**
Client: British Petroleum Development Ltd
Designers: Brown and Root Inc
Project managers: Brown and Root (UK) Ltd
Designers and contractors for graving dock and fabricating yard: George Wimpey and Co Ltd

**House of Commons underground car park**
Client: Department of the Environment
Engineer: W. V. Zinn and Associates
Contractor: Kier Ltd (main)

**Humber Bridge**
Client: Humber Bridge Board
Engineer: Freeman, Fox and Partners
Contractors: British Bridge Builders (superstructure)
John Howard and Co Ltd (sub-structure)
Tileman and Co Ltd (towers)
Clugston Construction and Costain Civil Engineering (approach roads)

**Kingston Bridge**
Client: Corporation of Glasgow
Engineer: W. A. Fairhurst and Partners
Contractor: Marples Ridgway Ltd jointly with Duncan Logan Ltd

**Merrick Park Water Tower**
Engineers: Hennebique & Mouchel

**Ninian Central Platform**
Client: Chevron Petroleum (UK) Ltd
Designers and main contractors: Howard Doris Ltd

**Pompidou Centre**
Client: Etablissement Publique du Centre Beaubourg
Architects: Piano and Rogers
Engineer: Ove Arup and Partners
Management Contractor: Grandes Travaux de Marseilles

**RIBA**
Architect: Grey Wornum.
Engineer: R. T. James & Partners

**The Ritz Hotel**
Architect: Mewes & Davis
Engineer: S. Bylander, Esq.

**Royal Liver Building**
Engineers: Hennebique & Mouchel

**Selfridges**
Architect: Frank Atkinson Esq., in association with Burnham & Co

**Tavanasa Bridge**
Engineer: Robert Maillart, Esq

**Thames Barrier**
Client: The Greater London Council (The cost has been met by the Ministry of Agriculture: Fisheries and Food and the GLC)
Design: Rendel Palmer and Tritton
Civil engineering contractor: Costain-Tarmac-Hollandsche Beton Maatschappij
Supply an installation of gates and operating machinery: Davy Cleveland Barrier Consortium

**Tower Bridge**
Architecture: Sir Horace Jones
Engineer: Sir John Wolfe Barry

**TP1**
Client: Elf Norge A/S
Designer: Sea Tank Company, Paris
Contractor: Sir Robert McAlpine and Sons

**Weavers Mill, Swansea**
Architect: H. G. Portsmouth, Esq
Engineers: Hennebique & Le Brun/Mouchel